ESSENTIALS OF MATHEMATICS

AN APPLIED APPROACH

9th Edition

RICHARD N. AUFMANN | JOANNE S. LOCKWOOD

CENGAGE
Learning·

Australia • Brazil • Japan • Korea • Mexico • Singapore • Spain • United Kingdom • United States

**ESSENTIALS OF MATHEMATICS,
AN APPLIED APPROACH, 9th Edition**

Senior Project Development Manager:
Linda deStefano

Market Development Manager:
Heather Kramer

Senior Production/Manufacturing Manager:
Donna M. Brown

Production Editorial Manager:
Kim Fry

Sr. Rights Acquisition Account Manager:
Todd Osborne

ESSENTIALS OF MATHEMATICS, AN APPLIED APPROACH, 9th Edition
AUFMANN | LOCKWOOD

© 2013 Cengage Learning. All rights reserved.

ENH WEBASSN START SMART GDE
Brooks/Cole

© 2007 Cengage Learning. All rights reserved.

For product information and technology assistance, contact us at
Cengage Learning Customer & Sales Support, 1-800-354-9706

For permission to use material from this text or product,
submit all requests online at **cengage.com/permissions**
Further permissions questions can be emailed to
permissionrequest@cengage.com

This book contains select works from existing Cengage Learning resources and was produced by Cengage Learning Custom Solutions for collegiate use. As such, those adopting and/or contributing to this work are responsible for editorial content accuracy, continuity and completeness.

Compilation © 2013 Cengage Learning
ISBN-13: 978-1-285-88401-1

ISBN-10: 1-285-88401-9

Cengage Learning
5191 Natorp Boulevard
Mason, Ohio 45040
USA
Cengage Learning is a leading provider of customized learning solutions with office locations around the globe, including Singapore, the United Kingdom, Australia, Mexico, Brazil, and Japan. Locate your local office at:
international.cengage.com/region.

Cengage Learning products are represented in Canada by Nelson Education, Ltd.
For your lifelong learning solutions, visit **www.cengage.com/custom.**
Visit our corporate website at **www.cengage.com.**

Printed in the United States of America

Brief Contents

ENHANCED
WEBASSIGN

The Start Smart Guide
for students

CENGAGE
Learning™

Australia • Brazil • Japan • Korea • Mexico • Singapore • Spain • United Kingdom • United States

CENGAGE
Learning™

Enhanced WebAssign: The Start Smart Guide for Students

Acquisitions Editor: Gary Whalen

Copyeditor: Deborah Todd

Media Editor: Lynh Pham

Cover Design: Fabio Fernandes

WebAssign © 2003–2007 by Advanced Instructional Systems, Inc.

All rights reserved.

WebAssign
Centennial Campus
730 Varsity Drive
Raleigh, NC 27606
Web: http://webassign.net
Tel: (800) 955-8275 or (919) 829-8181
Fax: (919) 829-1516
E-mail: info@webassign.net

WebAssign® is a registered service mark of North Carolina State University under license to Advanced Instructional Systems, Inc.

Enhanced WebAssign™ is a trademark of Advanced Instructional Systems and Cengage Learning.

© 2007 Cengage Learning

For product information and technology assistance, contact us at **Cengage Learning Customer & Sales Support, 1-800-354-9706**.
For permission to use material from this text or product, submit all requests online at **www.cengage.com/permissions**.
Further permissions questions can be emailed to **permissionrequest@cengage.com**.

ISBN-13: 978-0-495-38479-3

ISBN-10: 0-495-38479-8

Cengage Learning is a leading provider of customized learning solutions with office locations around the globe, including Singapore, the United Kingdom, Australia, Mexico, Brazil, and Japan. Locate your local office at: **www.cengage.com/global**.

Cengage Learning products are represented in Canada by Nelson Education, Ltd.

To learn more about Cengage Learning, visit **www.cengage.com**.

Purchase any of our products at your local college store or at our preferred online store **www.cengagebrain.com**.

Printed in the United States of America
10 11 12 13 14 15 14 13 12 11

CONTENTS

WebAssign works with any recent browser and computer. Some assignments may require an updated browser and/or plugins like Java, Flash, Shockwave, or Adobe Reader.

For technical support go to http://webassign.net/student.html or email support@webassign.net.

Contents

GETTING STARTED

Welcome to Enhanced WebAssign, the integrated, online learning system that gives you 24/7 access to your math, physics, astronomy, chemistry, biology, and statistics assignments.

Now, you can do homework, take quizzes and exams, and receive your scores and graded assignments from any computer with an Internet connection and web browser, any time of the day or night.

Note: As a live, web-based program, Enhanced WebAssign is updated regularly with new features and improvements. Please refer to WebAssign's online Help for the most current information.

Technical Startup Tips

Before you start, please note the following important points:

○ Most standard web connections should work with WebAssign. We recommend using Firefox 1.0 or later, or Internet Explorer 5.5 or later. *We do not recommend the AOL browser.*

○ You can use a 56 KBPS modem, broadband, or school network connection.

○ Your browser needs to have both JavaScript and Java enabled.

○ You *cannot skip the login page*. WebAssign must know it is you before delivering your assignments.

Note: If you'd like to bookmark WebAssign on your computer, we recommend that you bookmark **https://www.webassign.net/login.html** or the appropriate address for your school.

Login to WebAssign

In order to access WebAssign your instructor will provide you with login information or a Class Key. Login information will consist of a username, institution code, and an initial password. The Class Key will allow you to self-register and create your own login. You will need to remember the username and initial password you set after self-registering.

Please note that Class Keys are not the same as access codes. See pages 8–9 for instructions on registering your access code number. You will need to login first before you are able to register an access code.

➤ To get started

1. If you are using a shared computer, completely exit any browsers that are already open.

2. Open a new web browser and go to https://www.webassign.net/login.html, or the web address provided by your instructor.

   If your instructor has provided you with a **Username, Institution** (school code), and **Password,** continue with step 3. If you have been provided with a **Class Key** (usually your institution name and a series of numbers), skip to step 5.

3. Enter your **Username, Institution** (school code), and **Password** *provided by your instructor.*

   ### Institution

   If you do not know your **Institution,** you can search for it by clicking **(what's this?)** above the **Institution** entry box.

   In the **What's My Institution Code** pop-up window, enter your school name and click **go!**. The **Institution Search Results** table will give you choices of the School Names that most closely match your entry, and the **Institution Code** that you should enter in the **Institution** entry box on the **WebAssign Login** screen.

   ### Password

   If you have forgotten or do not know your **Password,** click **(Reset Password)** above the **Password** entry box, and follow the directions on the **WebAssign New Password Request** screen. You will need to submit your username, institution code, and the email address on file in your WebAssign account. If you are unsure of your username or listed email address, please check with your instructor. WebAssign cannot reset your username or password.

4. Click **Log In**.

5. If your instructor gave you a **Class Key,** you will use it to create your account. Click the **I have a Class Key** button. You will need to use this key only once when you register.

6. Enter the Class Key code in the field provided and click **Submit**. If your Class Key is recognized, you will be asked to confirm your class information. If the information provided is correct, then click the **Yes, this is my class** button. If the information provided is incorrect, then click the **No, this is not my class** button and reenter your Class Key.

7. When you verify that the class information is correct, you will be able to create a new WebAssign account. If you do not already have a WebAssign account, select "I need to create a WeAssign account." If you have a WebAssign account for any other course at the same institution then select "I already have a WebAssign account." When you have selected the appropriate option click the **Continue** button.

8. Enter a username in the field provided and then click **Check Availability** to determine whether or not your username is already in use. If it is, an available alternate username will be suggested. Remember your username because you will use it every time you login to WebAssign.

9. Enter and then re-enter a password. Remember your password because you will use it every time you login to WebAssign.

10. Under **Student Information** enter your first and last name, email address, and student ID.

11. Click **Create My Account**.

12. If you see confirmation of your account creation, you will now be able to login to WebAssign. Click **Log in now**.

Note: Before starting WebAssign on a shared computer, always exit any browsers and restart your browser application. *If you simply close the browser window or open a new window, login information contained in an encrypted key may not be yours.*

Logout

When you are finished with your work, click the **Logout** link in the upper right corner of your Home page, and *exit the browser completely* to avoid the possibility of someone else accessing your work.

YOUR ENHANCED WEBASSIGN HOME PAGE

Your personalized Home page is your hub for referencing and managing all of your Enhanced WebAssign assignments.

Using Access Codes

Some classes require an **access code** for admission. Please remember:

○ An **access code** is *not* the same as a Class Key or a login password.

○ An **access code** is good for *one class only* unless the textbook includes a two-term **access code**.

○ An **access code** is an alphanumeric code that is *usually* packaged with your textbook. It can begin with 2 or 3 letters, followed by an alphanumeric code, or it can have a longer prefix such as **BCEnhanced-S** followed by four sets of four characters.

○ If your textbook did not include an **access code**, you can buy one at your bookstore, or from your personalized Home page by clicking the **Purchase an access code online** button.

➤ **To enter an access code**

1. Under **WebAssign Notices**, select the proper prefix from the **Choose your access code prefix** pull-down menu.

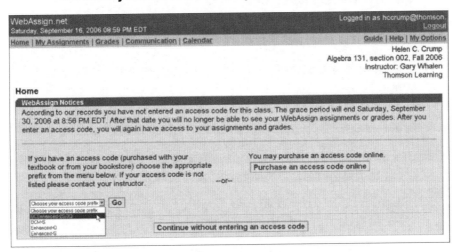

WebAssign notices

2. Click **Go**.

3. In the entry boxes, type in your access code *exactly* as it appears on your card. (When you purchase online, the access code is entered automatically.)

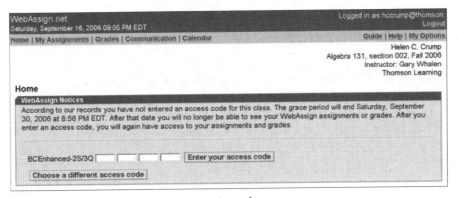

Access code entry

4. Click **Enter your access code.**

   If you have chosen the wrong prefix from the previous screen, you can click the **Choose a different access code** button to try again.

   If your **access code** is a valid unused code, you will receive a message that you have successfully entered the code for the class. Click the **Home** or **My Assignments** button to proceed.

Changing Your Password

For your personal security, it's a good idea to change the initial password provided by your instructor.

➢ To change your password

1. Click the **My Options** link in the upper right of your Home page.

2. In the **My Options** pop-up window, under the **Personal Info** tab:

   Enter your *new* password in the **Change Password** entry box next to **(enter new password)**, then

   Reenter your new password *exactly* the same in the entry box next to **(reenter for confirmation)**.

3. Enter your *current* password in the entry box under **If you made any changes above, enter your current password here and then click save:**, located at the bottom of the pop-up window.

4. Click the **Save** button in the bottom right corner of the pop-up window.

   If the change was successful, you will see the message **Your password has been changed**.

Note: Passwords are case-sensitive. This means that if you capitalize any of the letters, you must remember to capitalize them the same way each time you sign in to Enhanced WebAssign.

Changing Your Email Address

If your instructor provided you with an email address, you can easily change it to your own personal email address any time.

➢ To change your email address

1. Click the **My Options** link in the upper right of your Home page.

2. In the **My Options** pop-up window, under the **Personal Info** tab, enter your *valid* email address in the **Email Address** box.

3. Enter your current password in the entry box under **If you made any changes above enter your current password here and then click save:**, located at the bottom of the pop-up screen.

4. Click the **Save** button in the bottom right corner of the pop-up window.

   A confirmation email will be sent to your new email address.

Once you receive the confirmation email, you must click the link in the email to successfully complete and activate this change.

WORKING WITH ASSIGNMENTS

The courses that have been set up for you by your instructor(s) appear on your Enhanced WebAssign personalized Home page. If you have more than one course, simply select the course you want to work with from the pull-down menu.

Assignment Summary

There are two ways to get a quick summary of your assignments. On the Home page:

○ Click the **My Assignments** link in the upper left *menu bar,* or

○ Click the **Current Assignments** link in the **My Assignments** *module* on the Home page.

Accessing an Assignment

Once your assignments are displayed on your Home page, simply click the name of the assignment you'd like to begin.

○ If you have previously submitted an assignment, you will see your most recent responses, if your instructor allows this feature.

○ If you have already submitted the assignment, there will usually be a link to **Review All Submissions** on the page, if your instructor has allowed it.

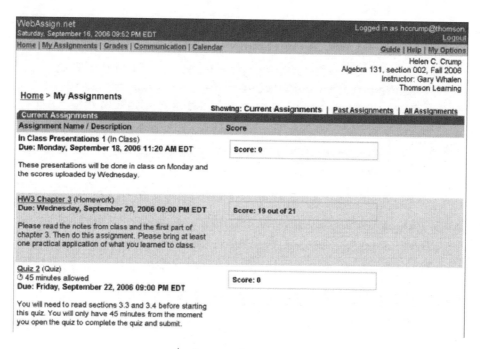

Assignment summary

Math assignment

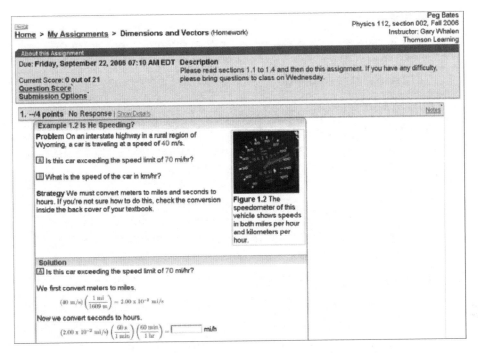

Physics assignment

Using the Assignment Page

When you click on an assignment name, your assignment will load. Within the **About this Assignment** page are links to valuable information about your assignment's score, submission options, and saving your work in progress. Within each question, there might also be "enhanced" action links to useful tutorial material such as book content, videos, animations, active figures, simulations, and practice problems. The links available may vary from one assignment to another.

Actions

Click a button or link to take one of the following actions:

Current Score

This gives you a quick look at your current score versus the maximum possible score.

Question Score

This gives you a pop-up window showing your score for each question.

Submission Options

This gives you a pop-up window explaining how you can submit the assignment and whether it can be submitted by question part, by whole question, or by the whole assignment.

Submissions Made

This shows you the number of submissions you've made. This information is only displayed on assignments that require submission of the entire assignment.

Notes

This feature gives you a pop-up window with a text box in which you can enter and save notes or show your work with a particular question.

Submit New Answers To Question

Use this button when you're ready to submit your answer for the question. This feature allows you to answer just the parts you want scored. If you leave any part of a question unanswered, the submission *will not* be recorded for that part.

Submit Whole Question

Use this button to submit your answer(s) for the entire question. If you leave any part of a question unanswered, the submission *will* be recorded as if the entire question has been answered, and will be graded as such.

Save Work

This button allows you to save the work you've done so far on a particular question, but does not submit that question for grading.

View Saved Work

Located in the question's header line, this link allows you to view work that you previously saved for that question.

Show Details

Located in the question's header line, this link shows your score on each part of the question, how many points each part of the question is worth, and how many submissions are allowed for each part if you can submit each part separately.

Submit All New Answers

This submits all of your new answers for all of the questions in the assignment.

Save All Work

This allows you to save all the work you've done on all of the questions in the assignment, but does not submit your work for grading.

Ask Your Teacher

This feature allows you to send a question about the assignment to your instructor.

Extension Request

This allows you to submit a request to your instructor for an extension of time on an assignment.

Home

This link takes you to your personalized Home page.

My Assignments

This link takes you to your assignments page.

Read it

This links to question-specific textbook material in PDF form.

Practice Another Version

This provides you with an alternate version of the assigned problem. Within the pop-up window you will be able to answer the practice problem and have that answer checked. You will also be able to practice additional versions of your assigned problem.

Practice it

This links to a practice problem or set of practice problems in a pop-up window. No grade is recorded on the work you do on practice problems.

Watch it

This links to a tutorial video.

Hint

This links to a pop-up window with helpful hints in case you get stuck on a question.

Hint: Active Figure

This links to an animated simulation to help you better understand the concepts being covered.

Note: Your instructor has the ability to turn on/off many of the options listed above.

ANSWERING QUESTIONS

Enhanced WebAssign uses a variety of question types that you're probably already familiar with using, such as multiple choice, true/false, free response, etc.

Always be sure to pay close attention to any instructions within the question regarding how you are supposed to submit your answers.

Numerical Questions

There are a few key points to keep in mind when working on numerical questions:

○ Numbers can be entered in both scientific notation and numerical expressions, such as fractions.

○ WebAssign uses the standard scientific notation "E" or "e" for "times 10 raised to the power." (Note: both uppercase E and lowercase e are acceptable in WebAssign.) For example, 1e3 is the scientific notation for 1000.

○ Numerical answers may not contain commas (,) or equal signs (=).

○ Numerical answers may only contain:

• Numbers

• E or e for scientific notation

• Mathematical operators +, -, *, /

○ Numerical answers within 1% of the actual answer are counted as correct, unless your instructor chooses a different tolerance. This is to account for rounding errors in calculations. In general, enter three significant figures for numerical answers.

➢ Example: Numerical Question

Let's suppose you're presented a question to which your answer is the fraction "one over sixty-four." Following are examples of Correct and Incorrect answer formats:

Correct Answers

Any of these formats would be correct:

1/64

0.015625

0.0156

.0156

1.5625E-2

Incorrect Answers

These formats would be graded as incorrect:

O.015625	The first character is the letter "O"
0. 015625	There is an improper space in the answer
1.5625 E-2	There is an improper space using E notation
l/64	The first character is lowercase letter "L"
5,400	There is a comma in the answer
1234.5=1230	There is an equal sign in the answer

Numerical Questions with Units

Some Enhanced WebAssign questions require a number and a unit, and this is generally, although not always, indicated in the instructions in the question.

You will know that a unit is expected when there is no unit after the answer box.

When you are expected to enter units and do not, you will get an error message telling you that units are required.

Note: Whether omission of the unit counts as a submission depends on the submission options chosen by the instructor.

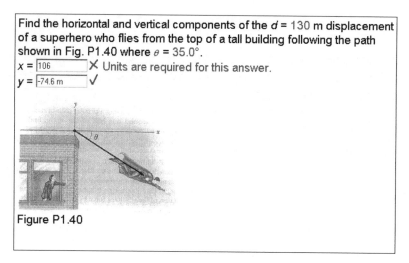

Find the horizontal and vertical components of the *d* = 130 m displacement of a superhero who flies from the top of a tall building following the path shown in Fig. P1.40 where *θ* = 35.0°.

x = ⟨106⟩ ✗ Units are required for this answer.

y = ⟨-74.6 m⟩ ✓

Figure P1.40

Numerical with units

The easiest units to use in this question are m, but the answer converted to yd would also be scored correct.

Numerical Questions with Significant Figures

Some numerical questions require a specific number of significant figures (sig figs) in your answer. If a question checks sig figs, you will see a sig fig icon next to the answer box.

If you enter the correct value with the wrong number of sig figs, you will not receive credit, but you will receive a hint that your number does not have the correct number of sig figs. The sig fig icon ⟨4.0✓⟩ is also a link to the rules used for sig figs in WebAssign.

Carry out the following arithmetic operations. (Use the correct number of significant figures.)

(a) the sum of the measured values 760., 37.2, 0.81, and 2.2

⟨4.0✓⟩ ⟨8e2⟩ ✗ Check the number of significant figures.

(b) the product 3.4 × 3.563

⟨4.0✓⟩ ⟨12⟩ ✓

(c) the product 5.7 × π

⟨4.0✓⟩ ⟨18⟩ ✓

Check for significant figures

Math Notation: Using the MathPad

In many math questions, Enhanced WebAssign gives you a **MathPad**. The **MathPad** provides easy input of math notation and symbols, even the more complicated ones. If your answer involves math notation or symbols, the MathPad will become available when you click the answer box.

         1   2   3

Top Symbols

The buttons on the top are single input buttons for frequently used operations.

Word Buttons

When you click one of the word buttons **Functions**, **Symbols**, **Relations**, or **Sets**, you are given a drop-down menu with symbols or notation from which to choose. For example, if you click the **Sets** button, you get set notation (figure 2 above). If you then click a right arrow button, additional symbols become available (figure 3 above).

To insert any available notation or symbol into your answer, simply click it.

Math Notation: Using the CalcPad

CalcPad, as its name implies, is designed for use with the more complicated symbol and notation entry in calculus. It functions in a similar manner to the MathPad described above. If your course uses **CalcPad**, check online for additional instructions.

Math Notation: Using the Keyboard

If you use your keyboard to enter math notation (calculator notation), *you must use the exact variables specified in the questions.*

The order is not important, as long as it is mathematically correct.

➤ Example: Math Notation Using Keyboard

In the example below, the keyboard is used to enter the answer in the answer field.

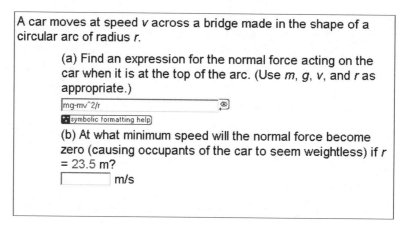

A car moves at speed *v* across a bridge made in the shape of a circular arc of radius *r*.

   (a) Find an expression for the normal force acting on the car when it is at the top of the arc. (Use *m*, *g*, *v*, and *r* as appropriate.)

   `mg-mv^2/r`

   symbolic formatting help

   (b) At what minimum speed will the normal force become zero (causing occupants of the car to seem weightless) if *r* = 23.5 m?

   [   ] m/s

Symbolic question

Expression Preview

Clicking the eye button ⊛ allows you to preview the expression you've entered in calculator notation.

Use this preview feature to help determine if you have properly placed your parentheses.

Symbolic Formatting Help

If you're unsure about how to symbolically enter your answer properly, use the **symbolic formatting help** button to display allowed notation.

Allowed Notation for Symbolic Formatting

+ for addition	x+1
- for subtraction	x-1, or -x
* or nothing for multiplication	4*x, or 4x
/ for division	x/4
** or ^ for exponential	x**3, or x^3
( ) where necessary to group terms	4/(x+1), or 3(x+1)
abs( ) to take the absolute value of a variable or expression	abs(-5) = 5
sin, cos, tan, sec, csc, cot, asin, acos, atan functions (angle x expressed in radians)	sin(2x)
sqrt( ) for square root of an expression	sqrt(x/5)
x^ (1/n) for the nth root of a number	x^ (1/3), or (x-3)^ (1/5)
pi for 3.14159…	2 pi x
e for scientific notation	1e3 = 1000
ln( ) for natural log	ln(x)
exp( ) for "e to the power of"	exp(x) = e^x

USING THE GRAPHING UTILITY

The Enhanced WebAssign Graphing Utility lets you graph one or more mathematical elements directly on a set of coordinate axes. Your graph is then scored automatically when you submit the assignment for grading.

The Graphing Utility currently supports points, rays, segments, lines, circles, and parabolas. Inequalities can also be indicated by filling one or more areas.

Graphing Utility Interface Overview

The middle of the Graphing Utility is the drawing area. It contains labeled coordinate axes, which may have different axis scales and extents, depending on the nature of the question you are working on.

On the left side of Graphing Utility is the list of Tools that let you create graph objects and select objects to edit.

The bottom of the Graphing Utility is the Object Properties Toolbar, which becomes active when you have a graph element selected. This toolbar shows you all the details about the selected graph object, and also lets you edit the object's properties.

On the right side of Graphing Utility is a list of Actions that lets you create fills and delete objects from your graph.

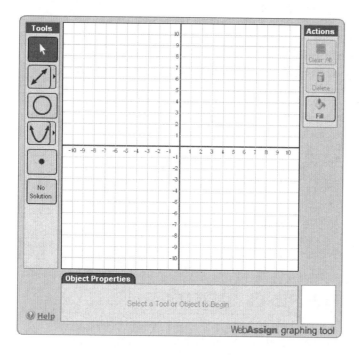

Drawing Tools	
Points:	Click the Point Tool, and then click where you want the point to appear.
Lines:	Click the Line Tool, and then place two points along the desired line. The arrows on the end of the line indicate that the line goes off to infinity on both ends.
Rays:	Click the Ray Tool, place the endpoint, and then place another point on the ray.
Line Segments:	Click the Line Segment Tool, and then place the two endpoints of the line segment.
Circles:	Click the Circle Tool, place the point at the center first, and then place a point on the circumference of the circle.
Parabolas:	Click the Parabola Tool (either vertical or horizontal), place the vertex first, and then place another point on the parabola.
No Solution:	If the question has no solution, simply click the No Solution Tool.

Note: Don't worry if you don't place the points exactly where you want them initially; you can move these points around before submitting for grading.

Selecting Graph Objects

To edit a graph object, it must be "selected" as the active object. (When you first draw an object, it is created in the selected state.) When a graph element is "selected," the color of the line changes and two "handles" are visible. The handles are the two square points you clicked to create the object. To select an object, click the Select Tool, and then click on the object. To deselect the object, click on a blank area on the drawing area or on a drawing tool.

Not Selected   *Selected*

Once an object is selected, you can modify it by using your mouse or the keyboard. As you move it, you'll notice that you cannot move the handles off the drawing area. To move an object with the mouse, click and drag the object's line. Or, click and drag one of the handles to move just that handle. On the keyboard, the arrow keys can also move the selected object by one unit at a time.

As you move the object or handle you'll see that the Object Properties toolbar reflects your changes.

Object Properties Toolbar	
Coordinate Fields: ● Point 1 (-13 , -9) ■ Point 2 (15 , -6)	You can use the Coordinate Fields to edit the coordinates of the handles directly. Use this method to enter decimal or fractional coordinates.
Endpoint Controls: Endpoint ⬛⭕ Endpoint ⬛⭕	If the selected object is a segment or ray, the Endpoint Controls are used to define the endpoint as closed or open. As a shortcut, you can also define an endpoint by clicking on the endpoint when the ray or segment is in the unselected state.
Solid/Dash Controls: Solid Dash	For any selected object other than a point, the Solid/Dash Controls are used to define the object as solid or dashed. To change graph objects to solid or dashed, select the object and then click the **Solid** or **Dash** button.

Using Fractions or Decimals as Coordinates

To draw an object with handle coordinates that are fractions or decimals, you must use the Object Properties Toolbar. Draw the desired object anywhere on the drawing area, then use the Coordinate Fields to change the endpoint(s) to the desired value. For example, to enter a fraction, just type "3/4."

Note: The points and lines you draw must be exactly correct when you submit for grading. This means you should not round any of your values—if you want a point at 11/3, you should enter 11/3 in the coordinate box rather than 3.667. Also, mixed fractions are not acceptable entries. This means that 3 2/3 is an incorrect entry.

Actions	
Fill Tool: Fill	To graph an inequality, you must specify a region on the graph. To do this, first draw the line(s), circle(s), or other object(s) that will define the region you want to represent your answer. Be sure to specify the objects as either solid or dashed, according to the inequality you are graphing! Then choose the Fill Tool and click inside the region that you want filled. If you decide you want the fill in a different area, click the filled region that you want to unfill, and then click the region that you do want to fill.
Delete Tool: Delete	To erase a single graph object, first select that element in the drawing area, then click the Delete Tool or press the Delete key on your keyboard.

Actions	
Clear All Tool: ![Clear All button]	The Clear All Tool will erase all of your graph objects. (If the drawing area is already empty, the Clear All Tool is disabled.)

➢ **Example**

Let's suppose you're asked to graph the inequality $y > 5x + \dfrac{1}{5}$, and you want to use the points $\left(0, \dfrac{1}{5}\right)$ and $\left(1, 5\dfrac{1}{5}\right)$. First, you would place any line on the drawing area.

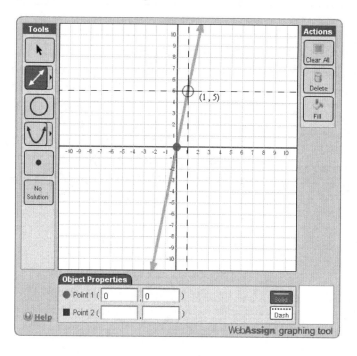

Then, you would adjust the points using the Coordinate Fields. Remember, you need to enter 5 1/5 as a decimal (5.2) or an improper fraction (26/5).

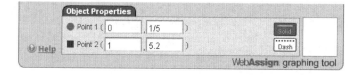

Next, you would define the line as dashed since the inequality does not include the values on the line.

Finally, you would select the Fill Tool and click on the desired region to complete the graph.

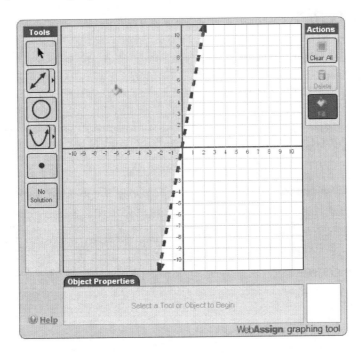

ADDITIONAL FEATURES

Calendar

The Calendar link presents you with a calendar showing all of your assignments on their due dates. You can also click on any date and enter your own personal events.

Communication

The Communication link gives you access to **Private Messages** and course **Forums**, if your instructor has enabled these features.

Forums

The **Forums** are for discussions with all the members of your class. Your instructor can create forums, and you can create topics within a forum or contribute to a current topic.

Private Messages

Private Messages are for communication between you and your instructor. If your instructor has enabled private messages, click the **New Message** link to send your instructor a message.

GRADES

The **Grades** link at the top of all your WebAssign pages gives you access to the raw scores and grades that your instructor posts. This page may also include statistics on the whole class, and a histogram of scores for each category of assignment and each individual assignment. It may have your individual average for each category of assignment, as well as the score on each of your assignments.

Your instructor will let you know what Scores and Grades will be posted in your course.

If your instructor has enabled all of the options, your display will be similar to the one below.

Grades

Overall Grade

This score is calculated from the various categories of assignments—for example, **Homework, Test**, **In Class**, **Quiz**, **Lab**, and **Exam**. Your instructor may have different categories.

Category Grades

The **Category Grades** give the contribution to your overall grade from each of the categories. If you click a grade that is a link, you will get a pop-up window explaining how the number was calculated.

Class Statistics

Class Statistics shows the averages, minimum scores, maximum scores, and standard deviation of the class at large.

My Scores Summary

This link presents a pop-up window with a summary of your raw scores and the class statistics on each assignment, if your teacher has posted these.

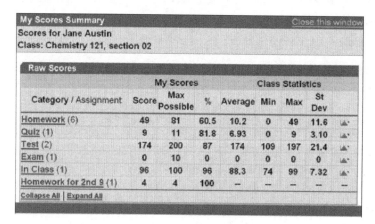

My Scores Summary								Close this window

Scores for Jane Austin
Class: Chemistry 121, section 02

Raw Scores

Category / Assignment	My Scores			Class Statistics				
	Score	Max Possible	%	Average	Min	Max	St Dev	
Homework (6)	49	81	60.5	10.2	0	49	11.6	⊾ᐟ
Quiz (1)	9	11	81.8	6.93	0	9	3.10	⊾ᐟ
Test (2)	174	200	87	174	109	197	21.4	⊾ᐟ
Exam (1)	0	10	0	0	0	0	0	⊾ᐟ
In Class (1)	96	100	96	88.3	74	99	7.32	⊾ᐟ
Homework for 2nd 9 (1)	4	4	100	--	--	--	--	--

Collapse All | Expand All

My Scores summary

TECHNICAL TIPS

Enhanced WebAssign relies on web browsers and other related technology that can lead to occasional technical issues. The following technical tips can help you avoid some common problems.

Cookies

Allow your browser to accept cookies.

WebAssign will work if you set your browser to not accept cookies; however, if an encrypted cookie is not saved to your computer during your session, you may be asked to login again more frequently. Once you logout and exit your browser, the cookie is deleted.

> **For technical support go to http://webassign.net/student.html or email support@webassign.net.**

Login and Credit

If you see an assignment that does not have your name at the top, you have not logged in properly.

You will not receive credit for any work you do on an assignment if your name is not associated with it. If you find yourself in the midst of this situation, make notes of your solution(s) and start over. Be aware that any randomized values in the questions will probably change.

Logout When You Finish Your Session

If someone wants to use your computer for WebAssign, logout and exit the browser before relinquishing control.

Otherwise, the work you have just completed may be written over by the next user.

Server

Although it is very rare, the WebAssign server may occasionally be unavailable.

If the WebAssign server is unavailable, instructors will provide instructions for submitting your assignments—possibly including new due dates. The policy for handling server problems will vary from instructor to instructor.

Use the Latest Browser Software

Use the latest version of Firefox, Mozilla, Netscape, or Internet Explorer browsers.

Older versions of browsers may not be supported by WebAssign.

For technical support go to http://webassign.net/student.html or email support@webassign.net.

Preface

Among the many questions we ask when we begin the process of revising a textbook, the most important is, "How can we improve the learning experience for the student?" We find answers to this question in a variety of ways, but most commonly by talking to students and instructors and by evaluating the written feedback we receive from instructors. Bearing this feedback in mind, our ultimate goal as we set out to create the ninth edition of *Essentials of Mathematics: An Applied Approach* was to provide students with more materials to help them better understand the underlying concepts presented in this course. As a result, we have made the following changes to the new edition.

New to this edition is the **Focus on Success** vignette that appears at the beginning of each chapter. **Focus on Success** offers practical tips for improving study habits and performance on tests and exams.

We now include an **Apply the Concept** box within the objectives that teach addition, subtraction, multiplication, and division. The arithmetic operation is applied to a real-world situation so that students can relate the operation to their everyday lives. For example, multiplication of whole numbers is applied to determining the total number of cans of soda in eight six-packs of soda.

The definition and key concept boxes have been enhanced in this edition; they now include examples to show how the general case translates to specific cases.

In each exercise set, the first group of exercises is now titled **Concept Check.** The **Concept Check** exercises focus on the concepts that lie behind the skills developed in the section. We consider an understanding of these concepts essential to a student's success in mastering the skills required to complete the exercises that follow.

Every chapter contains **Check Your Progress** exercises. This feature appears approximately mid-chapter and tests students' understanding of the concepts presented to that point in the chapter.

Critical Thinking exercises are included at the end of every exercise set. They may involve further exploration or analysis of the topic at hand. They may also integrate concepts introduced earlier in the text.

We trust that the new and enhanced features of the ninth edition will help students more successfully engage with the content. By narrowing the gap between the concrete and the abstract, between the real world and the theoretical, students should more plainly see that mastering the skills and topics presented is well within their reach and well worth the effort.

New to This Edition

- **Apply the Concept** boxes are provided within objectives that teach arithmetic operations.

- **Concept Check** exercises appear at the beginning of each exercise set.

- Enhanced definition/key concept boxes now provide examples that illustrate how the general case applies to specific cases.

- The **Focus on Success** feature at the beginning of each chapter offers practical guidance to help students develop positive study habits.

- **Check Your Progress** exercises appear approximately mid-chapter and test students' understanding of the concepts presented thus far in the chapter.

- **In the News** articles within the exercise sets have been updated, as have application problems throughout the text.

- **Critical Thinking** exercises appear at the end of each exercise set.

- **Projects or Group Activities** are now included at the end of each exercise set.

- **Chapter A, AIM for Success,** now appears as the first chapter of the text. This chapter describes skills used by students who have been successful in this course. Topics include how to stay motivated, making a commitment to success, time management, and how to prepare for and take tests. A guide to the textbook is included to help students use its features effectively.

- More annotations have been added to the worked Examples, to more effectively explain the steps of the solutions.

- Many of the **Chapter Summaries** have been expanded to include more entries and more descriptive explanations.

Organizational Changes

We have made the following changes in order to improve the effectiveness of the textbook and enhance the student's learning experience.

- In Chapter 1, the introductions to the four arithmetic operations were rewritten using real world applications to motivate the use of each operation.

- Section 1.5, Division of Whole Numbers, now includes additional exercises that focus on quotients and dividends that contain zero.

- Section 2.8, Order, Exponents, and the Order of Operations Agreement, was revised. Exponential notation is more fully integrated into the exercises that require the Order of Operations Agreement.

- Section 3.1 contains a new objective on comparing decimals. In the previous edition, this topic was covered later in the chapter. It was moved here to provide students with a better understanding of decimals and place value prior to the lessons on operations with decimals.

- Objective C in Section 3.6 was rewritten. There is now greater emphasis on the topic of comparing fractions and decimals.

- Section 5.1 now contains more examples of converting from a percent to a fraction or from a percent to a decimal. In Objective B of this section, students are given more practice in converting from a fraction or a decimal to a percent. The Section 5.1 exercise set was revised extensively to provide the student with a significantly improved selection of exercises.

- Section 6.1, Applications to Purchasing, was rewritten and now includes real world examples to motivate the topics of unit cost and finding the most economical purchase.

- Accompanying Chapter 6 are new and expanded compound interest rate tables as well as a new and expanded Monthly Payment Table to calculate mortgage and car loan payments.

- Section 6.4, Real Estate Expenses, was rewritten to include contemporary topics and interest rates.

Take AIM and Succeed!

An Objective-Based Approach

Essentials of Mathematics: An Applied Approach is organized around a carefully constructed hierarchy of **objectives.** This "objective-based" approach provides an integrated learning path that enables you to find resources such as assessment tools (both within the text and online), videos, tutorials, and additional exercises for each objective in the text.

1 Each Chapter Opener outlines the learning **OBJECTIVES** that appear in each section of the chapter. The list of objectives serves as a resource to guide you in your study and review of the topics.

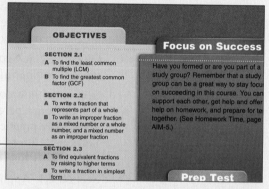

2 Taking the **PREP TEST** for each chapter will help you determine which topics you need to study more carefully and which topics you need only review. The **ANSWERS** to the **PREP TEST** provide references to the **OBJECTIVES** on which the exercises are based.

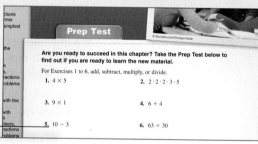

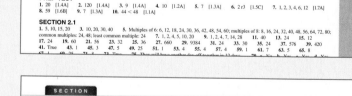

3 In every section, an **OBJECTIVE STATEMENT** introduces each new topic of discussion. Videos are available for each objective.

4 Section exercises are keyed to **OBJECTIVE STATEMENTS.**

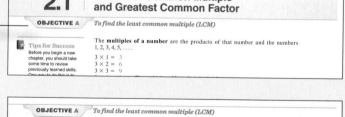

An Objective-Based Review

This "objective-based" approach continues through the end-of-chapter review and addresses a broad range of study styles by offering a **wide variety of review tools.**

 CHECK YOUR PROGRESS exercises appear approximately mid-chapter and test your understanding of the concepts presented up to that point in the chapter.

✔ **CHECK YOUR PROGRESS: CHAPTER 2**

1. Graph −3 on the number line.

    −6 −5 −4 −3 −2 −1 0 1 2 3 4 5 6

2. On the number line, which number is 5 units to the left of 2?

3. Place the correct symbol, < or >, between the two numbers.

    −12   −16

4. Write the given numbers in order from smallest to largest.

    −8, 7, −19, 4

At the end of each chapter, you will find a **CHAPTER SUMMARY** containing **KEY WORDS** and **ESSENTIAL RULES AND PROCEDURES** presented in the chapter. Each entry includes an objective reference and a page reference that show where in the chapter the concept was introduced. An example demonstrating the concept is also included.

CHAPTER

3   **Summary**

Key Words   **Examples**

A number written in **decimal notation** has three parts: a **whole-number part**, a **decimal point**, and a **decimal part**. The decimal part of a number represents a number less than 1. A number written in decimal notation is often simply called a **decimal**. [3.1A, p. 130]

For the decimal 31.25, 31 number part and 25 is the

By completing the **CHAPTER REVIEW EXERCISES,** you can practice working on problems in an order that is different from the order in which they were presented in the chapter. The **ANSWER** to each Chapter Review exercise includes a reference to the objective on which the exercise is based. This reference will help you quickly identify where to go if you need further practice with a particular concept.

CHAPTER

3   **Review Exercises**

1. Find the quotient of 3.6515 and 0.067.

2. Find the sum of 369.41, 88.3, 9.774,

Each **CHAPTER TEST** is designed to simulate a typical test of the concepts covered in the chapter. Each **ANSWER** includes an objective reference as well as a reference to a numbered Example, You Try It, or HOW TO in the text that is similar to the given test question.

CHAPTER

3   **TEST**

1. Place the correct symbol, < or >, between the two numbers.

    0.0068   0.000963

2. Subtract: $13.027 - 8.94$

CUMULATIVE REVIEW EXERCISES, which appear at the end of each chapter (beginning with Chapter 2), help you maintain previously learned skills. The **ANSWERS** include references to the section objectives on which the exercises are based.

Cumulative Review Exercises

1. Divide: $89\overline{)20,932}$

2. Simplify: $2^3 \cdot 4^2$

3. Simplify: $2^2 - (7 - 3) \div 2 + 1$

4. Find the LCM of 9, 12, and 24.

Understanding the Concepts

Each of the following features is designed to give you a fuller understanding of the key concepts.

 CONCEPT CHECK exercises promote conceptual understanding. Completing these exercises will deepen your understanding of the concepts you are learning and provide the foundation you need to successfully complete the remaining exercises in the exercise set.

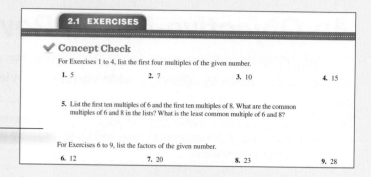

2.1 EXERCISES

✔ **Concept Check**

For Exercises 1 to 4, list the first four multiples of the given number.

1. 5   **2.** 7   **3.** 10   **4.** 15

5. List the first ten multiples of 6 and the first ten multiples of 8. What are the common multiples of 6 and 8 in the lists? What is the least common multiple of 6 and 8?

For Exercises 6 to 9, list the factors of the given number.

6. 12   **7.** 20   **8.** 23   **9.** 28

Definition/key concept boxes contain examples to illustrate how each definition or key concept is applied in practice.

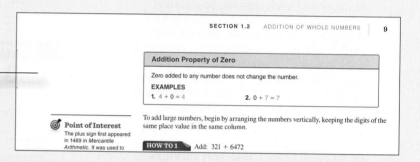

SECTION 1.2   ADDITION OF WHOLE NUMBERS   9

Addition Property of Zero

Zero added to any number does not change the number.

EXAMPLES

1. $4 + 0 = 4$ **2.** $0 + 7 = 7$

🎯 **Point of Interest**
The plus sign first appeared in 1489 in *Mercantile Arithmetic*. It was used to

To add large numbers, begin by arranging the numbers vertically, keeping the digits of the same place value in the same column.

HOW TO 1   Add: $321 + 6472$

TAKE NOTE boxes alert you to concepts that require special attention.

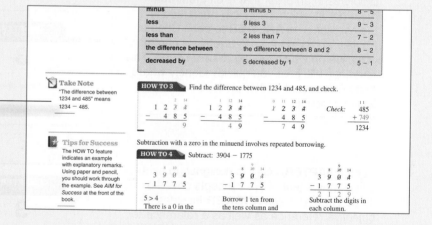

minus	8 minus 5	$8 - 5$
less	9 less 3	$9 - 3$
less than	2 less than 7	$7 - 2$
the difference between	the difference between 8 and 2	$8 - 2$
decreased by	5 decreased by 1	$5 - 1$

📝 **Take Note**
"The difference between 1234 and 485" means $1234 - 485$.

🗝 **Tips for Success**
The HOW TO feature indicates an example with explanatory remarks. Using paper and pencil, you should work through the example. See *AIM for Success* at the front of the book.

HOW TO 3   Find the difference between 1234 and 485, and check.

Check: 485
            $+ 749$
            1234

Subtraction with a zero in the minuend involves repeated borrowing.

HOW TO 4   Subtract: $3904 - 1775$

$5 > 4$
There is a 0 in the

Borrow 1 ten from the tens column and

Subtract the digits in each column.

POINT OF INTEREST boxes, which relate to the topic under discussion, may be historical in nature or of general interest.

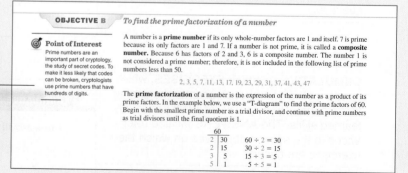

OBJECTIVE B   *To find the prime factorization of a number*

🎯 **Point of Interest**
Prime numbers are an important part of cryptology, the study of secret codes. To make it less likely that codes can be broken, cryptologists use prime numbers that have hundreds of digits.

A number is a **prime number** if its only whole-number factors are 1 and itself. 7 is prime because its only factors are 1 and 7. If a number is not prime, it is called a **composite number.** Because 6 has factors of 2 and 3, 6 is a composite number. The number 1 is not considered a prime number; therefore, it is not included in the following list of prime numbers less than 50.

2, 3, 5, 7, 11, 13, 17, 19, 23, 29, 31, 37, 41, 43, 47

The **prime factorization** of a number is the expression of the number as a product of its prime factors. In the example below, we use a "T-diagram" to find the prime factors of 60. Begin with the smallest prime number as a trial divisor, and continue with prime numbers as trial divisors until the final quotient is 1.

$60 \div 2 = 30$
$30 \div 2 = 15$
$15 \div 3 = 5$
$5 \div 5 = 1$

Application of the Concepts

The section exercises offer many opportunities to put the concepts you are learning into practice.

 APPLY THE CONCEPT boxes illustrate how an arithmetic operation is applied to a real-world situation so that you understand how the operation is used in everyday life.

OBJECTIVE A   *To multiply a number by a single digit*

Multiplication is used to find the total number of objects in several groups when each group contains the same number of objects.

APPLY THE CONCEPT ·····································

Sebastian purchased 8 six-packs of soda for a party. The total number of cans of soda he purchased can be found by adding 6 eight times. Sebastian purchased 48 cans of soda.

$$6 + 6 + 6 + 6 + 6 + 6 + 6 + 6 = 48$$

The number of cans can also be found by using multiplication.

$$6 \times 8 = 48$$

Multiplicand × Multiplier = Product

The **multiplicand** is the number of objects in each group (6 cans in each six-pack); the **multiplier** is the number of groups (8 six-packs); the **product** is the total number of objects (48 cans). Frequently we will discuss the *factors* of a product. A **factor** is one of the numbers that are multiplied to obtain a product. 6 and 8 are factors of 48.

Here is a table of basic multiplication facts. These facts should be memorized.

Basic Multiplication Facts

THINK ABOUT IT exercises promote deeper conceptual understanding. Completing these exercises will expand your understanding of the concepts being addressed.

---

30. $1347 - 103$ **31.** $9999 - 6794$ **32.** $1525 - 702$ **33.** $8843 - 7621$ **34.** 7806

 For Exercises 35 and 36, find two whole numbers with the given difference and sum.

35. Difference = 2; sum = 8   **36.** Difference = 5; sum = 9

 CRITICAL THINKING exercises may involve further exploration or analysis of the topic at hand. They may also integrate concepts introduced earlier in the text.

Critical Thinking

80. If you roll two ordinary six-sided dice and add the two numbers that appear on top, how many different sums are possible?

81. If you add two *different* whole numbers, is the sum always greater than either one of the numbers? If not, give an example.

82. If you add two whole numbers, is the sum always greater than either one of the numbers? If not, give an example. (Compare this with Exercise 81.)

83. Make up a word problem for which the answer is the sum of 34 and 28.

84. Call a number "lucky" if it ends in a 7. How many lucky numbers are less than 100?

Working through the application exercises that contain **REAL DATA** will prepare you to answer questions and solve problems that you encounter outside of class, using facts and information that you gather on your own.

IN THE NEWS exercises help you understand the importance of mathematics in our everyday world. These application exercises are based on information taken from popular media sources such as newspapers, magazines, and the Internet.

---

104. **College Education**   See the news clipping at the right.
   a. Find the average cost of tuition, room, and board for 4 years at a public university.
   b. Find the average cost of tuition, room, and board for 4 years at a private university.
   c. Find the difference in the average cost of tuition, room, and board for 4 years at a private university and 4 years at a public university.

Construction   The table at the right below shows the hourly wages for four types of jobs at a small construction company. Use this table for Exercises 105 to 107.

105. The owner of this company wants to provide the electrical installation for a new house. On the basis of the architectural plans, it is estimated that the installation will require 3 electricians, each working 50 hours, to complete

In the NEWS!

Comparing Tuition Costs

The average annual cost of tuition, room, and board at a four-year public university is $15,875. At a four-year private university, the average cost is $42,841.

Source: National Center for Education Statistics

By completing the **WRITING** exercises, you will improve your communication skills while increasing your understanding of mathematical concepts.

Critical Thinking

96. A survey was conducted to determine people's favorite color from among blue, green, red, purple, and other. The surveyor claims that $\frac{1}{3}$ of the people responded blue, $\frac{1}{6}$ responded green, $\frac{1}{8}$ responded red, $\frac{1}{12}$ responded purple, and $\frac{2}{5}$ responded some other color. Is this possible? Explain your answer.

Projects or Group Activities

A **unit fraction** is a fraction with numerator 1 and denominator greater than 1. For instance, $\frac{1}{2}$ and $\frac{1}{x}$ are unit fractions.

Focus on Study Skills

An emphasis on setting a foundation of good study habits is woven into the text.

UPDATED!

CHAPTER A, AIM FOR SUCCESS, outlines study skills that are used by students who have been successful in this course. By making Chapter A the first chapter of the text, the stage is set for a successful beginning to the course.

New ▸ FOCUS ON SUCCESS appears at the start of each Chapter Opener. These tips are designed to help you make the most of the text and your time as you progress through the course and prepare for tests and exams.

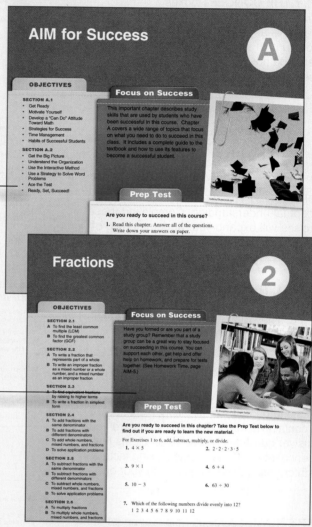

TIPS FOR SUCCESS boxes outline good study habits and function as reminders throughout the text.

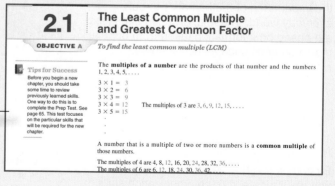

Focus on Skills and Problem Solving

The following features exemplify the emphasis on skills and the problem-solving process.

HOW TO examples provide solutions with detailed explanations for selected topics in each section.

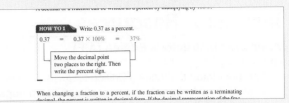

INTEGRATING TECHNOLOGY margin notes offer optional instruction in the use of a scientific calculator.

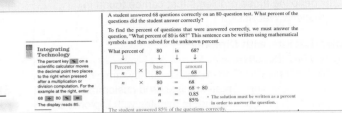

The EXAMPLE/YOU TRY IT matched pairs are designed to actively involve you in the learning process. The You Try Its are based on the Examples. These problems are paired so that you can easily refer to the steps in the Example as you work through the accompanying You Try It.

EXAMPLE 1

Write each percent as a decimal and as a fraction.
a. 120% **b.** 4.3% **c.** 0.45%

Solution

a. $120\% = 120 \times 0.01 = 1.2$

$120\% = 120 \times \dfrac{1}{100} = \dfrac{120}{100} = 1\dfrac{1}{5}$

b. $4.3\% = 4.3 \times 0.01 = 0.043$

$4.3\% = 4.3 \times \dfrac{1}{100}$

$= 4\dfrac{3}{10} \times \dfrac{1}{100}$ • $4.3 = 4\dfrac{3}{10}$

$= \dfrac{43}{10} \times \dfrac{1}{100} = \dfrac{43}{1000}$ • Multiply the fractions.

c. $0.45\% = 0.45 \times 0.01 = 0.0045$

YOU TRY IT 1

Write each percent as a decimal and as a fraction.
a. 125% **b.** 8.5% **c.** 0.25%

Your solution

Complete, WORKED-OUT SOLUTIONS to the You Try Its are included in an appendix at the back of the text. Compare your solution to the solution given in the appendix to obtain immediate feedback and reinforcement of the concept you are studying.

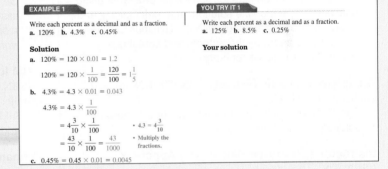

The PROBLEM-SOLVING APPROACH used throughout the text emphasizes the importance of problem-solving strategies. Model strategies are presented as guides for you to follow as you attempt the You Try Its that accompany the numbered Examples.

EXAMPLE 5

Scientists recently released one of the most comprehensive estimates of the number of species on Earth. Earth supports an estimated 8.7 million species, of which 2.2 million live in the ocean. What percent of the species live on land? Round to the nearest tenth of a percent.

Strategy

To find the percent of the species living on land:
- Subtract the number of species living in the ocean from the total number of species (8.7 million − 2.2 million). This gives the

YOU TRY IT 5

In a recent year, there were approximately 302.9 million wireless subscriber connections in the United States. Of these, approximately 112.1 million were subscribers using a smartphone. What percent of wireless subscribers were not using a smartphone? Round to the nearest tenth of a percent.

Your strategy

UPDATED!

PROJECTS OR GROUP ACTIVITIES appear at the end of each exercise set. Your instructor may assign these individually, or you may be asked to work through the activities in groups.

Projects or Group Activities

The table at the right shows how to determine weekly federal withholding tax for a single person in 2011. Use this table for Exercises 39 to 43.

39. What is the withholding tax for a person who earns $38 in one week?

40. What is the withholding tax for a person who earns $157

Income is between	Withholding amount
$0 and $40	$0
$40 and $204	$0 + 10% of amount over $40
$204 and $704	$16.40 + 15% of amount over $204
$704 and $1648	$91.40 + 25% of amount over $704
$1648 and $3394	$327.40 + 28% of amount over $1648
$3394 and $7332	$816.28 + 33% of amount over $3394
More than $7332	$2115.82 + 35% of amount over $7332

Additional Resources — Get More from Your Textbook!

Instructor Resources

Annotated Instructor's Edition (AIE)
(ISBN 978-1-285-09664-3)

The Annotated Instructor's Edition features answers to all of the problems in the text, as well as an appendix denoting those problems that can be found in Enhanced WebAssign.

PowerLecture with Diploma®
(ISBN 978-1-285-09462-5)

This DVD provides the instructor with dynamic media tools for teaching. Create, deliver, and customize tests (both print and online) in minutes with Diploma's Computerized Testing featuring algorithmic equations. Easily build solution sets for homework or exams using Solution Builder's online solutions manual. Quickly and easily update your syllabus with the Syllabus Creator, which was created by the authors and contains the new edition's table of contents.

Complete Solutions Manual (ISBN 978-1-285-09439-7)
Author: Carrie Green

The Complete Solutions Manual provides worked-out solutions to all of the problems in the text.

Instructor's Resource Binder with Appendix
(ISBN 978-1-285-09664-3)
Author: Maria H. Andersen, Muskegon Community College; Appendices by Richard N. Aufmann, Palomar College, and Joanne S. Lockwood, Nashua Community College

Each section of the main text is discussed in uniquely designed Teaching Guides that contain tips, examples, activities, worksheets, overheads, assessments, and solutions to all worksheets and activities.

Solution Builder

This online instructor database offers complete, worked-out solutions to all exercises in the text, allowing you to create customized, secure solutions printouts (in PDF format) matched exactly to the problems you assign in class. For more information, visit www.cengage.com/solutionbuilder.

Enhanced WebAssign® (ISBN 978-0-538-73810-1)

Exclusively from Cengage Learning, Enhanced WebAssign combines the exceptional mathematics content that you know and love with the most powerful online homework solution, WebAssign. Enhanced WebAssign engages students with immediate feedback, rich tutorial content, and interactive, fully customizable eBooks (YouBook), helping students to develop a deeper conceptual understanding of their subject matter. Online assignments can be built by selecting from thousands of text-specific problems or supplemented with problems from any Cengage Learning textbook.

Student Resources

Student Solutions Manual
(ISBN 978-1-285-09173-0)
Author: Carrie Green

Go beyond answers and improve your grade! This manual provides worked-out, step-by-step solutions to the odd-numbered problems in the text. The Student Solutions Manual gives you the information you need to truly understand how the problems are solved.

Student Workbook (ISBN 978-1-285-09466-3)
Author: Maria H. Andersen, Muskegon Community College

Get a head start. The Student Workbook contains assessments, activities, and worksheets for classroom discussions, in-class activities, and group work.

AIM for Success Student Practice Sheets
(ISBN 978-1-285-09719-0)
Author: Christine S. Verity

AIM for Success Student Practice Sheets provide additional problems to help you learn the material.

Enhanced WebAssign (ISBN 978-0-538-73810-1)

Enhanced WebAssign (assigned by the instructor) provides you with instant feedback on homework assignments. This online homework system is easy to use and includes helpful links to textbook sections, video examples, and problem-specific tutorials.

Acknowledgments

The authors would like to thank the people who have reviewed the ninth edition and provided many valuable suggestions.

Becky Bradshaw, *Lake Superior College*
Harvey Cartine, *Warren County Community College*
Jim Dawson, *College of Southern Idaho*
Cindy Dickson, *College of Southern Idaho*
Estella G. Elliott, *College of Southern Idaho*
Stephen Ester, *Saint Petersburg College*
Cassie Firth, *Northern Oklahoma College*
Lori L. Grady, *University of Wisconsin–Whitewater*
Nicholas Grener, *California State University, East Bay*
Ryan Grossman, *Ivy Tech Community College–Indiana*
Autumn Hoover, *Angelo State University*
Pat Horacek, *Pensacola State College*
Kelly Jackson, *Camden County College*
Thomas Judge, *California State University, East Bay*
Katy Koe, *Lincoln College*
William Lind, *Bryant and Stratton College*
Renee Lustig, *LeCordon Bleu College of Culinary Arts*
David Maina, *Columbia College, Chicago*
Connie Meade, *College of Southern Idaho*
Eugenia M. Moreno, *Butte Community College*
Dan Quynh Nguyen, *California State University, East Bay*
Rod Oberdick, *Delaware Technical Community College*
Scott Phelps, *University of La Verne*
David Poock, *Davenport University*
Nolan Thomas Rice, *College of Southern Idaho*
Daria Santerre, *Norwalk Community College*
Patricia Shepherd, *Ivy Tech Community College*
Darlyn Thomas, *Hennepin Technical College*
Sherri Urcavich, *University of Wisconsin–Green Bay*
Dr. Pamela D. Walker, *Northwestern College*
Donna M. Weglarz, *Westwood College–DuPage*
Lisa Williams, *College of the Abermarle*
Solomon Lee Willis, *Cleveland Community College*
Jerry Jacob Woods, *Westwood College*
Chen Zhixiong, *New Jersey City University*

Special thanks go to Jean Bermingham for copyediting the manuscript and proofreading pages, to Carrie Green for preparing the solutions manuals, and to Lauri Semarne for her work in ensuring the accuracy of the text. We would also like to thank the many people at Cengage Learning who worked to guide the manuscript for the ninth edition from development through production.

Index of Applications

AIM for Success

Focus on Success

This important chapter describes study skills that are used by students who have been successful in this course. Chapter A covers a wide range of topics that focus on what you need to do to succeed in this class. It includes a complete guide to the textbook and how to use its features to become a successful student.

hxdbzxy/Shutterstock.com

Prep Test

Are you ready to succeed in this course?

1. Read this chapter. Answer all of the questions. Write down your answers on paper.

2. Write down your instructor's name.

3. Write down the classroom number.

4. Write down the days and times the class meets.

5. Bring your textbook, a notebook, and a pen or pencil to every class.

6. Be an active participant, not a passive observer.

A.1

How to Succeed in This Course

Get Ready

We are committed to your success in learning mathematics and have developed many tools and resources to support you along the way.

DO YOU WANT TO EXCEL IN THIS COURSE?

Read on to learn about the skills you'll need and how best to use this book to get the results you want.

We have written this text in an *interactive* style. More about this later but, in short, this means that you are supposed to interact with the text. Do not just read the text! Work along with it. Ready? Let's begin!

WHY ARE YOU TAKING THIS COURSE?

Did you interact with the text, or did you just read the last question? Get some paper and a pencil or pen and answer the question. Really—you will have more success in math and other courses you take if you **actively participate.** Now, **interact.** Write down one reason you are taking this course.

Of course, we have no idea what you just wrote, but experience has shown us that many of you wrote something along the lines of "I have to take it to graduate" or "It is a prerequisite to another course I have to take" or "It is required for my major." Those reasons are perfectly fine. Every teacher has had to take courses that were not directly related to his or her major.

WHY DO YOU WANT TO SUCCEED IN THIS COURSE?

Think about why you want to succeed in this course. List the reasons here (not in your head . . . on the paper!):

One reason you may have listed is that math skills are important in order to be successful in your chosen career. That is certainly an important reason. Here are some other reasons.

- Math is a skill that applies across careers, which is certainly a benefit in our world of changing job requirements. A good foundation in math may enable you to more easily make a career change.
- Math can help you learn critical thinking skills, an attribute all employers want.
- Math can help you see relationships between ideas and identify patterns.

Take Note

Motivation alone won't lead to success. For example, suppose a person who cannot swim is rowed out to the middle of a lake and thrown overboard. That person has a lot of motivation to swim, but most likely will drown without some help. You'll need motivation *and* learning in order to succeed.

Motivate Yourself

You'll find many real-life problems in this book, relating to sports, money, cars, music, and more. We hope that these topics will help you understand how mathematics is used in everyday life. To learn all of the necessary skills and to understand how you can apply them to your life outside of this course, motivate yourself to learn.

One of the reasons we asked you why you are taking this course was to provide motivation for you to succeed. When there is a reason to do something, that task is easier to accomplish. We understand that you may not want to be taking this course but, to achieve your career goal, this is a necessary step. Let your career goal be your motivation for success.

MAKE THE COMMITMENT TO SUCCEED!

With practice, you will improve your math skills. Skeptical? Think about when you first learned to drive a car, ride a skateboard, dance, paint, surf, or any other talent that you now have. You may have felt self-conscious or concerned that you might fail. But with time and practice, you learned the skill.

List a situation in which you accomplished your goal by spending time practicing and perfecting your skills (such as learning to play the piano or to play basketball):

You do not get "good" at something by doing it once a week. **Practice** is the backbone of any successful endeavor—including math!

Develop a "Can Do" Attitude Toward Math

You can do math! When you first learned the skills you just listed above, you may not have done them well. With practice, you got better. With practice, you will get better at math. Stay focused, motivated, and committed to success.

We cannot emphasize enough how important it is to overcome the "I Can't Do Math" syndrome. If you listen to interviews of very successful athletes after a particularly bad performance, you will note that they focus on the positive aspects of what they did, not the negative. Sports psychologists encourage athletes always to be positive—to have a "can do" attitude. Develop this attitude toward math and you will succeed.

Change your conversation about mathematics. Do not say "I can't do math," "I hate math," or "Math is too hard." These comments just give you an excuse to fail. You don't want to fail, and we don't want you to fail. Write it down now: **I can do math!**

Strategies for Success

PREPARE TO SUCCEED

There are a number of things that may be worrisome to you as you begin a new semester. List some of those things now.

William Perugini/Shutterstock.com

_____

_____

Here are some of the concerns expressed by our students.

- **Tuition**
  Will I be able to afford school?
- **Job**
  I must work. Will my employer give me a schedule that will allow me to go to school?
- **Anxiety**
  Will I succeed?
- **Child care**
  What will I do with my kids while I'm in class or when I need to study?
- **Time**
  Will I be able to find the time to attend class and study?
- **Degree goals**
  How long will it take me to finish school and earn my degree?

These are all important and valid concerns. Whatever your concerns, acknowledge them. Choose an education path that allows you to accommodate your concerns. Make sure they don't prevent you from succeeding.

SELECT A COURSE

Many schools offer math assessment tests. These tests evaluate your present math skills. They don't evaluate how smart you are, so don't worry about your score on the test. If you are unsure about where you should start in the math curriculum, these tests can show you where to begin. You are better off starting at a level that is appropriate for you than starting with a more advanced class and then dropping it because you can't keep up. Dropping a class is a waste of time and money.

If you have difficulty with math, avoid short courses that compress the class into a few weeks. If you have struggled with math in the past, this environment does not give you the time to process math concepts. Similarly, avoid classes that meet once a week. The time delay between classes makes it difficult to make connections between concepts.

Some career goals require a number of math courses. If that is true of your major, try to take a math course every semester until you complete the requirements. Think about it this way. If you take, say, French I, and then wait two semesters before taking French II, you may forget a lot of material. Math is much the same. You must keep the concepts fresh in your mind.

Time Management

wavebreakmedia ltd/Shutterstock.com

One of the most important requirements in completing any task is to acknowledge the amount of time it will take to finish the job successfully. Before a construction company starts to build a skyscraper, the company spends months looking at how much time each of the phases of construction will take. This is done so that resources can be allocated when appropriate. For instance, it would not make sense to schedule the electricians to run wiring until the walls are up.

MANAGE YOUR TIME!

We know how busy you are outside of school. Do you have a full-time or a part-time job? Do you have children? Do you visit your family often? Do you play school sports or participate in the school orchestra or theater company? It can be stressful to balance all of the important activities and responsibilities in your life. Creating a time management plan will help you schedule enough time to do everything you need to do. Let's get started.

First, you need a calendar. You can use a daily planner, a calendar for a smartphone, or an online calendar, such as the ones offered by Google, MSN, or Yahoo. It is best to have a calendar on which you can fill in daily activities and be able to see a weekly or monthly view as well.

Start filling in your calendar now, even if it means stopping right here and finding a calendar. Some of the things you might include are:

- The hours each class meets
- Time for driving to and from work or school
- Leisure time, an important aspect of a healthy lifestyle
- Time for study. Plan at least one hour of study for each hour in class. This is a *minimum!*

- Time to eat
- Your work schedule
- Time for extracurricular activities such as sports, music lessons, or volunteer work
- Time for family and friends
- Time for sleep
- Time for exercise

Take Note

Be realistic about how much time you have. One gauge is that working 10 hours per week is approximately equivalent to taking one three-unit course. If your college considers 15 units a full load and you are working 10 hours per week, you should consider taking 12 units. The more you work, the fewer units you should take.

We really hope you did this. If not, please reconsider. One of the best pathways to success is understanding how much time it takes to succeed. When you finish your calendar, if it does not allow you enough time to stay physically and emotionally healthy, rethink some of your school or work activities. We don't want you to lose your job because you have to study math. On the other hand, we don't want you to fail in math because of your job.

If math is particularly difficult for you, consider taking fewer course units during the semesters you take math. This applies equally to any other subject that you may find difficult. There is no rule that you must finish college in four years. It is a myth—discard it now.

Now extend your calendar for the entire semester. Many of the entries will repeat, such as the time a class meets. In your extended calendar, include significant events that may disrupt your normal routine. These might include holidays, family outings, birthdays, anniversaries, or special events such as a concert or a football game. In addition to these events, be sure to include the dates of tests, the date of the final exam, and dates that projects or papers are due. These are all important semester events. Having them on your calendar will remind you that you need to make time for them.

CLASS TIME

To be successful, **attend class.** You should consider your commitment to attend class as serious as your commitment to your job or to keeping an appointment with a dear friend. It is difficult to overstate the importance of attending class. If you miss work, you don't get paid. If you miss class, you are not getting the full benefit of your tuition dollar. You are losing money.

If, by some unavoidable situation, you cannot attend class, find out as soon as possible what was covered in class. You might:

- Ask a friend for notes and the assignment.
- Contact your instructor and get the assignment. Missing class is no excuse for not being prepared for the next class.
- Determine whether there are online resources that you can use to help you with the topics and concepts that were discussed in the class you missed.

Going to class is important. Once you are there, **participate in class.** Stay involved and active. When your instructor asks a question, try to at least mentally answer the question. If you have a question, ask. Your instructor expects questions and wants you to understand the concept being discussed.

HOMEWORK TIME

In addition to attending class, you must **do homework.** Homework is the best way to reinforce the ideas presented in class. You should plan on at least one to two hours of homework and study for each hour you are in class. We've had many students tell us that one to two hours seems like a lot of time. That may be true, but if you want to attain your goals, you must be willing to devote the time to being successful in this math course.

You should schedule study time just as if it were class time. To do this, write down where and when you study best. For instance, do you study best at home, in the library, at the math center, under a tree, or somewhere else? Some psychologists who research successful study strategies suggest that just by varying where you study, you can increase the effectiveness of a study session. While you are considering where you prefer to study, also think about the time of day during which your study period will be most productive. Write down your thoughts.

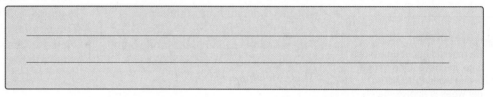

Look at what you have written, and be sure that you can consistently be in your favorite study environment at the time you have selected. Studying and homework are extremely important. Just as you should not miss class, **do not miss study time.**

Before we leave this important topic, we have a few suggestions. If at all possible, create a study hour right after class. The material will be fresh in your mind, and the immediate review, along with your homework, will help reinforce the concepts you are learning.

If you can't study right after class, make sure that you set aside some time *on the day of the class* to review notes and begin the homework. The longer you wait, the more difficult it will be to recall some of the important points covered during class. Study math in small chunks—one hour a day (perhaps not enough for most of us), every day, is better than seven hours in one sitting. If you are studying for an extended period of time, break up your study session by studying one subject for a while and then moving on to another subject. Try to alternate between similar or related courses. For instance, study math for a while, then science, and then back to math. Or study history for a while, then political science, and then back to history.

Meet some of the people in your class and try to **put together a study group.** The group could meet two or three times a week. During those meetings, you could quiz each other, prepare for a test, try to explain a concept to someone else in the group, or get help on a topic that is difficult for you.

After reading these suggestions, you may want to rethink where and when you study best. If so, do that now. Remember, however, that it is your individual style that is important. Choose what works for *you,* and stick to it.

Habits of Successful Students

There are a number of habits that successful students use. Think about what these might be, and write them down.

What you have written is very important. The habits you have listed are probably the things you know you must do to succeed. Here is a list of some responses from successful students we have known.

- **Set priorities.** You will encounter many distractions during the semester. Do not allow them to prevent you from reaching your goal.

- **Take responsibility.** Your instructor, this textbook, tutors, math centers, and other resources are there to help you succeed. Ultimately, however, you must choose to learn. You must choose success.

- **Hang out with successful students.** Success breeds success. When you work and study with successful students, you are in an environment that will help you succeed. Seek out people who are committed to their goals.

- **Study regularly.** We have mentioned this before, but it is too important not to be repeated.

- **Self test.** Once every few days, select homework exercises from previous assignments and use them to test your understanding. Try to do these exercises without getting help from examples in the text. These self tests will help you gain confidence that you can do these types of problems on a test given in class.

- **Try different strategies.** If you read the text and are still having difficulty understanding a concept, consider going a step further. Contact the instructor or find a tutor. Many campuses have some free tutorial services. Go to the math or learning center. Consult another textbook. Be active and get the help you need.

- **Make flash cards.** This is one of the strategies that some math students do not think to try. Flash cards are a very important part of learning math. For instance, your instructor may use words or phrases such as *linear, quadratic, exponent, base, rational,* and many others. If you don't know the meanings of these words, you will not know what is being discussed.

- **Plod along.** Your education is not a race. The primary goal is to finish. Taking too many classes and then dropping some does not get you to the end any faster. Take only as many classes as you can successfully manage.

SECTION

A.2 How to Use This Text to Succeed in This Course

Helder Almeida/Shutterstock.com

Get the Big Picture

One of the major resources that you will have access to the entire semester is this textbook. We have written this text with you and your success in mind. The following is a guide to the features of this text that will help you succeed.

Actually, we want you to get the *really* big picture. Take a few minutes to read the table of contents. You may feel some anxiety about all the new concepts you will be learning. Try to think of this as an exciting opportunity to learn math. Now look through the entire book. Move quickly. Don't spend more than a few seconds on each page. Scan titles, look at pictures, and notice diagrams.

Getting this "big picture" view will help you see where this course is going. To reach your goal, it's important to get an idea of the steps you will need to take along the way.

As you look through the book, find topics that interest you. What's your preference? Racing? Sailing? TV? Amusement parks? Find the Index of Applications at the front of the book, and pull out three subjects that interest you. Write those topics here.

Understand the Organization

Look again at the Table of Contents. There are six chapters in this book. You'll see that every chapter is divided into sections, and each section contains a number of learning objectives. Each learning objective is labeled with a letter from A to D. Knowing how this book is organized will help you locate important topics and concepts as you're studying.

Before you start a new objective, take a few minutes to read the Objective Statement for that objective. Then, browse through the objective material. Especially note the words or phrases in bold type—these are important concepts that you'll need to know as you move along in the course. These words are good candidates for flash cards. If possible, include an example of the concept on the flash card, as shown at the left.

You will also see important concepts and rules set off in boxes. Here is one about the Multiplication Property of One. These rules are also good candidates for flash cards.

Flash Card

> Multiplication Property of One
>
> Multiplying a number by 1 does not change the number.
>
> Examples:
> $8 \times 1 = 8$
> $1 \times 6 = 6$

Multiplication Property of One

Multiplying a number by 1 does not change the number.

EXAMPLES

1. $8 \times 1 = 8$ **2.** $1 \times 6 = 6$

Leaf through Section 1.2 of Chapter 1. Write down the words in bold and any concepts or rules that are displayed in boxes.

Use the Interactive Method

As we mentioned earlier, this textbook is based on an interactive approach. We want you to be actively involved in learning mathematics, and have given you many suggestions for getting "hands-on" with this book.

HOW TO Look on page 27. See HOW TO 2? A HOW TO introduces a concept (in this case, multiplying whole numbers) and includes a step-by-step solution of the type of exercise you will find in the homework.

HOW TO 2   Find the product of 47 and 23.

Multiply by the ones digit.	Multiply by the tens digit.	Add.

Multiply by the ones digit.

$$\begin{array}{r} 47 \\ \times\ 23 \\ \hline 141 \end{array} \quad (= 47 \times 3)$$

Multiply by the tens digit.

$$\begin{array}{r} 47 \\ \times\ 23 \\ \hline 141 \\ 940 \end{array} \quad (= 47 \times 20)$$

↑
Writing the 0 keeps the columns aligned correctly.

Add.

$$\begin{array}{r} 47 \\ \times\ 23 \\ \hline 141 \\ 940 \\ \hline 1081 \end{array}$$

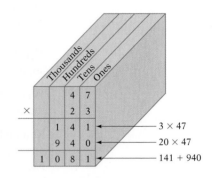

Grab paper and a pencil and work along as you're reading through the HOW TO. When you're done, get a clean sheet of paper. Write down the problem and try to complete the solution without looking at your notes or at the book. When you're done, check your answer. If you got it right, you're ready to move on.

Look through the text and find three instances of a HOW TO. Write the concept illustrated in each HOW TO here.

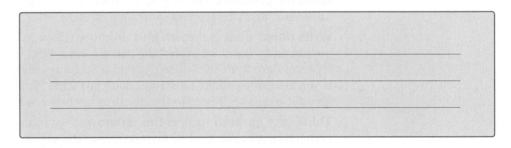

Example/You Try It Pair You'll need hands-on practice to succeed in mathematics. When we show you an example, work it out yourself, right beside the solution. Use the Example/You Try It pairs to get the practice you need.

Take a look at page 27. Example 2 and You Try It 2 are shown here.

EXAMPLE 2

Find 829 multiplied by 603.

Solution

$$\begin{array}{r} 829 \\ \times\ \ \ 603 \\ \hline 2487 \\ 49740 \\ \hline 499{,}887 \end{array}$$

- $3 \times 829 = 2487$
- Write a zero in the tens column for 0×829.
- $6 \times 829 = 4974$

YOU TRY IT 2

Multiply: 756×305

Your solution

Solution on p. S2

You'll see that each Example is fully worked out. Study the Example by carefully working through each step. Then, try to complete the You Try It. Use the solution to the Example as a model for solving the You Try It. If you get stuck, the solutions to the You Try Its are provided in the back of the book. There is a page number directly following the You Try It that shows you where you can find the completely-worked-out solution. Use the solution to get a hint for the step on which you are stuck. Then, try again!

When you've arrived at your solution, check your work against the solution in the back of the book. Turn to page S2 to see the solution for You Try It 2.

Remember that sometimes there is more than one way to solve a problem. But your answer should always match the answer we've given in the back of the book. If you have any questions about whether your method will always work, check with your instructor.

Use a Strategy to Solve Word Problems

Learning to solve word problems is one of the reasons you are studying math. This is where you combine all of the critical thinking skills you have learned to solve practical problems.

Try not to be intimidated by word problems. Basically, what you need is a strategy that will help you come up with the equation you will need to solve the problem. When you are looking at a word problem, try the following:

- **Read the problem.** This may seem pretty obvious, but we mean really **read** it. Don't just scan it. Read the problem slowly and carefully.

- **Write down what is known and unknown.** Now that you have read the problem, go back and write down everything that is known. Next, write down what it is you are trying to find. *Write* this—don't just think it! Be as specific as you can. For instance, if you are asked to find a distance, don't just write "I need to find the distance." Be specific and write "I need to find the distance between Earth and the moon."

- **Think of a method to find the unknown.** For instance, should you use addition, subtraction, multiplication, or division to find the unknown quantity? This is certainly the most difficult step.

- **Solve the problem.** Be careful as you solve the problem. There is no sense in getting to this point and then making a careless mistake. The unknown in most problems will include a unit such as feet, dollars, or miles per hour. When you write your answer, include a unit. An answer such as 20 doesn't mean much. Is it 20 feet, 20 dollars, 20 miles per hour, or something else?

- **Check your solution.** Now that you have an answer, go back to the problem and ask yourself whether it makes sense. This is an important step. For instance, if, according to your answer, the cost of a car is $2.51, you know that something went wrong.

In this text, the solution of every word problem is broken down into two steps, **Strategy** and **Solution.** The Strategy consists of the first three steps discussed above. The Solution is the last two steps. Here is an Example from page 28 of the text. Because you have not yet studied the concepts involved in the problem, you may not be able to solve it. However, note the detail in the Strategy. When you do the You Try It following an Example, be sure to include your own Strategy.

EXAMPLE 4

A pharmacist's assistant earns $640 for working a 40-hour week. This week the assistant also worked 7 hours of overtime at $26 an hour. Find the assistant's total pay for the week.

Strategy

To find the assistant's total pay for the week:
- Find the overtime pay by multiplying the hours of overtime (7) by the overtime rate of pay (26).
- Add the weekly salary (640) to the overtime pay.

Solution

$$\begin{array}{r} 26 \\ \times\ 7 \\ \hline 182 \end{array} \text{ overtime pay} \qquad \begin{array}{r} 640 \\ +\ 182 \\ \hline 822 \end{array}$$

The assistant earned $822 this week.

YOU TRY IT 4

The buyer for Ross Department Store can buy 80 men's suits for $7600. Each sports jacket will cost the store $62. The manager orders 80 men's suits and 25 sports jackets. What is the total cost of the order?

Your strategy

Your solution

Solutions on p. S2

When you have finished studying a section, **do the exercises your instructor has selected.** Math is not a spectator sport. You must practice every day. Do the homework and do not get behind.

Ace the Test

There are a number of features in this text that will help you prepare for a test. These features will help you even more if you do just one simple thing: When you are doing your homework, go back to each previous homework assignment for the current chapter and rework two exercises. That's right—just *two* exercises. You will be surprised at how much better prepared you will be for a test by doing this.

Here are some additional aids to help you **ace the test.**

Chapter Summary Once you've completed a chapter, look at the Chapter Summary. The Chapter Summary is divided into two sections: **Key Words** and **Essential Rules and Procedures.** Flip to page 196 to see the Chapter Summary for Chapter 4. The summary shows all of the important topics covered in the chapter. Do you see the reference following each topic? This reference shows you the objective and page in the text where you can find more information on the concept.

Write down one Key Word and one Essential Rule or Procedure. Explain the meaning of the reference "4.1A, page 178."

Chapter Review Exercises Turn to page 197 to see the Chapter Review Exercises for Chapter 4. When you do the review exercises, you're giving yourself an important opportunity to test your understanding of the chapter. The answer to each review exercise is given at the back of the book, along with the objective the question relates to. When you're done with the Chapter Review Exercises, check your answers. If you had trouble with any of the questions, you can restudy the objectives and retry some of the exercises in those objectives for extra help.

Go to the Answer Section at the back of the text. Find the answers for the Chapter Review Exercises for Chapter 4. Write down the answer to Exercise 6. Explain the meaning of the reference "4.2B."

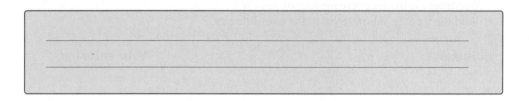

Chapter Test The Chapter Test for each chapter can be found after the Chapter Review Exercises and can be used to help you prepare for your exam. The answer to each question is given at the back of the book, along with both an objective reference and a reference to a HOW TO, Example, or You Try It that the question relates to. Think of these tests as "practice runs" for your in-class tests. Take the test in a quiet place, and try to work through it in the same amount of time that will be allowed for your actual exam.

The aids we have mentioned above will help you prepare for a test. You should begin your review *at least* two days before the test—three days is better. These aids will get you ready for the test.

Here are some suggestions to try while you are actually taking the test.

- **Try to relax.** We know that test situations make some students quite nervous or anxious. These feelings are normal. Try to stay calm and focused on what you know. If you have prepared as we have suggested, the answers will begin to come to you.
- **Scan the test.** Get a feeling for the big picture.
- **Read the directions carefully.** Make sure you answer each question fully.
- **Work the problems that are easiest for you first.** This will help you with your confidence and help reduce any nervous feelings you may have.

Ready, Set, Succeed!

It takes hard work and commitment to succeed, but we know you can do it! Doing well in mathematics is just one step you'll take on your path to success. Good luck. We wish you success.

hxdbzxy/Shutterstock.com

Whole Numbers

Focus on Success

Have you read Chapter A, AIM for Success? It describes study skills used by students who have been successful in their math courses. It gives you tips on how to stay motivated, how to manage your time, and how to prepare for exams. Chapter A also includes a complete guide to the textbook and how to use its features to be successful in this course. It starts on page AIM-1.

Andresr/Shutterstock.com

Prep Test

Are you ready to succeed in this chapter? Take the Prep Test below to find out if you are ready to learn the new material.

1. Name the number of ◆s shown below.

◆ ◆ ◆ ◆ ◆ ◆ ◆

2. Write the numbers from 1 to 10.

1 __ __ __ __ __ __ __ __ 10

3. Match the number with its word form.
a. 4   A. five
b. 2   B. one
c. 5   C. zero
d. 1   D. four
e. 3   E. two
f. 0   F. three

1

1.1   Introduction to Whole Numbers

OBJECTIVE A   *To identify the order relation between two numbers*

The **whole numbers** are 0, 1, 2, 3, 4, 5, 6, 7, 8, 9, 10, 11, 12, 13, 14, ...

The three dots mean that the list continues on and on and that there is no largest whole number.

Just as distances are associated with the markings on the edge of a ruler, the whole numbers can be associated with points on a line. This line is called the **number line.** The arrow on the number line below indicates that there is no largest whole number.

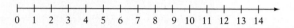

The **graph of a whole number** is shown by placing a heavy dot directly above that number on the number line. Here is the graph of 7 on the number line:

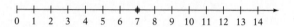

The number line can be used to show the order of whole numbers. A number that appears to the left of a given number **is less than (<)** the given number. A number that appears to the right of a given number **is greater than (>)** the given number.

Four is less than seven.
4 < 7

Twelve is greater than seven.
12 > 7

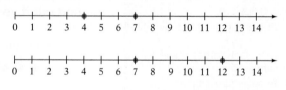

EXAMPLE 1

Graph 11 on the number line.

Solution

YOU TRY IT 1

Graph 6 on the number line.

Your solution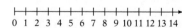

EXAMPLE 2

Place the correct symbol, < or >, between the two numbers.
a. 39   24
b.   0   51

Solution
a. 39 > 24
b.   0 < 51

YOU TRY IT 2

Place the correct symbol, < or >, between the two numbers.
a. 45   29
b. 27   0

Your solution
a.
b.

Solutions on p. S1

OBJECTIVE B *To write whole numbers in words and in standard form*

Point of Interest

The Babylonians had a place-value system based on 60. Its influence is still with us in angle measurement and time: 60 seconds in 1 minute, 60 minutes in 1 hour. It appears that the earliest record of a base-10 place-value system for natural numbers dates from the 8th century.

When a whole number is written using the digits 0, 1, 2, 3, 4, 5, 6, 7, 8, and 9, it is said to be in **standard form.** The position of each digit in the number determines the digit's **place value.** The diagram below shows a **place-value chart** naming the first 12 place values. The number 37,462 is in standard form and has been entered in the chart.

In the number 37,462, the position of the digit 3 determines that its place value is ten-thousands.

When a number is written in standard form, each group of digits separated from the other digits by a comma (or commas) is called a **period.** The number 3,786,451,294 has four periods. The period names are shown in red in the place-value chart above.

To write a number in words, start from the left. Name the number in each period. Then write the period name in place of the comma.

3,786,451,294 is read "three billion seven hundred eighty-six million four hundred fifty-one thousand two hundred ninety-four."

To write a whole number in standard form, write the number named in each period, and replace each period name with a comma.

Four million sixty-two thousand five hundred eighty-four is written 4,062,584. The zero is used as a place holder for the hundred-thousands place.

EXAMPLE 3

Write 25,478,083 in words.

Solution

Twenty-five million four hundred seventy-eight thousand eighty-three

YOU TRY IT 3

Write 36,462,075 in words.

Your solution

EXAMPLE 4

Write three hundred three thousand three in standard form.

Solution

303,003

YOU TRY IT 4

Write four hundred fifty-two thousand seven in standard form.

Your solution

Solutions on p. S1

OBJECTIVE C *To write whole numbers in expanded form*

The whole number 26,429 can be written in **expanded form** as

20,000 + 6000 + 400 + 20 + 9.

The place-value chart can be used to find the expanded form of a number.

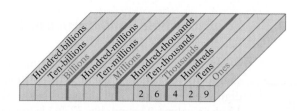

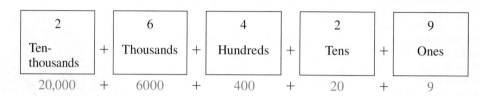

The number 420,806 is written in expanded form below. Note the effect of having zeros in the number.

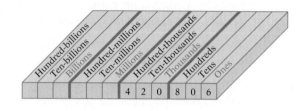

or simply 400,000 + 20,000 + 800 + 6.

EXAMPLE 5

Write 23,859 in expanded form.

Solution

20,000 + 3000 + 800 + 50 + 9

YOU TRY IT 5

Write 68,281 in expanded form.

Your solution

EXAMPLE 6

Write 709,542 in expanded form.

Solution

700,000 + 9000 + 500 + 40 + 2

YOU TRY IT 6

Write 109,207 in expanded form.

Your solution

Solutions on p. S1

OBJECTIVE D   *To round a whole number to a given place value*

When the distance to the moon is given as 240,000 miles, the number represents an approximation to the true distance. Taking an approximate value for an exact number is called **rounding.** A rounded number is always rounded to a given place value.

37 is closer to 40 than it is to 30. 37 rounded to the nearest ten is 40.

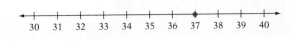

673 rounded to the nearest ten is 670. 673 rounded to the nearest hundred is 700.

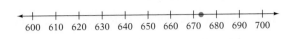

A whole number is rounded to a given place value without using the number line by looking at the first digit to the right of the given place value.

HOW TO 1 Round 13,834 to the nearest hundred.

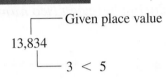

• If the digit to the right of the given place value is less than 5, that digit and all digits to the right are replaced by zeros.

13,834 rounded to the nearest hundred is 13,800.

HOW TO 2 Round 386,217 to the nearest ten-thousand.

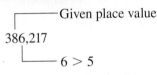

• If the digit to the right of the given place value is greater than or equal to 5, increase the digit in the given place value by 1, and replace all other digits to the right by zeros.

386,217 rounded to the nearest ten-thousand is 390,000.

EXAMPLE 7

Round 525,453 to the nearest ten-thousand.

Solution

```
         ┌── Given place value
525,453
     └── 5 = 5
```

525,453 rounded to the nearest ten-thousand is 530,000.

YOU TRY IT 7

Round 368,492 to the nearest ten-thousand.

Your solution

EXAMPLE 8

Round 1972 to the nearest hundred.

Solution

```
     ┌── Given place value
1972
    └── 7 > 5
```

1972 rounded to the nearest hundred is 2000.

YOU TRY IT 8

Round 3962 to the nearest hundred.

Your solution

Solutions on p. S1

1.1 EXERCISES

✔ Concept Check

1. Determine whether the statement is true or false.

   a. $23 > 48$ **b.** $0 < 14$ **c.** $15 > 0$ **d.** $47 < 74$

2. Name the place value of the digit 3 in each number.

   a. 83,479   **b.** 3,491,507   **c.** 2,634,958   **d.** 76,319,204

OBJECTIVE A   *To identify the order relation between two numbers*

For Exercises 3 to 6, graph the number on the number line.

3. 3   `0 1 2 3 4 5 6 7 8 9 10 11 12`   **4.** 5   `0 1 2 3 4 5 6 7 8 9 10 11 12`

5. 9   `0 1 2 3 4 5 6 7 8 9 10 11 12`   **6.** 0   `0 1 2 3 4 5 6 7 8 9 10 11 12`

For Exercises 7 to 14, place the correct symbol, $<$ or $>$, between the two numbers.

7. 37   49   **8.** 58   21   **9.** 101   87   **10.** 245   158

11. 2701   2071   **12.** 0   45   **13.** 107   0   **14.** 815   928

15. Do the inequalities $21 < 30$ and $30 > 21$ express the same order relation?

OBJECTIVE B   *To write whole numbers in words and in standard form*

For Exercises 16 to 23, write the number in words.

16. 2675   **17.** 3790   **18.** 42,928   **19.** 58,473

20. 356,943   **21.** 498,512   **22.** 3,697,483   **23.** 6,842,715

For Exercises 24 to 29, write the number in standard form.

24. Eighty-five

25. Three hundred fifty-seven

26. Three thousand four hundred fifty-six

27. Sixty-three thousand seven hundred eighty

28. Six hundred nine thousand nine hundred forty-eight

29. Seven million twenty-four thousand seven hundred nine

30. What is the place value of the first digit on the left in a seven-digit whole number?

OBJECTIVE C   *To write whole numbers in expanded form*

For Exercises 31 to 38, write the number in expanded form.

31. 5287

32. 6295

33. 58,943

34. 453,921

35. 200,583

36. 301,809

37. 403,705

38. 3,000,642

39. The expanded form of a number consists of four numbers added together. Must the number be a four-digit number?

OBJECTIVE D   *To round a whole number to a given place value*

For Exercises 40 to 51, round the number to the given place value.

40. 926   Tens

41. 845   Tens

42. 1439   Hundreds

43. 3973   Hundreds

44. 43,607   Thousands

45. 52,715   Thousands

46. 389,702   Thousands

47. 629,513   Thousands

48. 647,989   Ten-thousands

49. 253,678   Ten-thousands

50. 36,702,599   Millions

51. 71,834,250   Millions

52. True or false? If a number rounded to the nearest ten is less than the original number, then the ones digit of the original number is greater than 5.

Critical Thinking

53. If 3846 is rounded to the nearest ten and then that number is rounded to the nearest hundred, is the result the same as the result you get when you round 3846 to the nearest hundred? If not, which method is correct for rounding to the nearest hundred?

Projects or Group Activities

54. The U.S. House of Representatives has 435 members. The number of representatives that each state sends to the House of Representatives is based on the population of the state. State populations are determined every 10 years by the Census Bureau. Use the Census Bureau's Internet site to determine which states gained or lost a seat in the House of Representatives after the 2010 census.

1.2 Addition of Whole Numbers

OBJECTIVE A   *To add whole numbers*

Addition is the process of finding the total of two or more numbers.

APPLY THE CONCEPT

Maryka carried 4 soccer balls from her car to the soccer field. She returned to her car and carried 3 more balls to the field. By counting, the total of 4 balls and 3 balls is 7 balls. Maryka carried a total of 7 balls from her car to the field.

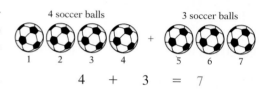

4 soccer balls   3 soccer balls

1 2 3 4   5 6 7

4   +   3   =   7

Addend + Addend = Sum

Here is a table of basic addition facts. These facts should be memorized.

Basic Addition Facts

+	1	2	3	4	5	6	7	8	9
1	1 + 1 = 2	1 + 2 = 3	1 + 3 = 4	1 + 4 = 5	1 + 5 = 6	1 + 6 = 7	1 + 7 = 8	1 + 8 = 9	1 + 9 = 10
2	2 + 1 = 3	2 + 2 = 4	2 + 3 = 5	2 + 4 = 6	2 + 5 = 7	2 + 6 = 8	2 + 7 = 9	2 + 8 = 10	2 + 9 = 11
3	3 + 1 = 4	3 + 2 = 5	3 + 3 = 6	3 + 4 = 7	3 + 5 = 8	3 + 6 = 9	3 + 7 = 10	3 + 8 = 11	3 + 9 = 12
4	4 + 1 = 5	4 + 2 = 6	4 + 3 = 7	4 + 4 = 8	4 + 5 = 9	4 + 6 = 10	4 + 7 = 11	4 + 8 = 12	4 + 9 = 13
5	5 + 1 = 6	5 + 2 = 7	5 + 3 = 8	5 + 4 = 9	5 + 5 = 10	5 + 6 = 11	5 + 7 = 12	5 + 8 = 13	5 + 9 = 14
6	6 + 1 = 7	6 + 2 = 8	6 + 3 = 9	6 + 4 = 10	6 + 5 = 11	6 + 6 = 12	6 + 7 = 13	6 + 8 = 14	6 + 9 = 15
7	7 + 1 = 8	7 + 2 = 9	7 + 3 = 10	7 + 4 = 11	7 + 5 = 12	7 + 6 = 13	7 + 7 = 14	7 + 8 = 15	7 + 9 = 16
8	8 + 1 = 9	8 + 2 = 10	8 + 3 = 11	8 + 4 = 12	8 + 5 = 13	8 + 6 = 14	8 + 7 = 15	8 + 8 = 16	8 + 9 = 17
9	9 + 1 = 10	9 + 2 = 11	9 + 3 = 12	9 + 4 = 13	9 + 5 = 14	9 + 6 = 15	9 + 7 = 16	9 + 8 = 17	9 + 9 = 18

Some special properties of addition that are used frequently are given below.

Commutative Property of Addition

Two numbers can be added in either order; the sum will be the same.

EXAMPLES

1. 4 + 8 = 8 + 4
         12 = 12

2. 9 + 6 = 6 + 9
         15 = 15

Associative Property of Addition

Grouping an addition in any order gives the same result. Parentheses are grouping symbols that mean "Do operations inside parentheses first."

EXAMPLES

1. (3 + 2) + 4 = 3 + (2 + 4)
         5   + 4 = 3 +   6
              9 = 9

2. (3 + 6) + 2 = 3 + (6 + 2)
         9   + 2 = 3 +   8
              11 = 11

> **Addition Property of Zero**
>
> Zero added to any number does not change the number.
>
> **EXAMPLES**
>
> **1.** $4 + 0 = 4$ **2.** $0 + 7 = 7$

To add large numbers, begin by arranging the numbers vertically, keeping the digits of the same place value in the same column.

HOW TO 1   Add: $321 + 6472$

$$
\begin{array}{c}
\text{THOUSANDS} \quad \text{HUNDREDS} \quad \text{TENS} \quad \text{ONES} \\
\begin{array}{r} 3\ 2\ 1 \\ +\ 6\ 4\ 7\ 2 \\ \hline 6\ 7\ 9\ 3 \end{array}
\end{array}
$$

• Add the digits in each column.

There are several words or phrases in English that indicate the operation of addition. Here are some examples:

added to	3 added to 5	$5 + 3$
more than	7 more than 5	$5 + 7$
the sum of	the sum of 3 and 9	$3 + 9$
increased by	4 increased by 6	$4 + 6$
the total of	the total of 8 and 3	$8 + 3$
plus	5 plus 10	$5 + 10$

Integrating Technology

Most scientific calculators use *algebraic logic:* the add ($+$), subtract ($-$), multiply ($\times$), and divide ($\div$) keys perform the indicated operation using the number in the display and the next number keyed in. For instance, for HOW TO 2 at the right, enter 24 $+$ 71 $=$. The display reads 95.

When the sum of the digits in a column exceeds 9, the addition will involve **carrying.**

HOW TO 2   What is the sum of 487 and 369?

$$
\begin{array}{r}
\text{HUNDREDS} \quad \text{TENS} \quad \text{ONES} \\
\overset{1}{} \\
4\ 8\ 7 \\
+\ 3\ 6\ 9 \\
\hline
6
\end{array}
$$

• The phrase *the sum of* means to add.
• Add the ones column.
  $7 + 9 = 16$ (1 ten + 6 ones).
  Write the 6 in the ones column and carry the 1 ten to the tens column.

$$
\begin{array}{r}
\overset{1}{4}\ \overset{1}{8}\ 7 \\
+\ 3\ 6\ 9 \\
\hline
5\ 6
\end{array}
$$

• Add the tens column.
  $1 + 8 + 6 = 15$ (1 hundred + 5 tens).
  Write the 5 in the tens column and carry the 1 hundred to the hundreds column.

$$
\begin{array}{r}
\overset{1}{4}\ \overset{1}{8}\ 7 \\
+\ 3\ 6\ 9 \\
\hline
8\ 5\ 6
\end{array}
$$

• Add the hundreds column.
  $1 + 4 + 3 = 8$ (8 hundreds).
  Write the 8 in the hundreds column.

The sum is 856.

EXAMPLE 1

Find the total of 17, 103, and 8.

Solution

$$\begin{array}{r} \overset{1}{17} \\ 103 \\ +8 \\ \hline 128 \end{array}$$

• 7 + 3 + 8 = 18
Write the 8 in the ones
column. Carry the 1 to
the tens column.

YOU TRY IT 1

What is 347 increased by 12,453?

Your solution

EXAMPLE 2

Find the sum of 89, 36, and 98.

Solution

$$\begin{array}{r} \overset{2}{89} \\ 36 \\ +98 \\ \hline 223 \end{array}$$

• 9 + 6 + 8 = 23
Write the 3 in the ones
column. Carry the 2 to
the tens column.

YOU TRY IT 2

Add: 95 + 88 + 67

Your solution

EXAMPLE 3

Add: 41,395
       4,327
       497,625
    +   32,991

Solution

$$\begin{array}{r} \overset{1\,1\,2\ \,2\,1}{41,395} \\ 4,327 \\ 497,625 \\ +32,991 \\ \hline 576,338 \end{array}$$

YOU TRY IT 3

Add: 392
        4,079
       89,035
    +   4,992

Your solution

Solutions on p. S1

**Integrating
Technology**

This example illustrates that
estimation is important when
one is using a calculator.

ESTIMATION: Estimation and Calculators

At some places in the text, you will be asked to use your calculator. Effective use of a calculator requires that you estimate the answer to the problem. This helps ensure that you have entered the numbers correctly and pressed the correct keys.

For example, if you use your calculator to find 22,347 + 5896 and the answer in the calculator's display is 131,757,912, you should realize that you have entered some part of the calculation incorrectly. In this case, you pressed ⨉ instead of ＋ . By estimating the answer to a problem, you can help ensure the accuracy of your calculations. There is a special symbol for **approximately equal to:** ≈.

For example, to estimate the answer to 22,347 + 5896, round each number to the same place value. In this case, we will round to the nearest thousand. Then add.

$$\begin{array}{r} 22,347 \approx 22,000 \\ +5,896 \approx +6,000 \\ \hline 28,000 \end{array}$$

The sum 22,347 + 5896 is approximately 28,000. Knowing this, you would know that 131,757,912 is much too large and is therefore incorrect.

To estimate the sum of two numbers, first round each number to the same place value, and then add. Compare this answer with the calculator's answer.

OBJECTIVE B   *To solve application problems*

To solve an application problem, first read the problem carefully. Devising a **strategy** involves identifying the quantity to be found and planning the steps that are necessary to find that quantity. Finding the **solution of an application problem** involves performing each operation stated in the strategy and writing the answer.

HOW TO 3

The table below displays the Walmart store count and square footage in the United States as reported in the Walmart 2011 Annual Report.

	Discount Stores	Supercenters	Sam's Clubs	Neighborhood Markets
Number of units	629	3029	611	168
Square footage (in millions)	68	560	81	7

Find the total number of Walmart discount stores and Supercenters in the United States.

Strategy   To find the total number of Walmart discount stores and Supercenters in the United States, read the table to find the number of each type of store in the United States. Then add the numbers.

Solution
$$\begin{array}{r} 629 \\ + \; 3029 \\ \hline 3658 \end{array}$$

Walmart has a total of 3658 discount stores and Supercenters in the United States.

EXAMPLE 4

Use the table above to find the total number of Sam's Clubs and neighborhood markets that Walmart owns in the United States.

Strategy

To determine the total number of Sam's Clubs and neighborhood markets, read the table to find the number of Sam's Clubs and the number of neighborhood markets. Then add the two numbers.

Solution
$$\begin{array}{r} 611 \\ + \; 168 \\ \hline 779 \end{array}$$

Walmart owns a total of 779 Sam's Clubs and neighborhood markets.

YOU TRY IT 4

Use the table above to determine the total square footage of Walmart stores in the United States.

Your strategy

Your solution

Solution on p. S1

1.2 EXERCISES

✔ Concept Check

For Exercises 1 to 6, identify the property on page 8 or 9 that justifies the statement.

1. $347 + 0 = 347$

2. $6 + (8 + 1) = (6 + 8) + 1$

3. $(3 + 7) + 4 = 3 + (7 + 4)$

4. $13 + 302 = 302 + 13$

5. $(9 + 8) + 3 = (8 + 9) + 3$

6. $23 + (0 + 9) = 23 + 9$

OBJECTIVE A   *To add whole numbers*

For Exercises 7 to 36, add.

7.
$$\begin{array}{r} 17 \\ + 11 \\ \hline \end{array}$$

8.
$$\begin{array}{r} 25 \\ + 63 \\ \hline \end{array}$$

9.
$$\begin{array}{r} 83 \\ + 42 \\ \hline \end{array}$$

10.
$$\begin{array}{r} 63 \\ + 94 \\ \hline \end{array}$$

11.
$$\begin{array}{r} 77 \\ + 25 \\ \hline \end{array}$$

12.
$$\begin{array}{r} 63 \\ + 49 \\ \hline \end{array}$$

13.
$$\begin{array}{r} 56 \\ + 98 \\ \hline \end{array}$$

14.
$$\begin{array}{r} 86 \\ + 68 \\ \hline \end{array}$$

15.
$$\begin{array}{r} 658 \\ + 831 \\ \hline \end{array}$$

16.
$$\begin{array}{r} 842 \\ + 936 \\ \hline \end{array}$$

17.
$$\begin{array}{r} 735 \\ + 93 \\ \hline \end{array}$$

18.
$$\begin{array}{r} 189 \\ + 50 \\ \hline \end{array}$$

19.
$$\begin{array}{r} 859 \\ + 725 \\ \hline \end{array}$$

20.
$$\begin{array}{r} 637 \\ + 829 \\ \hline \end{array}$$

21.
$$\begin{array}{r} 36,925 \\ + 65,392 \\ \hline \end{array}$$

22.
$$\begin{array}{r} 56,772 \\ + 51,239 \\ \hline \end{array}$$

23.
$$\begin{array}{r} 50,873 \\ + 28,453 \\ \hline \end{array}$$

24.
$$\begin{array}{r} 34,872 \\ + 46,079 \\ \hline \end{array}$$

25.
$$\begin{array}{r} 878 \\ 737 \\ + 189 \\ \hline \end{array}$$

26.
$$\begin{array}{r} 768 \\ 461 \\ + 669 \\ \hline \end{array}$$

27.
$$\begin{array}{r} 319 \\ 348 \\ + 912 \\ \hline \end{array}$$

28.
$$\begin{array}{r} 292 \\ 579 \\ + 315 \\ \hline \end{array}$$

29.
$$\begin{array}{r} 9409 \\ 3253 \\ + 7078 \\ \hline \end{array}$$

30.
$$\begin{array}{r} 8188 \\ 8020 \\ + 7104 \\ \hline \end{array}$$

31.
$$\begin{array}{r} 2038 \\ 2243 \\ + 3139 \\ \hline \end{array}$$

32.
$$\begin{array}{r} 4252 \\ 6882 \\ + 5235 \\ \hline \end{array}$$

33.
$$\begin{array}{r} 67,428 \\ 32,171 \\ + 20,971 \\ \hline \end{array}$$

34.
$$\begin{array}{r} 52,801 \\ 11,664 \\ + 89,638 \\ \hline \end{array}$$

35.
$$\begin{array}{r} 76,290 \\ 43,761 \\ + 87,402 \\ \hline \end{array}$$

36.
$$\begin{array}{r} 43,901 \\ 98,301 \\ + 67,943 \\ \hline \end{array}$$

For Exercises 37 to 44, add.

37. 20,958 + 3218 + 42

38. 80,973 + 5168 + 29

39. 392 + 37 + 10,924 + 621

40. 694 + 62 + 70,129 + 217

41. 294 + 1029 + 7935 + 65

42. 692 + 2107 + 3196 + 92

43. 97 + 7234 + 69,532 + 276

44. 87 + 1698 + 27,317 + 727

45. What is 9874 plus 4509?

46. What is 7988 plus 5678?

47. What is 3487 increased by 5986?

48. What is 99,567 increased by 126,863?

49. What is 23,569 more than 9678?

50. What is 7894 more than 45,872?

51. What is 479 added to 4579?

52. What is 23,902 added to 23,885?

53. Find the total of 659, 55, and 1278.

54. Find the total of 4561, 56, and 2309.

55. Find the sum of 34, 329, 8, and 67,892.

56. Find the sum of 45, 1289, 7, and 32,876.

For Exercises 57 to 60, use a calculator to add. Then round the numbers to the nearest hundred, and use estimation to determine whether the sum is reasonable.

57. 1234 + 9780 + 6740

58. 919 + 3642 + 8796

59. 241 + 569 + 390 + 1672

60. 107 + 984 + 1035 + 2904

For Exercises 61 to 64, use a calculator to add. Then round the numbers to the nearest thousand, and use estimation to determine whether the sum is reasonable.

61.   32,461
            9,844
         + 59,407

62.   29,036
           22,904
         + 7,903

63.   25,432
           62,941
         + 70,390

64.   66,541
           29,365
         + 98,742

For Exercises 65 to 68, use a calculator to add. Then round the numbers to the nearest ten-thousand, and use estimation to determine whether the sum is reasonable.

65.	67,421	66.	21,896	67.	281,421	68.	542,698
	82,984		4,235		9,874		97,327
	66,361		62,544		34,394		7,235
	10,792		21,892		526,398		73,667
	+ 34,037		+ 1,334		+ 94,631		+ 173,201

69. Which property of addition (see pages 8 and 9) allows you to use either arrangement shown at the right to find the sum of 691 and 452?

$$691 \quad\quad 452$$
$$+ 452 \quad\quad + 691$$

OBJECTIVE B   *To solve application problems*

70. Use the table of Walmart data on page 11. What does the sum 68 + 560 represent?

71. **Demographics**   In a recent year, according to the Centers for Disease Control and Prevention, there were 138,660 twin births in this country, 5877 triplet births, 345 quadruplet deliveries, and 46 quintuplet and other higher-order multiple births. Find the total number of multiple births during the year.

Melissa King/Shutterstock.com

72. **Demographics**   The Census Bureau estimated that the U.S. population would grow by 296 million people from 2000 to 2100. Given that the U.S. population in 2000 was 281 million, find the Census Bureau's estimate of the U.S. population in 2100.

The Film Industry   The graph at the right shows the domestic box-office gross income from the first eight *Harry Potter* movies. Use this information for Exercises 73 to 75.

73. Find the total gross income from the eight *Harry Potter* movies.

74. Find the total gross income from the two lowest-grossing *Harry Potter* movies.

75. Find the total gross income from the two highest-grossing *Harry Potter* movies.

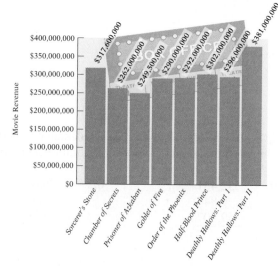

(*Source:* www.the-numbers.com/movies/series/HarryPotter.php)

76. Geometry The perimeter of a triangle is the sum of the lengths of the three sides of the triangle. Find the perimeter of a triangle that has sides that measure 12 inches, 14 inches, and 17 inches.

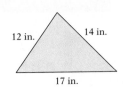

77. Travel The odometer on a moving van reads 68,692. The driver plans to drive 515 miles the first day, 492 miles the second day, and 278 miles the third day.
a. How many miles will be driven during the three days?
b. What will the odometer reading be at the end of the trip?

78. ● **Internet** Thirty-seven million U.S. households do not have broadband Internet access. Seventy-eight million U.S. households do have broadband Internet access. How many households are there in the United States? (*Source:* U.S. Department of Commerce)

79. ● **Energy** In a recent year, the United States produced 5,633,000 barrels of crude oil per day and imported 9,003,300 barrels of crude oil per day. Find the total number of barrels of crude oil produced and imported per day in the United States. (*Source:* Energy Information Administration)

Critical Thinking

80. If you roll two ordinary six-sided dice and add the two numbers that appear on top, how many different sums are possible?

81. If you add two *different* whole numbers, is the sum always greater than either one of the numbers? If not, give an example.

82. If you add two whole numbers, is the sum always greater than either one of the numbers? If not, give an example. (Compare this with Exercise 81.)

83. ◣ Make up a word problem for which the answer is the sum of 34 and 28.

84. Call a number "lucky" if it ends in a 7. How many lucky numbers are less than 100?

Projects or Group Activities

The size, or magnitude, of a number can be represented on the number line by an arrow.

The number 3 can be represented anywhere on the number line by an arrow that is 3 units in length.

To add on the number line, place the arrows representing the addends head to tail, with the first arrow starting at zero. The sum is represented by an arrow starting at zero and stopping at the tip of the last arrow.

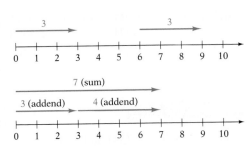

85. Represent the sum of 2 and 6 using arrows on the number line.

86. Represent the sum of 5 and 4 using arrows on the number line.

SECTION

1.3 Subtraction of Whole Numbers

OBJECTIVE A *To subtract whole numbers without borrowing*

Subtraction is the process of finding the difference between two numbers.

APPLY THE CONCEPT

A store had 7 iPads in stock. Nathan sold 3 iPads from the stock. By counting, the difference between 7 iPads and 3 iPads is 4. There are 4 iPads remaining in stock.

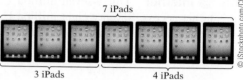

7 iPads

3 iPads   4 iPads

7 iPads	−	3 iPads	=	4 iPads
Minuend	−	**Subtrahend**	=	**Difference**

Subtraction can be related to addition as shown at the right. This relationship can be used to check a subtraction.

Subtrahend	3
+ Difference	+ 4
= Minuend	7

Point of Interest
The minus sign dates from the same period as the plus sign, around 1515.

To subtract large numbers, begin by arranging the numbers vertically, keeping the digits that have the same place value in the same column. Then subtract the digits in each column.

HOW TO 1   Subtract 8955 − 2432 and check.

THOUSANDS
HUNDREDS
TENS
ONES

$$
\begin{array}{r}
8\ 9\ 5\ 5 \\
-\ 2\ 4\ 3\ 2 \\
\hline
6\ 5\ 2\ 3
\end{array}
$$

Check:	Subtrahend	2432
	+ Difference	+ 6523
	= Minuend	8955

EXAMPLE 1

Subtract 6594 − 3271 and check.

Solution

6594	*Check:*	3271
− 3271		+ 3323
3323		6594

YOU TRY IT 1

Subtract 8925 − 6413 and check.

Your solution

EXAMPLE 2

Subtract 15,762 − 7541 and check.

Solution

15,762	*Check:*	7,541
− 7,541		+ 8,221
8,221		15,762

YOU TRY IT 2

Subtract 17,504 − 9302 and check.

Your solution

Solutions on p. S1

OBJECTIVE B   *To subtract whole numbers with borrowing*

In all the subtraction problems in the preceding objective, for each place value, the lower digit was smaller than the upper digit. When the lower digit is larger than the upper digit, subtraction will involve **borrowing.**

HOW TO 2   Subtract: $692 - 378$

$\begin{array}{ccc} \text{HUNDREDS} & \text{TENS} & \text{ONES} \\ & 8+1 & \\ 6 & 9 & 2 \\ -\ 3 & 7 & 8 \end{array}$	Because $8 > 2$, borrowing is necessary. 9 tens = 8 tens + 1 ten.
$\begin{array}{ccc} \text{HUNDREDS} & \text{TENS} & \text{ONES} \\ & 8+① & 10 \\ 6 & 9 & 2 \\ -\ 3 & 7 & 8 \end{array}$	Borrow 1 ten from the tens column and write 10 in the ones column.
$\begin{array}{ccc} \text{HUNDREDS} & \text{TENS} & \text{ONES} \\ & 8 & 12 \\ 6 & 9 & 2 \\ -\ 3 & 7 & 8 \end{array}$	Add the borrowed 10 to 2.
$\begin{array}{ccc} \text{HUNDREDS} & \text{TENS} & \text{ONES} \\ & 8 & 12 \\ 6 & 9 & 2 \\ -\ 3 & 7 & 8 \end{array}$	Subtract the digits in each column.

The phrases below are used to indicate the operation of subtraction. An example is shown at the right of each phrase.

minus	8 minus 5	$8 - 5$
less	9 less 3	$9 - 3$
less than	2 less than 7	$7 - 2$
the difference between	the difference between 8 and 2	$8 - 2$
decreased by	5 decreased by 1	$5 - 1$

> **Take Note**
> "The difference between 1234 and 485" means $1234 - 485$.

HOW TO 3   Find the difference between 1234 and 485, and check.

$$\begin{array}{ccccc} & & 2 & 14 & \\ 1 & 2 & \cancel{3} & \cancel{4} \\ - & & 4 & 8 & 5 \\ \hline & & & & 9 \end{array} \qquad \begin{array}{ccccc} & 1 & 12 & 14 & \\ 1 & \cancel{2} & \cancel{3} & \cancel{4} \\ - & & 4 & 8 & 5 \\ \hline & & 4 & 9 \end{array} \qquad \begin{array}{ccccc} 0 & 11 & 12 & 14 \\ \cancel{1} & \cancel{2} & \cancel{3} & \cancel{4} \\ - & & 4 & 8 & 5 \\ \hline & 7 & 4 & 9 \end{array}$$

Check:
$$\begin{array}{r} {}^{1\,1} \\ 485 \\ +\ 749 \\ \hline 1234 \end{array}$$

> **Tips for Success**
> The HOW TO feature indicates an example with explanatory remarks. Using paper and pencil, you should work through the example. See *AIM for Success* at the front of the book.

Subtraction with a zero in the minuend involves repeated borrowing.

HOW TO 4   Subtract: $3904 - 1775$

$\begin{array}{cccc} & 8 & 10 & \\ 3 & \cancel{9} & \cancel{0} & 4 \\ -\ 1 & 7 & 7 & 5 \end{array}$	$5 > 4$ There is a 0 in the tens column. Borrow 1 hundred (= 10 tens) from the hundreds column and write 10 in the tens column.
$\begin{array}{cccc} & & 9 & \\ & 8 & \cancel{10} & 14 \\ 3 & \cancel{9} & \cancel{0} & \cancel{4} \\ -\ 1 & 7 & 7 & 5 \end{array}$	Borrow 1 ten from the tens column and add 10 to the 4 in the ones column.
$\begin{array}{cccc} & & 9 & \\ & 8 & \cancel{10} & 14 \\ 3 & \cancel{9} & \cancel{0} & \cancel{4} \\ -\ 1 & 7 & 7 & 5 \\ \hline 2 & 1 & 2 & 9 \end{array}$	Subtract the digits in each column.

EXAMPLE 3

Subtract 4392 − 678 and check.

Solution

$$\begin{array}{r} \overset{3}{\cancel{4}}\ \overset{13}{\cancel{3}}\ \overset{8}{\cancel{9}}\ \overset{12}{\cancel{2}} \\ -\ \ 6\ 7\ 8 \\ \hline 3\ 7\ 1\ 4 \end{array}$$

Check:
$$\begin{array}{r} 678 \\ +\ 3714 \\ \hline 4392 \end{array}$$

YOU TRY IT 3

Subtract 3481 − 865 and check.

Your solution

EXAMPLE 4

Find 23,954 less than 63,221 and check.

Solution

$$\begin{array}{r} \overset{5}{\cancel{6}}\ \overset{12}{\cancel{3}},\overset{11}{\cancel{2}}\ \overset{11}{\cancel{2}}\ \overset{11}{\cancel{1}} \\ -\ 2\ 3,9\ 5\ 4 \\ \hline 3\ 9,2\ 6\ 7 \end{array}$$

Check:
$$\begin{array}{r} 23,954 \\ +\ 39{,}267 \\ \hline 63,221 \end{array}$$

YOU TRY IT 4

Find 54,562 decreased by 14,485 and check.

Your solution

EXAMPLE 5

Subtract 46,005 − 32,167 and check.

Solution

$$\begin{array}{r} 4\ \overset{5}{\cancel{6}},\overset{10}{\cancel{0}}\ 0\ 5 \\ -\ 3\ 2,1\ 6\ 7 \end{array}$$

• There are two zeros in the minuend. Borrow 1 thousand from the thousands column and write 10 in the hundreds column.

$$\begin{array}{r} 4\ \overset{5}{\cancel{6}},\overset{\overset{9}{\cancel{10}}}{\cancel{0}}\ \overset{10}{\cancel{0}}\ 5 \\ -\ 3\ 2,1\ 6\ 7 \end{array}$$

• Borrow 1 hundred from the hundreds column and write 10 in the tens column.

$$\begin{array}{r} 4\ \overset{5}{\cancel{6}},\overset{\overset{9}{\cancel{10}}}{\cancel{0}}\ \overset{\overset{9}{\cancel{10}}}{\cancel{0}}\ \overset{15}{\cancel{5}} \\ -\ 3\ 2,1\ 6\ 7 \\ \hline 1\ 3,8\ 3\ 8 \end{array}$$

• Borrow 1 ten from the tens column and add 10 to the 5 in the ones column.

Check:
$$\begin{array}{r} 32,167 \\ +\ 13,838 \\ \hline 46,005 \end{array}$$

YOU TRY IT 5

Subtract 64,003 − 54,936 and check.

Your solution

Solutions on pp. S1–S2

ESTIMATION: Estimating the Difference Between Two Whole Numbers

Calculate 323,502 − 28,912. Then use estimation to determine whether the difference is reasonable.

Subtract to find the exact difference. To estimate the difference, round each number to the same place value. Here we have rounded to the nearest ten-thousand. Then subtract. The estimated answer is 290,000, which is very close to the exact difference 294,590.

$$\begin{array}{r} 323{,}502 \approx \\ -\ \ \ 28{,}912 \approx \\ \hline 294{,}590 \end{array} \quad \begin{array}{r} 320{,}000 \\ -\ 30{,}000 \\ \hline 290{,}000 \end{array}$$

OBJECTIVE C   *To solve application problems*

The table at the right shows the populations of the four regions of the United States. Use this table for Example 6 and You Try It 6.

Region	Population
Northeast	55,317,240
Midwest	66,927,001
South	114,555,744
West	71,945,553

Source: U.S. Census Bureau

EXAMPLE 6

Find the difference between the population of the most populous region and the population of the least populous region.

Strategy

To find the difference:

- Identify the most populous region (the South) and the least populous region (the Northeast).
- Subtract the population of the Northeast (55,317,240) from the population of the South (114,555,744).

Solution   114,555,744
              − 55,317,240
               59,238,504

There are 59,238,504 more people living in the South than in the Northeast.

YOU TRY IT 6

Find the difference between the population of the Midwest and the population of the Northeast.

Your strategy

Your solution

EXAMPLE 7

You had a balance of $415 on your student debit card. You then used the card, deducting $197 for books, $48 for art supplies, and $24 for theater tickets. What is your new student debit card balance?

Strategy

To find your new debit card balance:

- Add to find the total of the three deductions (197 + 48 + 24).
- Subtract the total of the three deductions from the original balance (415).

Solution

197   415
 48   − 269
+ 24   146
─────
269 total deductions

Your new debit card balance is $146.

YOU TRY IT 7

Your total weekly salary is $638. Deductions of $127 for taxes, $18 for insurance, and $35 for savings are taken from your pay. Find your weekly take-home pay.

Your strategy

Your solution

Solutions on p. S2

1.3 EXERCISES

✔ Concept Check

For Exercises 1 to 4, find the difference. Then write the related addition problem using Subtrahend + Difference = Minuend.

1. $9 - 5$ **2.** $7 - 2$ **3.** $11 - 0$ **4.** $8 - 8$

OBJECTIVE A   *To subtract whole numbers without borrowing*

For Exercises 5 to 34, subtract.

5. $\begin{array}{r} 12 \\ -\ 8 \\ \hline \end{array}$ **6.** $\begin{array}{r} 11 \\ -\ 4 \\ \hline \end{array}$ **7.** $\begin{array}{r} 15 \\ -\ 6 \\ \hline \end{array}$ **8.** $\begin{array}{r} 19 \\ -\ 8 \\ \hline \end{array}$ **9.** $\begin{array}{r} 25 \\ -\ 3 \\ \hline \end{array}$

10. $\begin{array}{r} 16 \\ -\ 7 \\ \hline \end{array}$ **11.** $\begin{array}{r} 68 \\ -\ 8 \\ \hline \end{array}$ **12.** $\begin{array}{r} 55 \\ -\ 4 \\ \hline \end{array}$ **13.** $\begin{array}{r} 89 \\ -23 \\ \hline \end{array}$ **14.** $\begin{array}{r} 77 \\ -\ 3 \\ \hline \end{array}$

15. $\begin{array}{r} 88 \\ -57 \\ \hline \end{array}$ **16.** $\begin{array}{r} 54 \\ -21 \\ \hline \end{array}$ **17.** $\begin{array}{r} 1305 \\ -\ 404 \\ \hline \end{array}$ **18.** $\begin{array}{r} 1202 \\ -\ 701 \\ \hline \end{array}$ **19.** $\begin{array}{r} 1497 \\ -\ 706 \\ \hline \end{array}$

20. $\begin{array}{r} 1763 \\ -\ 801 \\ \hline \end{array}$ **21.** $\begin{array}{r} 2836 \\ -1711 \\ \hline \end{array}$ **22.** $\begin{array}{r} 8974 \\ -3972 \\ \hline \end{array}$ **23.** $\begin{array}{r} 9273 \\ -6142 \\ \hline \end{array}$ **24.** $\begin{array}{r} 8976 \\ -7463 \\ \hline \end{array}$

25. $129 - 82$ **26.** $77 - 36$ **27.** $969 - 44$ **28.** $132 - 61$ **29.** $4865 - 304$

30. $1347 - 103$ **31.** $9999 - 6794$ **32.** $1525 - 702$ **33.** $8843 - 7621$ **34.** $7806 - 3405$

For Exercises 35 and 36, find two whole numbers with the given difference and sum.

35.   Difference = 2; sum = 8   **36.**   Difference = 5; sum = 9

OBJECTIVE B   *To subtract whole numbers with borrowing*

For Exercises 37 to 80, subtract.

37. $\begin{array}{r} 71 \\ -18 \\ \hline \end{array}$ **38.** $\begin{array}{r} 93 \\ -28 \\ \hline \end{array}$ **39.** $\begin{array}{r} 47 \\ -18 \\ \hline \end{array}$ **40.** $\begin{array}{r} 44 \\ -27 \\ \hline \end{array}$

41. $\begin{array}{r} 37 \\ -29 \\ \hline \end{array}$ **42.** $\begin{array}{r} 50 \\ -27 \\ \hline \end{array}$ **43.** $\begin{array}{r} 70 \\ -33 \\ \hline \end{array}$ **44.** $\begin{array}{r} 993 \\ -537 \\ \hline \end{array}$

45.
$$\begin{array}{r} 250 \\ -192 \\ \hline \end{array}$$

46.
$$\begin{array}{r} 840 \\ -783 \\ \hline \end{array}$$

47.
$$\begin{array}{r} 768 \\ -194 \\ \hline \end{array}$$

48.
$$\begin{array}{r} 770 \\ -395 \\ \hline \end{array}$$

49. $674 - 337$

50. $3526 - 387$

51. $1712 - 289$

52. $4350 - 729$

53. $1702 - 948$

54. $1607 - 869$

55. $5933 - 3754$

56. $7293 - 3748$

57. $9407 - 2918$

58. $3706 - 2957$

59. $8605 - 7716$

60. $8052 - 2709$

61. $80,305 - 9176$

62. $70,702 - 4239$

63. $10,004 - 9306$

64. $80,009 - 63,419$

65. $70,618 - 41,213$

66. $80,053 - 27,649$

67. $70,700 - 21,076$

68. $80,800 - 42,023$

69.
$$\begin{array}{r} 2600 \\ -1972 \\ \hline \end{array}$$

70.
$$\begin{array}{r} 8400 \\ -3762 \\ \hline \end{array}$$

71.
$$\begin{array}{r} 9003 \\ -2471 \\ \hline \end{array}$$

72.
$$\begin{array}{r} 6004 \\ -2392 \\ \hline \end{array}$$

73.
$$\begin{array}{r} 8202 \\ -3916 \\ \hline \end{array}$$

74.
$$\begin{array}{r} 7050 \\ -4137 \\ \hline \end{array}$$

75.
$$\begin{array}{r} 7015 \\ -2973 \\ \hline \end{array}$$

76.
$$\begin{array}{r} 4207 \\ -1624 \\ \hline \end{array}$$

77.
$$\begin{array}{r} 7005 \\ -1796 \\ \hline \end{array}$$

78.
$$\begin{array}{r} 8003 \\ -2735 \\ \hline \end{array}$$

79.
$$\begin{array}{r} 20,005 \\ -9,627 \\ \hline \end{array}$$

80.
$$\begin{array}{r} 80,004 \\ -8,237 \\ \hline \end{array}$$

81. Which of the following phrases represent the subtraction $673 - 571$?

(i) 571 less 673   **(ii)** 571 less than 673   **(iii)** 673 decreased by 571

82. Find 10,051 less 9027.

83. Find 17,031 less 5792.

84. Find the difference between 1003 and 447.

85. What is 29,874 minus 21,392?

86. What is 29,797 less than 68,005?

87. What is 69,379 less than 70,004?

88. What is 25,432 decreased by 7994?

89. What is 86,701 decreased by 9976?

For Exercises 90 to 93, use the relationship between addition and subtraction to complete the statement.

90. ___ + 39 = 104   **91.** 67 + ___ = 90   **92.** ___ + 497 = 862   **93.** 253 + ____ = 4901

For Exercises 94 to 99, use a calculator to subtract. Then round the numbers to the nearest ten-thousand and use estimation to determine whether the difference is reasonable.

94.   80,032
       − 19,605

95.   90,765
       − 60,928

96.   32,574
       − 10,961

97.   96,430
       − 59,762

98.   567,423
       − 208,444

99.   300,712
       − 198,714

OBJECTIVE C   *To solve application problems*

100. Banking You have $304 in your checking account. If you write a check for $139, how much is left in your checking account?

101.  **Insects** The table at the right shows the number of taste genes and the number of smell genes in the mosquito, fruit fly, and honey bee.
  a. How many more smell genes does the honey bee have than the mosquito?
  b. How many more taste genes does the mosquito have than the fruit fly?
  c. Which of these insects has the best sense of smell?
  d. Which of these insects has the worst sense of taste?

	Mosquito	Fruit Fly	Honey Bee
Taste genes	76	68	10
Smell genes	79	62	170

Source: www.sciencedaily.com
Images: mosquito, © iStockphoto.com/Henrik Larsson; fruit fly, © iStockphoto.com/arlindo71; honey bee, © iStockphoto.com/beti gorse

102. ● **Electric Car Sales** The graph at the right shows the projected sales of electric cars in the United States from 2015 to 2020.
  a. Are sales of electric cars projected to increase for the years shown?
  b. How many more electric cars are projected to be sold in 2020 than in 2015?
  c. Between which two consecutive years is the number of electric cars sold projected to increase the most?

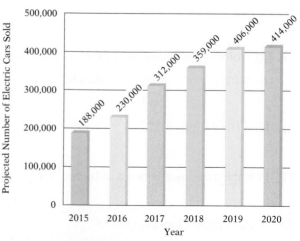

Projected Sales of Electric Cars in the United States
(*Source: An Analysis of Battery Electric Vehicle Production Projections;* Cunnigham, John; MIT, 2009)

103. 🌐 **Earth Science**   Use the graph at the right to find the difference between the maximum heights to which the Great Fountain and Valentine geysers erupt.

104. 🌐 **Earth Science**   According to the graph at the right, how much higher is the eruption of the Giant than that of Old Faithful?

105. 🌐 **Education**   In a recent year, 775,424 women and 573,079 men earned a bachelor's degree. How many more women than men earned a bachelor's degree that year? (*Source:* The National Center for Education Statistics)

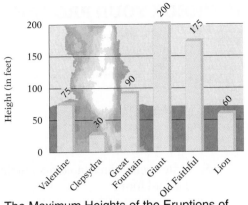

The Maximum Heights of the Eruptions of Six Geysers at Yellowstone National Park

🌐 **Demographics**   The graph at the right shows the expected U.S. population aged 100 and over for every 2 years from 2010 to 2020. Use this information for Exercises 106 to 108.

106. What is the expected growth in the population aged 100 and over during the 10-year period?

107. a. Which 2-year period has the smallest expected increase in the number of people aged 100 and over?
b. Which 2-year period has the greatest expected increase?

108. 🔲 What does the difference 208,000 − 166,000 represent?

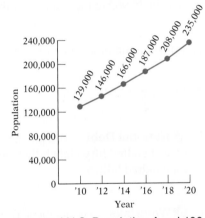

Expected U.S. Population Aged 100 and Over

Source: U.S. Census Bureau

109. Finances   You had a credit card balance of $409 before you used the card to purchase books for $168, CDs for $36, and a pair of shoes for $97. You then made a payment to the credit card company of $350. Find your new credit card balance.

Critical Thinking

110. Answer true or false.
a. 9 − (5 − 3) = (9 − 5) − 3
b. Subtraction is an associative operation. *Hint:* See part (a) of this exercise.

111. 🔲 Make up a word problem for which the difference between 15 and 8 is the answer.

Projects or Group Activities

112. Write down a five-digit number in which all of the digits are different. Now reverse the order of the digits to form a new five-digit number. Subtract the smaller number from the larger one. Add the digits of the difference. If the result is a two-digit number, add the digits again. What is the result? Try this with a four-digit or six-digit number. Is the result always the same?

✔ CHECK YOUR PROGRESS: CHAPTER 1

1. Graph 7 on the number line.

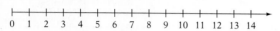

2. Place the correct symbol, < or >, between the two numbers.
   107   97

3. Write 82,743 in words.

4. Write 2,530,021 in words.

5. Write twenty-three thousand four hundred one in standard form.

6. Write nine hundred three thousand three in standard form.

7. Write 63,291 in expanded form.

8. Round 592,455 to the nearest thousand.

9. Round 45,962 to the nearest ten-thousand.

10. Add: 90,361 + 2955 + 750,679

11. Find the sum of 2034 and 12,598.

12. Find 40,781 increased by 156,742.

13. Subtract: 12,045 − 4987

14. Find 823 less than 9361.

15. ◐ **National Debt**   An estimate of the national debt is fourteen trillion seven hundred fifty-eight billion dollars. Round this number to the nearest hundred billion.

16. ◐ **Waterfalls**   The height of Yosemite Falls is 2425 feet, and the height of Colonial Falls is 2585 feet. How much higher is Colonial Falls than Yosemite Falls?

17. **Charity**   Janice decided to donate some money to a charity. Her contributions for a six-month period were $25, $30, $13, $15, $20, and $27. Find the total amount of her contribution for the six months.

◐ **Health Statistics**   The table at the right shows the median height, in centimeters (cm), from birth to age 5 for boys and girls. Use this chart for Exercises 18 and 19. (*Source:* National Center for Health Statistics)

18. How many centimeters do boys grow from birth to age 5?

19. Between which two consecutive years do girls grow the most?

Age	Height of Girls (cm)	Height of Boys (cm)
Birth	49	50
1	74	75
2	84	87
3	95	91
4	100	102
5	108	110

20. **Sports**   The scores for a professional golfer for four rounds of golf were 68, 72, 69, and 66. What was the total score for the golfer for the four rounds of golf?

SECTION

1.4 Multiplication of Whole Numbers

OBJECTIVE A · *To multiply a number by a single digit*

Multiplication is used to find the total number of objects in several groups when each group contains the same number of objects.

APPLY THE CONCEPT

Sebastian purchased 8 six-packs of soda for a party. The total number of cans of soda he purchased can be found by adding 6 eight times. Sebastian purchased 48 cans of soda.

6 + 6 + 6 + 6 + 6 + 6 + 6 + 6 = 48

The number of cans can also be found by using multiplication.

$$6 \times 8 = 48$$

Multiplicand × Multiplier = Product

The **multiplicand** is the number of objects in each group (6 cans in each six-pack); the **multiplier** is the number of groups (8 six-packs); the **product** is the total number of objects (48 cans). Frequently we will discuss the *factors* of a product. A **factor** is one of the numbers that are multiplied to obtain a product. 6 and 8 are factors of 48.

Here is a table of basic multiplication facts. These facts should be memorized.

Basic Multiplication Facts

×	1	2	3	4	5	6	7	8	9
1	$1 \times 1 = 1$	$1 \times 2 = 2$	$1 \times 3 = 3$	$1 \times 4 = 4$	$1 \times 5 = 5$	$1 \times 6 = 6$	$1 \times 7 = 7$	$1 \times 8 = 8$	$1 \times 9 = 9$
2	$2 \times 1 = 2$	$2 \times 2 = 4$	$2 \times 3 = 6$	$2 \times 4 = 8$	$2 \times 5 = 10$	$2 \times 6 = 12$	$2 \times 7 = 14$	$2 \times 8 = 16$	$2 \times 9 = 18$
3	$3 \times 1 = 3$	$3 \times 2 = 6$	$3 \times 3 = 9$	$3 \times 4 = 12$	$3 \times 5 = 15$	$3 \times 6 = 18$	$3 \times 7 = 21$	$3 \times 8 = 24$	$3 \times 9 = 27$
4	$4 \times 1 = 4$	$4 \times 2 = 8$	$4 \times 3 = 12$	$4 \times 4 = 16$	$4 \times 5 = 20$	$4 \times 6 = 24$	$4 \times 7 = 28$	$4 \times 8 = 32$	$4 \times 9 = 36$
5	$5 \times 1 = 5$	$5 \times 2 = 10$	$5 \times 3 = 15$	$5 \times 4 = 20$	$5 \times 5 = 25$	$5 \times 6 = 30$	$5 \times 7 = 35$	$5 \times 8 = 40$	$5 \times 9 = 45$
6	$6 \times 1 = 6$	$6 \times 2 = 12$	$6 \times 3 = 18$	$6 \times 4 = 24$	$6 \times 5 = 30$	$6 \times 6 = 36$	$6 \times 7 = 42$	$6 \times 8 = 48$	$6 \times 9 = 54$
7	$7 \times 1 = 7$	$7 \times 2 = 14$	$7 \times 3 = 21$	$7 \times 4 = 28$	$7 \times 5 = 35$	$7 \times 6 = 42$	$7 \times 7 = 49$	$7 \times 8 = 56$	$7 \times 9 = 63$
8	$8 \times 1 = 8$	$8 \times 2 = 16$	$8 \times 3 = 24$	$8 \times 4 = 32$	$8 \times 5 = 40$	$8 \times 6 = 48$	$8 \times 7 = 56$	$8 \times 8 = 64$	$8 \times 9 = 72$
9	$9 \times 1 = 9$	$9 \times 2 = 18$	$9 \times 3 = 27$	$9 \times 4 = 36$	$9 \times 5 = 45$	$9 \times 6 = 54$	$9 \times 7 = 63$	$9 \times 8 = 72$	$9 \times 9 = 81$

Tips for Success

Some students think that they can "coast" at the beginning of this course because the topic of Chapter 1 is whole numbers. However, this chapter lays the foundation for the entire course. Be sure you know and understand all of the concepts presented. For example, study the properties of multiplication presented in this lesson.

The times sign "×" is only one symbol that is used to indicate multiplication. Each of the expressions that follow represents multiplication.

$$7 \times 8 \qquad 7 \cdot 8 \qquad 7(8) \qquad (7)(8) \qquad (7)8$$

As with addition, there are some useful properties of multiplication.

Commutative Property of Multiplication

Two numbers can be multiplied in either order; the product will be the same.

EXAMPLES

1. $4 \times 3 = 3 \times 4$
$12 = 12$

2. $9 \times 7 = 7 \times 9$
$63 = 63$

Associative Property of Multiplication

Grouping numbers to be multiplied in any order gives the same result. Do the multiplication inside the parentheses first.

EXAMPLES

1. $(4 \times 2) \times 3 = 4 \times (2 \times 3)$

$\qquad 8 \quad \times 3 = 4 \times \quad 6$

$\qquad\qquad 24 = 24$

2. $3 \times (2 \times 5) = (3 \times 2) \times 5$

$\qquad 3 \times \quad 10 \quad = \quad 6 \quad \times 5$

$\qquad\qquad 30 = 30$

Multiplication Property of One

Multiplying a number by 1 does not change the number.

EXAMPLES

1. $8 \times 1 = 8$

2. $1 \times 6 = 6$

Multiplication Property of Zero

A number multiplied by zero is zero.

EXAMPLES

1. $7 \times 0 = 0$

2. $0 \times 4 = 0$

★ **Tips for Success**

One of the key instructional features of this text is the Example/You Try It pairs. Each Example is completely worked. You are to solve the You Try It problems. When you are ready, check your solution against the one given in the Solutions section. The solution for You Try It 1 below is on page S2 (see the reference at the bottom right of the You Try It). See *AIM for Success* at the front of the book.

Multiplication of larger numbers requires repeated use of the basic multiplication facts.

HOW TO 1   Multiply: 37×4

$$\begin{array}{r} \overset{2}{37} \\ \times\ 4 \\ \hline 8 \end{array}$$

• $4 \times 7 = 28$ (2 tens + 8 ones)
  Write the 8 in the ones column and carry the 2 to the tens column.

$$\begin{array}{r} \overset{2}{37} \\ \times\ 4 \\ \hline 148 \end{array}$$

• **The 3 in 37 is 3 tens.**

$\qquad 4 \times 3$ tens $=\ \ \mathbf{12\ tens}$

Add the carry digit. $\underline{+\ 2\ tens}$

$\qquad\qquad\qquad\qquad \mathbf{14\ tens}$

The product is 148.

The phrases below are used to indicate the operation of multiplication. An example is shown at the right of each phrase.

times	7 times 3	$7 \cdot 3$
the product of	the product of 6 and 9	$6 \cdot 9$
multiplied by	8 multiplied by 2	$8 \cdot 2$

EXAMPLE 1

Find the product of 735 and 9.

Solution

$$\begin{array}{r} \overset{3\ 4}{735} \\ \times\ \ 9 \\ \hline 6615 \end{array}$$

• $9 \times 5 = 45$
  Write the 5 in the ones column.
  Carry the 4 to the tens column.
  $9 \times 3 = 27, 27 + 4 = 31$
  $9 \times 7 = 63, 63 + 3 = 66$

YOU TRY IT 1

Multiply: 648×7

Your solution

Solution on p. S2

OBJECTIVE B *To multiply larger whole numbers*

Note the pattern in the products shown at the right.

Multiply the nonzero parts of the factors.

Then attach the same number of zeros to the product as the total number of zeros in the factors.

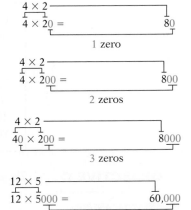

4×2
$4 \times 20 = 80$
1 zero

4×2
$4 \times 200 = 800$
2 zeros

4×2
$40 \times 200 = 8000$
3 zeros

12×5
$12 \times 5000 = 60,000$
3 zeros

HOW TO 2 Find the product of 47 and 23.

Multiply by the ones digit.	Multiply by the tens digit.	Add.
47	47	47
× 23	× 23	× 23
141 (= 47 × 3)	141	141
	940 (= 47 × 20)	940
		1081

Writing the 0 keeps the columns aligned correctly.

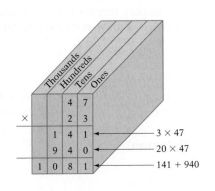

	Thousands	Hundreds	Tens	Ones	
			4	7	
×			2	3	
		1	4	1	3 × 47
		9	4	0	20 × 47
	1	0	8	1	141 + 940

The place-value chart on the right above illustrates the placement of the products.

Note the placement of the products when multiplying by a factor that contains a zero.

HOW TO 3 Multiply: 439 × 206

439
× 206
2634
000   0 × 439
878
90,434

When working the problem, we usually write only one zero. Writing this zero ensures the proper placement of the products.

439
× 206
2634
8780
90,434

EXAMPLE 2

Find 829 multiplied by 603.

Solution

829
× 603
2487
49740
499,887

• 3 × 829 = 2487
• Write a zero in the tens column for 0 × 829.
• 6 × 829 = 4974

YOU TRY IT 2

Multiply: 756 × 305

Your solution

Solution on p. S2

ESTIMATION: Estimating the Product of Two Whole Numbers

Calculate 3267 × 389. Then use estimation to determine whether the product is reasonable.

Multiply to find the exact product.   3267 **×** 389 **=** 1,270,863

To estimate the product, round each number $3267 \approx$ 3000
so that it has only one nonzero digit. Then multiply. $\times\ 389 \approx$ $\times\ \ 400$
The estimated answer is 1,200,000, which is   1,200,000
very close to the exact product 1,270,863.

OBJECTIVE C   *To solve application problems*

EXAMPLE 3

A state park forester receives a salary of $1050 each week. How much does the forester earn in 4 weeks?

Strategy

To find the forester's earnings for 4 weeks, multiply the weekly salary (1050) by the number of weeks (4).

Solution

    1050
 ×   4
    4200

The forester earns $4200 in 4 weeks.

YOU TRY IT 3

An elephant will eat approximately 150 pounds of food each day. How many pounds of food will an elephant eat in a 365-day year?

Your strategy

Your solution

EXAMPLE 4

A pharmacist's assistant earns $640 for working a 40-hour week. This week the assistant also worked 7 hours of overtime at $26 an hour. Find the assistant's total pay for the week.

Strategy

To find the assistant's total pay for the week:
• Find the overtime pay by multiplying the hours of overtime (7) by the overtime rate of pay (26).
• Add the weekly salary (640) to the overtime pay.

Solution

    26   640
 × 7   + 182
   182 overtime pay   822

The assistant earned $822 this week.

YOU TRY IT 4

The buyer for Ross Department Store can buy 80 men's suits for $7600. Each sports jacket will cost the store $62. The manager orders 80 men's suits and 25 sports jackets. What is the total cost of the order?

Your strategy

Your solution

1.4 EXERCISES

✔ **Concept Check**

For Exercises 1 to 4, write the expression as a product.

1. $2 + 2 + 2 + 2 + 2 + 2$ **2.** $4 + 4 + 4 + 4 + 4$ **3.** $7 + 7 + 7 + 7$ **4.** $18 + 18 + 18$

For Exercises 5 to 8, identify the property on pages 25–26 that justifies the statement.

5. $1 \times 23 = 23$ **6.** $(9 \times 5) \times 7 = 9 \times (5 \times 7)$ **7.** $8 \times 12 = 12 \times 8$ **8.** $(9 \times 5) \times 7 = (5 \times 9) \times 7$

OBJECTIVE A   *To multiply a number by a single digit*

For Exercises 9 to 43, multiply.

9. $\begin{array}{r} 3 \\ \times\, 4 \\ \hline \end{array}$
10. $\begin{array}{r} 2 \\ \times\, 8 \\ \hline \end{array}$
11. $\begin{array}{r} 5 \\ \times\, 7 \\ \hline \end{array}$
12. $\begin{array}{r} 6 \\ \times\, 4 \\ \hline \end{array}$
13. $\begin{array}{r} 5 \\ \times\, 5 \\ \hline \end{array}$

14. $\begin{array}{r} 7 \\ \times\, 7 \\ \hline \end{array}$
15. $\begin{array}{r} 0 \\ \times\, 7 \\ \hline \end{array}$
16. $\begin{array}{r} 8 \\ \times\, 0 \\ \hline \end{array}$
17. $\begin{array}{r} 8 \\ \times\, 9 \\ \hline \end{array}$
18. $\begin{array}{r} 7 \\ \times\, 6 \\ \hline \end{array}$

19. $\begin{array}{r} 66 \\ \times\, 3 \\ \hline \end{array}$
20. $\begin{array}{r} 70 \\ \times\, 4 \\ \hline \end{array}$
21. $\begin{array}{r} 67 \\ \times\, 5 \\ \hline \end{array}$
22. $\begin{array}{r} 127 \\ \times\, 9 \\ \hline \end{array}$
23. $\begin{array}{r} 623 \\ \times\, 4 \\ \hline \end{array}$

24. $\begin{array}{r} 802 \\ \times\, 5 \\ \hline \end{array}$
25. $\begin{array}{r} 607 \\ \times\, 9 \\ \hline \end{array}$
26. $\begin{array}{r} 300 \\ \times\, 5 \\ \hline \end{array}$
27. $\begin{array}{r} 600 \\ \times\, 7 \\ \hline \end{array}$
28. $\begin{array}{r} 906 \\ \times\, 8 \\ \hline \end{array}$

29. $\begin{array}{r} 703 \\ \times\, 9 \\ \hline \end{array}$
30. $\begin{array}{r} 127 \\ \times\, 5 \\ \hline \end{array}$
31. $\begin{array}{r} 632 \\ \times\, 3 \\ \hline \end{array}$
32. $\begin{array}{r} 559 \\ \times\, 4 \\ \hline \end{array}$
33. $\begin{array}{r} 632 \\ \times\, 8 \\ \hline \end{array}$

34. $\begin{array}{r} 524 \\ \times\, 4 \\ \hline \end{array}$
35. $\begin{array}{r} 337 \\ \times\, 5 \\ \hline \end{array}$
36. $\begin{array}{r} 841 \\ \times\, 6 \\ \hline \end{array}$
37. $\begin{array}{r} 6709 \\ \times\, 7 \\ \hline \end{array}$
38. $\begin{array}{r} 3608 \\ \times\, 5 \\ \hline \end{array}$

39. $\begin{array}{r} 8568 \\ \times\, 7 \\ \hline \end{array}$
40. $\begin{array}{r} 5495 \\ \times\, 4 \\ \hline \end{array}$
41. $\begin{array}{r} 4780 \\ \times\, 4 \\ \hline \end{array}$
42. $\begin{array}{r} 3690 \\ \times\, 5 \\ \hline \end{array}$
43. $\begin{array}{r} 9895 \\ \times\, 2 \\ \hline \end{array}$

44. True or false? The product of two one-digit whole numbers must be a two-digit whole number.

45. Find the product of 5, 7, and 4.

46. Find the product of 6, 2, and 9.

47. What is 3208 multiplied by 7?

48. What is 5009 multiplied by 4?

49. What is 3105 times 6?

50. What is 8957 times 8?

OBJECTIVE B   *To multiply larger whole numbers*

For Exercises 51 to 82, multiply.

51.
$$\begin{array}{r} 16 \\ \times\ 21 \\ \hline \end{array}$$

52.
$$\begin{array}{r} 18 \\ \times\ 24 \\ \hline \end{array}$$

53.
$$\begin{array}{r} 35 \\ \times\ 26 \\ \hline \end{array}$$

54.
$$\begin{array}{r} 27 \\ \times\ 72 \\ \hline \end{array}$$

55.
$$\begin{array}{r} 693 \\ \times\ 91 \\ \hline \end{array}$$

56.
$$\begin{array}{r} 581 \\ \times\ 72 \\ \hline \end{array}$$

57.
$$\begin{array}{r} 419 \\ \times\ 80 \\ \hline \end{array}$$

58.
$$\begin{array}{r} 727 \\ \times\ 60 \\ \hline \end{array}$$

59.
$$\begin{array}{r} 8279 \\ \times\ 46 \\ \hline \end{array}$$

60.
$$\begin{array}{r} 9577 \\ \times\ 35 \\ \hline \end{array}$$

61.
$$\begin{array}{r} 6938 \\ \times\ 78 \\ \hline \end{array}$$

62.
$$\begin{array}{r} 8875 \\ \times\ 67 \\ \hline \end{array}$$

63.
$$\begin{array}{r} 7035 \\ \times\ 57 \\ \hline \end{array}$$

64.
$$\begin{array}{r} 6702 \\ \times\ 48 \\ \hline \end{array}$$

65.
$$\begin{array}{r} 3009 \\ \times\ 35 \\ \hline \end{array}$$

66.
$$\begin{array}{r} 6003 \\ \times\ 57 \\ \hline \end{array}$$

67.
$$\begin{array}{r} 809 \\ \times\ 530 \\ \hline \end{array}$$

68.
$$\begin{array}{r} 607 \\ \times\ 460 \\ \hline \end{array}$$

69.
$$\begin{array}{r} 800 \\ \times\ 325 \\ \hline \end{array}$$

70.
$$\begin{array}{r} 700 \\ \times\ 274 \\ \hline \end{array}$$

71.
$$\begin{array}{r} 987 \\ \times\ 349 \\ \hline \end{array}$$

72.
$$\begin{array}{r} 688 \\ \times\ 674 \\ \hline \end{array}$$

73.
$$\begin{array}{r} 312 \\ \times\ 134 \\ \hline \end{array}$$

74.
$$\begin{array}{r} 423 \\ \times\ 427 \\ \hline \end{array}$$

75.
$$\begin{array}{r} 379 \\ \times\ 500 \\ \hline \end{array}$$

76.
$$\begin{array}{r} 684 \\ \times\ 700 \\ \hline \end{array}$$

77.
$$\begin{array}{r} 985 \\ \times\ 408 \\ \hline \end{array}$$

78.
$$\begin{array}{r} 758 \\ \times\ 209 \\ \hline \end{array}$$

79.
$$\begin{array}{r} 3407 \\ \times\ 309 \\ \hline \end{array}$$

80.
$$\begin{array}{r} 5207 \\ \times\ 902 \\ \hline \end{array}$$

81.
$$\begin{array}{r} 4258 \\ \times\ 986 \\ \hline \end{array}$$

82.
$$\begin{array}{r} 6327 \\ \times\ 876 \\ \hline \end{array}$$

83. 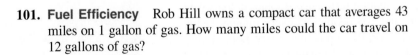 Find a one-digit number and a two-digit number whose product is a number that ends in two zeros.

84. What is 5763 times 45?

85. What is 7349 times 27?

86. Find the product of 2, 19, and 34.

87. Find the product of 6, 73, and 43.

88. What is 376 multiplied by 402?

89. What is 842 multiplied by 309?

For Exercises 90 to 97, use a calculator to multiply. Then use estimation to determine whether the product is reasonable.

90. 8745
  × 63

91. 4732
  × 93

92. 2937
  × 206

93. 8941
  × 726

94. 3097
  × 1025

95. 6379
  × 2936

96. 32,508
  × 591

97. 62,504
  × 923

OBJECTIVE C   *To solve application problems*

98. Geometry The perimeter of a square is equal to four times the length of a side of the square. Find the perimeter of the square herb box garden shown at the right.

99. Geometry The area of a rectangle is equal to the product of the length and the width. Find the area of the rectangular tennis court shown at the right.

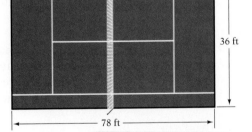

100. The price of grapes is $3 per pound, and the price of cherries is $5 per pound. Which of the following represents the price of 4 pounds of grapes and 2 pounds of cherries?
  (i) $(4 \times 3) + (4 \times 5)$ **(ii)** $(2 \times 3) + (4 \times 5)$
  (iii) $5 \times (3 + 5)$ **(iv)** $(4 \times 3) + (2 \times 5)$

101. Fuel Efficiency Rob Hill owns a compact car that averages 43 miles on 1 gallon of gas. How many miles could the car travel on 12 gallons of gas?

102. Fuel Efficiency A plane flying from Los Angeles to Boston uses 865 gallons of jet fuel each hour. How many gallons of jet fuel were used on a 6-hour flight?

103. ● **Matchmaking Services** See the news clipping at the right.
  a. How many marriages occur between eHarmony members each week?
  b. How many marriages occur each year? Use a 365-day year.

In the NEWS!

Find Your Match Online

eHarmony, the online matchmaking service, boasts marriages among its members at the rate of 542 a day.
Source: www.eharmony.com

104. ● **College Education** See the news clipping at the right.
  a. Find the average cost of tuition, room, and board for 4 years at a public university.
  b. Find the average cost of tuition, room, and board for 4 years at a private university.
  c. Find the difference in the average cost of tuition, room, and board for 4 years at a private university and 4 years at a public university.

> ## In the NEWS!
>
> ### Comparing Tuition Costs
>
> The average annual cost of tuition, room, and board at a four-year public university is $15,875. At a four-year private university, the average cost is $42,841.
> *Source:* National Center for Education Statistics

Construction The table at the right below shows the hourly wages for four types of jobs at a small construction company. Use this table for Exercises 105 to 107.

105. The owner of this company wants to provide the electrical installation for a new house. On the basis of the architectural plans, it is estimated that the installation will require 3 electricians, each working 50 hours, to complete the job. What is the estimated cost for the electricians' labor?

106. Carlos Vasquez, a plumbing contractor, hires 4 plumbers from this company at the hourly wage given in the table. If each plumber works 23 hours, what are the total wages paid by Carlos?

Type of Work	Wage per Hour
Electrician	$34
Plumber	$30
Clerk	$16
Bookkeeper	$20

107. The owner of this company estimates that a kitchen remodel will require 1 electrician working 30 hours and 1 plumber working 33 hours. This project also requires 3 hours of clerical work and 4 hours of bookkeeping. What is the total cost for these four components of the remodel?

Critical Thinking

108. Determine whether each statement is always true, sometimes true, or never true.
  a. A whole number times zero is zero.
  b. A whole number times 1 is the whole number.
  c. The product of two whole numbers is greater than either of the numbers.

109. ● **Safety** According to the National Safety Council, in a recent year, a death resulting from an accident occurred at the rate of 1 every 5 minutes. At this rate, how many accidental deaths occurred each hour? Each day? Throughout the year? Explain how you arrived at your answers.

110. ● **Demographics** According to the Population Reference Bureau, in the world today, 267 people are born every minute and 108 people die every minute. Using this statistic, what is the increase in the world's population every hour? Every day? Every week? Every year? Use a 365-day year. Explain how you arrived at your answers.

Projects or Group Activities

111. What multiplication problem is shown at the right? The letters S, T, R, A, and W stand for five different digits.

$$\begin{array}{r} \text{STRAW} \\ \times \quad\quad 4 \\ \hline \text{WARTS} \end{array}$$

SECTION

1.5 | Division of Whole Numbers

OBJECTIVE A *To divide by a single digit with no remainder in the quotient*

Division is used to separate objects into equal groups.

APPLY THE CONCEPT ....

Four friends want to share equally in the cost of a $24 birthday present for their friend Bianca. From the diagram below, each friend's share of the cost is $6.

Cost of the present
$24

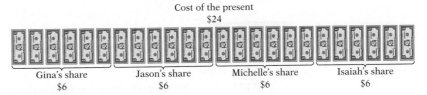

| Gina's share | Jason's share | Michelle's share | Isaiah's share |
| $6 | $6 | $6 | $6 |

The solution of this division problem is written as follows:

Each friend's share

Number of friends   6 ⟵ **Quotient**

Divisor ⟶ 4)‾2‾4‾

Cost of the present
Dividend

Note that the quotient multiplied by the divisor equals the dividend.

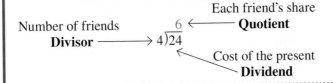

$$\frac{6}{4)\overline{24}} \quad \text{because} \quad \boxed{\begin{array}{c}6\\ \text{Quotient}\end{array}} \times \boxed{\begin{array}{c}4\\ \text{Divisor}\end{array}} = \boxed{\begin{array}{c}24\\ \text{Dividend}\end{array}}$$

$$\frac{6}{9)\overline{54}} \quad \text{because} \quad 6 \quad \times \quad 9 \quad = \quad 54$$

$$\frac{5}{8)\overline{40}} \quad \text{because} \quad 5 \quad \times \quad 8 \quad = \quad 40$$

Property of One in Division

Any whole number, except zero, divided by itself is 1.

EXAMPLES

1. $8)\overline{8}$ (quotient 1)
2. $14)\overline{14}$ (quotient 1)

Property of Zero in Division

Zero divided by any whole number other than zero is zero.

EXAMPLES

1. $7)\overline{0}$ (quotient 0)
2. $13)\overline{0}$ (quotient 0)

Note that the Property of Zero in Division states that zero divided by any whole number *other than zero* is zero. Division by zero is not allowed. Here is an example of why this is so.

Suppose we try to divide 0 into 8, and write $0\overline{)8}^{?}$. The quotient—the number that replaces the question mark—times the divisor, 0, must equal the dividend, 8. In other words, $\boxed{?} \times 0$ would have to be 8. However, any number times zero is zero. There is no number whose product with 0 is 8, and therefore no number that can replace the question mark to make a true statement.

Integrating Technology

Enter 8 ÷ 0 = on your calculator. An error message is displayed because division by zero is not allowed.

When the dividend is a larger whole number, the digits in the quotient are found in steps.

HOW TO 1   Divide $4\overline{)3192}$ and check.

$$
\begin{array}{r}
7 \\
4\overline{)3192} \\
-28 \\
\hline
39
\end{array}
$$

• Think $4\overline{)31}^{\,7}$. Place 7 in the quotient.
• Multiply 7×4.
• Subtract: $31 - 28 = 3$. Bring down the 9.

$$
\begin{array}{r}
79 \\
4\overline{)3192} \\
-28 \\
\hline
39 \\
-36 \\
\hline
32
\end{array}
$$

• Think $4\overline{)39}^{\,9}$. Place 9 in the quotient.
• Multiply 9×4.
• Subtract: $39 - 36 = 3$. Bring down the 2.

$$
\begin{array}{r}
798 \\
4\overline{)3192} \\
-28 \\
\hline
39 \\
-36 \\
\hline
32 \\
-32 \\
\hline
0
\end{array}
$$

• Think $4\overline{)32}^{\,8}$. Place 8 in the quotient.
• Multiply 8×4.
• Subtract: $32 - 32 = 0$.

Check:
$$
\begin{array}{r}
798 \\
\times 4 \\
\hline
3192
\end{array}
$$

The place-value chart can be used to show why this method works.

$$
\begin{array}{r}
\text{H T O} \\
7\ 9\ 8 \\
4\overline{)\ 3\ 1\ 9\ 2} \\
-\ 2\ 8\ 0\ 0 \\
\hline
3\ 9\ 2 \\
-\ 3\ 6\ 0 \\
\hline
3\ 2 \\
-\ 3\ 2 \\
\hline
0
\end{array}
$$

7 hundreds × 4

9 tens × 4

8 ones × 4

There are other ways of expressing division.

54 divided by 9 equals 6.

54 ÷ 9 equals 6.

$\dfrac{54}{9}$ equals 6.

EXAMPLE 1

Divide 7)56 and check.

Solution

$\overset{8}{7)\overline{56}}$

Check: $8 \times 7 = 56$

YOU TRY IT 1

Divide 9)63 and check.

Your solution

EXAMPLE 2

Divide 2808 ÷ 8 and check.

Solution

```
     351
8) 2808
  −24
    40
   −40
    08
   − 8
     0
```

Check: $351 \times 8 = 2808$

YOU TRY IT 2

Divide 4077 ÷ 9 and check.

Your solution

EXAMPLE 3

Divide 7)2856 and check.

Solution

```
    408
7) 2856
  −28
   05      • Think 7)5̄. Place 0 in the quotient.
  −0       • Multiply 0 × 7.
   56      • Subtract: 5 − 0 = 5. Bring down the 6.
  −56
    0
```

Check: $408 \times 7 = 2856$

YOU TRY IT 3

Divide 9)6345 and check.

Your solution

Solutions on pp. S2–S3

To divide by a single digit with a remainder in the quotient

Sometimes it is not possible to separate objects into a whole number of equal groups.

APPLY THE CONCEPT

A baker has 14 muffins to pack into 3 boxes. Each box holds 4 muffins. From the diagram, we see that after the baker places 4 muffins in each box, there are 2 left over. The 2 leftover muffins represent the **remainder.**

The baker's division problem can be written as follows.

$$
\begin{array}{r}
\textbf{Quotient} \\
\text{(Number in each box)} \\
\textbf{Divisor} \longrightarrow 3\overline{)\,14} \longleftarrow \textbf{Dividend} \\
\text{(Number of boxes)} \quad -12 \quad \text{(Total number of muffins)} \\
2 \longleftarrow \textbf{Remainder} \\
\text{(Number left over)}
\end{array}
$$

The answer to a division problem with a remainder is frequently written

$$
3\overline{)14}^{\,4\ \text{r}2}
$$

Note that
$$\boxed{\begin{matrix}4\\ \text{Quotient}\end{matrix}} \times \boxed{\begin{matrix}3\\ \text{Divisor}\end{matrix}} + \boxed{\begin{matrix}2\\ \text{Remainder}\end{matrix}} = \boxed{\begin{matrix}14\\ \text{Dividend}\end{matrix}}.$$

EXAMPLE 4

Divide $4\overline{)2522}$ and check.

Solution

$$
\begin{array}{r}
630\ \text{r}2 \\
4\overline{)\,2522} \\
-24 \\
\hline
12 \\
-12 \\
\hline
02 \\
-0 \\
\hline
2
\end{array}
$$

• Think $4\overline{)2}$. Place 0 in the quotient.
• Multiply 0×4.
• Subtract: $2 - 0 = 2$.

Check: $(630 \times 4) + 2 =$
$\qquad 2520 \ \ + 2 = 2522$

YOU TRY IT 4

Divide $6\overline{)5225}$ and check.

Your solution

EXAMPLE 5

Divide $9\overline{)27{,}438}$ and check.

Solution

$$
\begin{array}{r}
3{,}048 \text{ r6} \\
9\overline{)\ 27{,}438} \\
-27\phantom{{,}438} \\
\hline
0\,4 \\
-0 \\
\hline
43 \\
-36 \\
\hline
78 \\
-72 \\
\hline
6
\end{array}
$$

- Think $9\overset{0}{\overline{)4}}$. Place 0 in the quotient.
- Multiply 0×9.
- Subtract: $4 - 0 = 4$. Bring down the 3.

Check: $(3048 \times 9) + 6 =$
$27{,}432\ \ + 6 = 27{,}438$

YOU TRY IT 5

Divide $7\overline{)21{,}409}$ and check.

Your solution

Solution on p. S3

OBJECTIVE C   *To divide by larger whole numbers*

When the divisor has more than one digit, estimate at each step by using the first digit of the divisor. If that product is too large, lower the guess by 1 and try again.

HOW TO 2   Divide $34\overline{)1598}$ and check.

$$
\begin{array}{r}
5 \\
34\overline{)\ 1598} \\
-170 \\
\hline
\end{array}
$$

- Think $3\overline{)15}$.
- Multiply 5×34.

170 is too large. Lower the guess by 1 and try again.

$$
\begin{array}{r}
4 \\
34\overline{)\ 1598} \\
-136 \\
\hline
238
\end{array}
$$

- Multiply 4×34.
- Subtract $159 - 136 = 23$. Bring down the 8.

$$
\begin{array}{r}
47 \\
34\overline{)\ 1598} \\
-136 \\
\hline
238 \\
-238 \\
\hline
0
\end{array}
$$

- Think $3\overline{)23}$.
- Multiply 7×34.
- Subtract.

Check:
$$
\begin{array}{r}
47 \\
\times 34 \\
\hline
188 \\
141 \\
\hline
1598
\end{array}
$$

The phrases below are used to indicate the operation of division. An example is shown at the right of each phrase.

the quotient of	the quotient of 9 and 3	$9 \div 3$
divided by	6 divided by 2	$6 \div 2$

EXAMPLE 6

Find 7077 divided by 34 and check.

Solution

$$
\begin{array}{r}
208 \text{ r5} \\
34\overline{)7077} \\
-68 \\
\hline
27 \\
-0 \\
\hline
277 \\
-272 \\
\hline
5
\end{array}
$$

$\overset{0}{}$
• Think $34\overline{)27}$. Place 0 in the quotient.
• Multiply 0×34.
• Subtract: $27 - 0 = 27$. Bring down the 7.

Check: $(208 \times 34) + 5 =$
$\ 7072 \ + 5 = 7077$

YOU TRY IT 6

Divide $4578 \div 42$ and check.

Your solution

EXAMPLE 7

Find the quotient of 21,312 and 56, and check.

Solution

$$
\begin{array}{r}
380 \text{ r32} \\
56\overline{)21{,}312} \\
-16\,8 \\
\hline
4\,51 \\
-4\,48 \\
\hline
32 \\
-0 \\
\hline
32
\end{array}
$$

$\overset{4}{}$
• Think $5\overline{)21}$. 4×56 is too large. Try 3.

Check: $(380 \times 56) + 32 =$
$\ 21{,}280 \ + 32 = 21{,}312$

YOU TRY IT 7

Divide $18{,}359 \div 39$ and check.

Your solution

EXAMPLE 8

Divide $427\overline{)24{,}782}$ and check.

Solution

$$
\begin{array}{r}
58 \text{ r16} \\
427\overline{)24{,}782} \\
-21\,35 \\
\hline
3\,432 \\
-3\,416 \\
\hline
16
\end{array}
$$

Check: $(58 \times 427) + 16 =$
$\ 24{,}766 \ + 16 = 24{,}782$

YOU TRY IT 8

Divide $534\overline{)33{,}219}$ and check.

Your solution

EXAMPLE 9

Divide $386\overline{)206,149}$ and check.

Solution

$$
\begin{array}{r}
534 \text{ r}25 \\
386\overline{)206,149} \\
-193\,0 \\
\hline
13\,14 \\
-11\,58 \\
\hline
1\,569 \\
-1\,544 \\
\hline
25
\end{array}
$$

Check: $(534 \times 386) + 25 =$
$206,124 \;\; + 25 = 206,149$

YOU TRY IT 9

Divide $515\overline{)216,848}$ and check.

Your solution

Solution on p. S3

ESTIMATION: Estimating the Quotient of Two Whole Numbers

Calculate $38,772 \div 54$. Then use estimation to determine whether the quotient is reasonable.

Divide to find the exact quotient.

$38,772 \;\boxed{\div}\; 54 \;\boxed{=}\; 718$

To estimate the quotient, round each number so that it contains one nonzero digit. Then divide. The estimated answer is 800, which is close to the exact quotient 718.

$38,772 \div 54 \approx$
$40,000 \div 50 = 800$

OBJECTIVE D   *To solve application problems*

The **average** of several numbers is the sum of all the numbers divided by the number of those numbers.

A student has six test grades in a Spanish class. They are 81, 87, 80, 85, 79, and 86. To find the student's average of test score, divide the sum of the six test scores by 6.

$$
\text{Average test score} = \frac{81 + 87 + 80 + 85 + 79 + 86}{6} = \frac{498}{6} = 83
$$

The student's average test score in the Spanish class is 83.

HOW TO 3

🕐 The table below shows how much a median-income family can expect to spend raising a child to the age of 17 years. Find the average amount spent each year. Round to the nearest dollar.

Expenses to Raise a Child	
Housing	$70,020
Food	$35,970
Transportation	$28,590
Child care/education	$37,740
Clothing	$13,260
Health care	$17,760
Other	$19,030

Source: Department of Agriculture, *Expenditures on Children by Families*

Julie Keen/Shutterstock.com

Strategy

To find the average amount spent each year:

• Add all the numbers in the table to find the total amount spent during the 17 years.
• Divide the sum by 17.

Solution

$$\begin{array}{r} 70,020 \\ 35,970 \\ 28,590 \\ 37,740 \\ 13,260 \\ 17,760 \\ +\ 19,030 \\ \hline 222,370 \end{array}$$ • Sum of all the costs

$$\begin{array}{r} 13{,}080\ r10 \\ 17\overline{)222{,}370} \\ -17 \\ \hline 52 \\ -51 \\ \hline 13 \\ -\ 0 \\ \hline 137 \\ -136 \\ \hline 10 \\ -\ 0 \\ \hline 10 \end{array}$$

• When rounding to the nearest whole number, compare twice the remainder to the divisor. If twice the remainder is less than the divisor, drop the remainder. If twice the remainder is greater than or equal to the divisor, add 1 to the units digit of the quotient and drop the remainder.

• Twice the remainder is 2 × 10 = 20. Because 20 > 17, add 1 to the units digit of the quotient.

The average amount spent each year to raise a child to the age of 17 is $13,081.

EXAMPLE 10

Ngan Hui, a freight supervisor, shipped 35,640 bushels of wheat in 9 railroad cars. Find the amount of wheat shipped in each car.

Strategy

To find the amount of wheat shipped in each car, divide the number of bushels (35,640) by the number of cars (9).

Solution

$$
\begin{array}{r}
3\,960 \\
9\overline{)\,35{,}640} \\
-27 \\
\hline
86 \\
-81 \\
\hline
54 \\
-54 \\
\hline
0
\end{array}
$$

Each car carried 3960 bushels of wheat.

EXAMPLE 11

The used car you are buying costs $11,216. A down payment of $2000 is required. The remaining balance is paid in 48 equal monthly payments. What is the monthly payment?

Strategy

To find the monthly payment:

- Find the remaining balance by subtracting the down payment (2000) from the total cost of the car (11,216).
- Divide the remaining balance by the number of equal monthly payments (48).

Solution

$$
\begin{array}{r}
11{,}216 \\
-\,2{,}000 \\
\hline
9{,}216
\end{array}
$$

• **Remaining balance**

$$
\begin{array}{r}
192 \\
48\overline{)\,9216} \\
-48 \\
\hline
441 \\
-432 \\
\hline
96 \\
-96 \\
\hline
0
\end{array}
$$

The monthly payment is $192.

YOU TRY IT 10

Suppose a Michelin retail outlet can store 270 tires on 15 shelves. How many tires can be stored on each shelf?

Your strategy

Your solution

YOU TRY IT 11

A soft-drink manufacturer produces 12,600 cans of soft drink each hour. Cans are packed 24 to a case. How many cases of soft drink are produced in 8 hours?

Your strategy

Your solution

Solutions on pp. S3–S4

1.5 EXERCISES

✔ Concept Check

For Exercises 1 to 4, find the quotient. Then write the related multiplication problem using Quotient × Divisor = Dividend.

1. $4\overline{)8}$ **2.** $3\overline{)12}$ **3.** $5\overline{)30}$ **4.** $9\overline{)63}$

For Exercises 5 to 8, use the relationship between multiplication and division to complete the multiplication problem.

5. __ × 9 = 54   **6.** 12 × __ = 60   **7.** 8 × __ = 96   **8.** __ × 15 = 90

OBJECTIVE A   *To divide by a single digit with no remainder in the quotient*

For Exercises 9 to 24, divide.

9. $7\overline{)49}$ **10.** $5\overline{)80}$ **11.** $6\overline{)96}$ **12.** $6\overline{)480}$

13. $4\overline{)840}$ **14.** $3\overline{)690}$ **15.** $7\overline{)308}$ **16.** $7\overline{)203}$

17. $9\overline{)6327}$ **18.** $4\overline{)2120}$ **19.** $8\overline{)7280}$ **20.** $9\overline{)8118}$

21. $7\overline{)35,042}$ **22.** $4\overline{)28,032}$ **23.** $9\overline{)54,450}$ **24.** $8\overline{)25,632}$

25. What is 7525 divided by 7?   **26.** What is 32,364 divided by 4?

27. 🖐 If the dividend and the divisor in a division problem are the same number, what is the quotient?

OBJECTIVE B   *To divide by a single digit with a remainder in the quotient*

For Exercises 28 to 50, divide.

28. $4\overline{)9}$ **29.** $2\overline{)7}$ **30.** $5\overline{)27}$ **31.** $9\overline{)88}$ **32.** $3\overline{)40}$

33. $6\overline{)97}$ **34.** $8\overline{)83}$ **35.** $5\overline{)54}$ **36.** $7\overline{)632}$ **37.** $4\overline{)363}$

38. $4\overline{)921}$ **39.** $7\overline{)845}$ **40.** $8\overline{)1635}$ **41.** $5\overline{)1548}$ **42.** $7\overline{)9432}$

43. $7\overline{)8124}$ **44.** $3\overline{)5162}$ **45.** $5\overline{)3542}$ **46.** $8\overline{)3274}$

47. $4\overline{)15,301}$ **48.** $7\overline{)43,500}$ **49.** $6\overline{)34,263}$ **50.** $7\overline{)21,495}$

51. What is 45,738 divided by 4? Round to the nearest ten.

52. What is 37,896 divided by 9? Round to the nearest hundred.

53. What is 3572 divided by 7? Round to the nearest ten.

54. What is 78,345 divided by 4? Round to the nearest hundred.

55. True or false? When a three-digit number is divided by a one-digit number, the quotient can be a one-digit number.

OBJECTIVE C   *To divide by larger whole numbers*

For Exercises 56 to 83, divide.

56. $27\overline{)96}$ **57.** $44\overline{)82}$ **58.** $42\overline{)87}$ **59.** $67\overline{)93}$

60. $41\overline{)897}$ **61.** $32\overline{)693}$ **62.** $23\overline{)784}$ **63.** $25\overline{)772}$

64. $74\overline{)600}$ **65.** $92\overline{)500}$ **66.** $70\overline{)329}$ **67.** $50\overline{)467}$

68. $36\overline{)7225}$ **69.** $44\overline{)8821}$ **70.** $19\overline{)3859}$ **71.** $32\overline{)9697}$

72. $88\overline{)3127}$ **73.** $92\overline{)6177}$ **74.** $29\overline{)14,721}$ **75.** $63\overline{)44,653}$

76. $22\overline{)98,654}$ **77.** $77\overline{)83,629}$ **78.** $57\overline{)114,545}$ **79.** $73\overline{)365,566}$

80. $206\overline{)3097}$ **81.** $504\overline{)6504}$ **82.** $654\overline{)1217}$ **83.** $546\overline{)2344}$

84. Find the quotient of 5432 and 21.

85. Find the quotient of 8507 and 53.

86. What is 37,294 divided by 72?

87. What is 76,788 divided by 46?

88. Find 23,457 divided by 43. Round to the nearest hundred.

89. Find 341,781 divided by 43. Round to the nearest ten.

90. True or false? If the remainder of a division problem is 210, then the divisor was less than 210.

For Exercises 91 to 102, use a calculator to divide. Then use estimation to determine whether the quotient is reasonable.

91. $76\overline{)389,804}$ **92.** $53\overline{)117,925}$ **93.** $29\overline{)637,072}$ **94.** $67\overline{)738,072}$

95. $38\overline{)934,648}$ **96.** $34\overline{)906,304}$ **97.** $309\overline{)876,324}$ **98.** $642\overline{)323,568}$

99. $209\overline{)632,016}$ **100.** $614\overline{)332,174}$ **101.** $179\overline{)5,734,444}$ **102.** $374\overline{)7,712,254}$

OBJECTIVE D *To solve application problems*

103. Salaries Melissa's annual starting salary as a chemical engineer is $69,048. What is her monthly salary?

104. Cooking A chef is making 120 meatballs from 6 pounds of hamburger. Six pounds of hamburger contain 7200 calories.
  a. How many calories are in one meatball?
  b. How many calories are in one pound of hamburger?

105. Jewelry A jeweler is making 15 identical gold necklaces from 30 ounces of a gold alloy that costs $375 per ounce. What is the cost of the gold alloy in each necklace?

106. Manufacturing It costs a manufacturer of the energy drink Z-ENG $126,000 to make 63,000 bottles of the drink. The manufacturer packages the Z-ENG in cartons of four bottles. What is the cost of a carton of four bottles of Z-ENG?

107. Education A nursing student received scores of 86, 94, 79, and 93 on four anatomy exams. What was the nursing student's average score for the four exams?

108. Education To receive an A grade in a Spanish course, a professor requires a minimum score of 450 points on the five semester exams. If Richard receives a score of 82 on the first exam, what average score must Richard receive on the remaining four tests to achieve the minimum total of 450 points?

109. Electronics The cost of a 3D television that you are purchasing is $3180. If you make a down payment of $1620 and agree to pay off the remaining balance in 12 equal monthly payments, what is the monthly payment?

110. Wages A sales associate earns $440 for working a 40-hour week. Last week, the associate worked an additional 9 hours at $13 an hour. What is the difference between the associate's hourly overtime pay rate and the regular hourly pay rate?

● **Insurance**   The table at the right shows the sources of insurance claims for losses of laptop computers in a recent year. Claims have been rounded to the nearest ten thousand dollars. Use this information for Exercises 111 and 112.

Source	Claims
Accidents	$560,000
Theft	$300,000
Power surge	$80,000
Lightning	$50,000
Transit	$20,000
Water/flood	$20,000
Other	$110,000

Source: Safeware, The Insurance Company

111.   What was the average monthly claim for theft?

112.   For all sources combined, find the average claim per month.

● **Work Hours**   The table at the right shows, for different countries, the average numbers of hours per year that employees work. Use this information for Exercises 113 to 115. Use a 50-week year. Round answers to the nearest whole number.

Country	Annual Number of Hours Worked
France	1554
Germany	1390
Greece	2119
United Kingdom	1646
United States	1768

Source: Organization for Economic Cooperation and Development

113.   What is the average number of hours worked per week by employees in the United Kingdom?

114.   On average, how many more hours per week do employees in the United States work than employees in France?

115.   On average, how many more hours per week do employees work in the country with the most hours worked per year than in the country with the least hours worked per year?

116.   ● **Weather**   The daily low temperatures, in degrees Fahrenheit, for 9 consecutive summer days in Fargo, North Dakota, were 66, 55, 55, 61, 62, 66, 65, 52, and 58. What was the average low temperature for those 9 days?

117.   ● **U.S. Postal Service**   Use the information in the news clipping at the right to determine, on average, how many pieces of mail the U.S. Postal Service processed per day this year. Assume there are 300 working days in a year.

In the NEWS!

Decline in USPS Mail Volume

This year, the U.S. Postal Service processed 117 billion pieces of mail. This is a decline of 6 billion pieces from last year.

Source: www.usps.com

118.   ▧ Which problems below require division to solve?
   (i)   Four friends want to share a restaurant bill of $48 equally. Find the amount that each friend should pay.
   (ii)   On average, Sam spends $30 a week on gas. Find Sam's average yearly expenditure for gas.
   (iii)   Emma's 12 phone bills for last year totaled $660. Find Emma's average monthly phone bill.

Critical Thinking

119.   **Payroll Deductions**   Your paycheck shows deductions of $225 for savings, $98 for taxes, and $27 for insurance. Find the total of the three deductions.

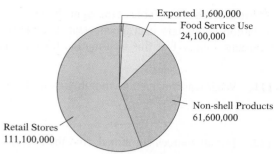

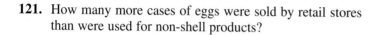

Dairy Products   The topic of the graph at the right is the eggs produced in the United States during a recent year. It shows where the eggs that were produced went or how they were used. Use this graph for Exercises 120 and 121.

120. Use the graph to determine the total number of cases of eggs produced during the year.

121. How many more cases of eggs were sold by retail stores than were used for non-shell products?

Eggs Produced in the United States (in cases)
Source: American Egg Board

Finances   The graph at the right shows the annual expenditures, for a recent year, of an average household in the United States. Use this information for Exercises 122 to 124. Round answers to the nearest whole number.

122. What is the total amount spent annually by an average household in the United States?

123. What is the average monthly expense for housing?

124. What is the difference between the average monthly expense for food and the average monthly expense for health care?

125. Finances   You purchase a used car with a down payment of $2500 and monthly payments of $195 for 48 months. Find the total amount paid for the car.

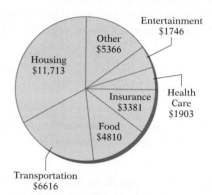

Average Annual Household Expenses
Source: Bureau of Labor Statistics
Consumer Expenditure Survey

Projects or Group Activities

126. A **factor** of a given number is a number that divides the given number evenly. For instance, 6 is a factor of 54 but 8 is not a factor of 54.
   a. Find all the factors of 48.
   b. Find all the factors of 144.
   c. Find all the factors of 97.

For Exercises 127 to 130, state which operation—addition, subtraction, multiplication, or division—you would use to solve the problem. Do not solve.

127. Mary and Jose are building a brick walkway. They have 35 bricks, 7 of which are unusable. How many usable bricks do they have?

128. Mary and Jose are building a brick walkway. They want to have a walkway that has 7 bricks in each row and 35 rows. How many bricks do they need?

129. Mary and Jose are building a brick walkway. They have 35 bricks and want a walkway that is 7 bricks wide. How many rows of bricks can they make?

130. Mary and Jose are building a brick walkway. They have 7 bricks and purchase 35 more bricks. How many bricks do they now have?

1.6

Exponential Notation and the Order of Operations Agreement

OBJECTIVE A   *To simplify expressions that contain exponents*

Repeated multiplication of the same factor can be written in two ways:

$$3 \cdot 3 \cdot 3 \cdot 3 \cdot 3 \quad \text{or} \quad 3^5 \leftarrow \textbf{Exponent}$$

The **exponent** indicates how many times the factor occurs in the multiplication. The expression 3^5 is in **exponential notation.**

It is important to be able to read numbers written in exponential notation.

$6 = 6^1$ is read "six to the first power" or just "six." Usually the exponent 1 is not written.

$6 \cdot 6 = 6^2$ is read "six squared" or "six to the second power."

$6 \cdot 6 \cdot 6 = 6^3$ is read "six cubed" or "six to the third power."

$6 \cdot 6 \cdot 6 \cdot 6 = 6^4$ is read "six to the fourth power."

$6 \cdot 6 \cdot 6 \cdot 6 \cdot 6 = 6^5$ is read "six to the fifth power."

Each place value in the place-value chart can be expressed as a power of 10.

Ten =	10 =	10	$= 10^1$
Hundred =	100 =	$10 \cdot 10$	$= 10^2$
Thousand =	1000 =	$10 \cdot 10 \cdot 10$	$= 10^3$
Ten-thousand =	10,000 =	$10 \cdot 10 \cdot 10 \cdot 10$	$= 10^4$
Hundred-thousand =	100,000 =	$10 \cdot 10 \cdot 10 \cdot 10 \cdot 10$	$= 10^5$
Million =	1,000,000 =	$10 \cdot 10 \cdot 10 \cdot 10 \cdot 10 \cdot 10$	$= 10^6$

Integrating Technology

A calculator can be used to evaluate an exponential expression. The y^x key (or, on some calculators, an x^y or $\wedge$ key) is used to enter the exponent. For instance, for the example at the right, enter 4 y^x 3 $=$. The display reads 64.

To simplify a numerical expression containing exponents, write each factor as many times as indicated by the exponent, and then carry out the indicated multiplication.

$$4^3 = 4 \cdot 4 \cdot 4 = 64$$

$$2^2 \cdot 3^4 = (2 \cdot 2) \cdot (3 \cdot 3 \cdot 3 \cdot 3) = 4 \cdot 81 = 324$$

EXAMPLE 1

Write $3 \cdot 3 \cdot 3 \cdot 5 \cdot 5$ in exponential notation.

Solution

$3 \cdot 3 \cdot 3 \cdot 5 \cdot 5 = 3^3 \cdot 5^2$

YOU TRY IT 1

Write $2 \cdot 2 \cdot 2 \cdot 2 \cdot 3 \cdot 3 \cdot 3$ in exponential notation.

Your solution

Solution on p. S4

EXAMPLE 2

Write as a power of 10: $10 \cdot 10 \cdot 10 \cdot 10$

Solution

$10 \cdot 10 \cdot 10 \cdot 10 = 10^4$

YOU TRY IT 2

Write as a power of 10: $10 \cdot 10 \cdot 10 \cdot 10 \cdot 10 \cdot 10 \cdot 10$

Your solution

EXAMPLE 3

Simplify $3^2 \cdot 5^3$.

Solution

$$
\begin{aligned}
3^2 \cdot 5^3 &= (3 \cdot 3) \cdot (5 \cdot 5 \cdot 5) \\
&= 9 \cdot 125 \\
&= 1125
\end{aligned}
$$

YOU TRY IT 3

Simplify $2^3 \cdot 5^2$.

Your solution

Solutions on p. S4

OBJECTIVE B   *To use the Order of Operations Agreement to simplify expressions*

More than one operation may occur in a numerical expression. The answer may be different depending on the order in which the operations are performed. For example, consider $3 + 4 \times 5$.

Multiply first, then add.

$$
\begin{aligned}
3 + &\underbrace{4 \times 5} \\
&\underbrace{3 + 20} \\
&23
\end{aligned}
$$

Add first, then multiply.

$$
\begin{aligned}
&\underbrace{3 + 4} \times 5 \\
&\underbrace{7 \times 5} \\
&35
\end{aligned}
$$

An Order of Operations Agreement is used so that only one answer is possible.

Order of Operations Agreement
Step 1. Perform operations inside grouping symbols such as parentheses.
Step 2. Simplify exponential expressions.
Step 3. Do multiplication and division as they occur from left to right.
Step 4. Do addition and subtraction as they occur from left to right.

EXAMPLES

1. $3(7 - 2) = 3(5)$ • Perform operations inside grouping symbols. [Step 1]
   $ = 15$ • Multiply. [Step 3]

2. $5 \cdot 4^2 = 5 \cdot 16$ • Simplify exponential expressions. [Step 2]
   $ = 80$ • Multiply. [Step 3]

3. $18 \div 9 \cdot 4 = 2 \cdot 4$ • Do multiplication and division from left to right. [Step 3]
   $ = 8$

4. $12 - 2 \cdot 4 = 12 - 8$ • Do multiplication and division from left to right. [Step 3]
   $ = 4$ • Do addition and subtraction from left to right. [Step 4]

Integrating Technology

Many scientific calculators have an x^2 key. This key is used to square the displayed number. For example, after the user presses 4 x^2 = , the display reads 16.

HOW TO 1 Simplify: $3 \times (2 + 1) - 2^2 + 4 \div 2$

Use the Order of Operations Agreement.

$3 \times (2 + 1) - 2^2 + 4 \div 2$

$3 \times 3 - 2^2 + 4 \div 2$ 1. Perform operations inside parentheses.

$3 \times 3 - 4 + 4 \div 2$ 2. Simplify expressions with exponents.

$9 - 4 + 4 \div 2$ 3. Do multiplication and division as they occur from left to right.

$9 - 4 + 2$

$5 + 2$ 4. Do addition and subtraction as they occur from left to right.

7

One or more of the steps of the Order of Operations Agreement may not be needed to simplify an expression. In that case, proceed to the next step in the Order of Operations Agreement.

HOW TO 2 Simplify $5 + 8 \div 2$.

There are no parentheses or exponents, so Steps 1 and 2 of the Order of Operations Agreement are not needed. Proceed to Step 3 of the agreement.

$5 + 8 \div 2$

$5 + 4$ 3. Do multiplication or division.

9 4. Do addition or subtraction.

EXAMPLE 4

Simplify: $64 \div (8 - 4)^2 \cdot 9 - 5^2$

Solution

$64 \div (8 - 4)^2 \cdot 9 - 5^2$

$= 64 \div 4^2 \cdot 9 - 5^2$ • **Parentheses**

$= 64 \div 16 \cdot 9 - 25$ • **Exponents**

$= 4 \cdot 9 - 25$ • **Division and multiplication**

$= 36 - 25$

$= 11$ • **Subtraction**

YOU TRY IT 4

Simplify: $5 \cdot (8 - 4)^2 \div 4 - 2$

Your solution

Solution on p. S4

1.6 EXERCISES

✔ Concept Check

1. How many times does 7 occur as a factor in the expression 7^5?

2. Using the Order of Operations Agreement, does $8 \cdot (4 \cdot 2) = (8 \cdot 4) \cdot 2$? If so, what Property of Multiplication does this show? See pages 25 and 26 for the Properties of Multiplication.

3. Which expressions below have the same value?
   (i) $8 \div 4 \div 2$ **(ii)** $8 \div (4 \div 2)$ **(iii)** $(8 \div 4) \div 2$?

4. Which expressions below have the same value?
   (i) $8 - 4 - 2$ **(ii)** $(8 - 4) - 2$ **(iii)** $8 - (4 - 2)$

OBJECTIVE A   *To simplify expressions that contain exponents*

For Exercises 5 to 16, write the number in exponential notation.

5. $2 \cdot 2 \cdot 2$

6. $7 \cdot 7 \cdot 7 \cdot 7 \cdot 7$

7. $6 \cdot 6 \cdot 6 \cdot 7 \cdot 7 \cdot 7 \cdot 7$

8. $6 \cdot 6 \cdot 9 \cdot 9 \cdot 9 \cdot 9$

9. $2 \cdot 2 \cdot 2 \cdot 3 \cdot 3 \cdot 3$

10. $3 \cdot 3 \cdot 10 \cdot 10$

11. $5 \cdot 7 \cdot 7 \cdot 7 \cdot 7 \cdot 7$

12. $4 \cdot 4 \cdot 4 \cdot 5 \cdot 5 \cdot 5$

13. $3 \cdot 3 \cdot 3 \cdot 6 \cdot 6 \cdot 6 \cdot 6$

14. $2 \cdot 2 \cdot 5 \cdot 5 \cdot 5 \cdot 8$

15. $3 \cdot 3 \cdot 3 \cdot 5 \cdot 9 \cdot 9 \cdot 9$

16. $2 \cdot 2 \cdot 2 \cdot 4 \cdot 7 \cdot 7 \cdot 7$

For Exercises 17 to 41, simplify.

17. 2^3

18. 2^6

19. $2^4 \cdot 5^2$

20. $2^6 \cdot 3^2$

21. $3^2 \cdot 10^2$

22. $2^3 \cdot 10^4$

23. $6^2 \cdot 3^3$

24. $4^3 \cdot 5^2$

25. $5 \cdot 2^3 \cdot 3$

26. $6 \cdot 3^2 \cdot 4$

27. $2^2 \cdot 3^2 \cdot 10$

28. $3^2 \cdot 5^2 \cdot 10$

29. $0^2 \cdot 4^3$

30. $6^2 \cdot 0^3$

31. $3^2 \cdot 10^4$

32. $5^3 \cdot 10^3$ **33.** $2^2 \cdot 3^3 \cdot 5$ **34.** $5^2 \cdot 7^3 \cdot 2$ **35.** $2 \cdot 3^4 \cdot 5^2$ **36.** $6 \cdot 2^6 \cdot 7^2$

37. $5^2 \cdot 3^2 \cdot 7^2$ **38.** $4^2 \cdot 9^2 \cdot 6^2$ **39.** $3^4 \cdot 2^6 \cdot 5$ **40.** $4^3 \cdot 6^3 \cdot 7$ **41.** $4^2 \cdot 3^3 \cdot 10^4$

42. ⬚ Rewrite the expression using the numbers 3 and 5 exactly once. Then simplify
the expression.
   a. $3 + 3 + 3 + 3 + 3$
   b. $3 \cdot 3 \cdot 3 \cdot 3 \cdot 3$

OBJECTIVE B   *To use the Order of Operations Agreement to simplify expressions*

For Exercises 43 to 81, simplify by using the Order of Operations Agreement.

43. $4 - 2 + 3$ **44.** $6 - 3 + 2$ **45.** $6 \cdot 3 + 5$

46. $5 \cdot 9 + 2$ **47.** $14 - 2 \cdot 4$ **48.** $12 + 3 \cdot 5$

49. $3 + 6 \div 3$ **50.** $12 + 8 \div 4$ **51.** $2 \cdot 3^2$

52. $5 \cdot 2^3$ **53.** $4 \cdot (5 - 3) + 2$ **54.** $3 + (4 + 2) \div 3$

55. $5 + (8 + 4) \div 6$ **56.** $8 - 2^2 + 4$ **57.** $16 \cdot (3 + 2) \div 10$

58. $12 \cdot (1 + 5) \div 12$ **59.** $10 - 2^3 + 4$ **60.** $5 \cdot 3^2 + 8$

61. $16 + 4 \cdot 3^2$ **62.** $12 + 4 \cdot 2^3$ **63.** $16 + (8 - 3) \cdot 2$

64. $7 + (9 - 5) \cdot 3$ **65.** $2^2 + 3 \cdot (6 - 2)^2$ **66.** $3^3 + 5 \cdot (8 - 6)^3$

67. $2^2 \cdot 3^2 + 2 \cdot 3$ **68.** $4 \cdot 6 + 3^2 \cdot 4^2$ **69.** $3 \cdot (6 - 2) + 4$

70. $5 \cdot (8 - 4) - 6$

71. $8 - (8 - 2) \div 3$

72. $12 - (12 - 4) \div 4$

73. $8 + 2 - 3 \cdot 2 \div 3$

74. $10 + 1 - 5 \cdot 2 \div 5$

75. $3 \cdot (4 + 2) \div 6$

76. $(7 - 3)^2 \div 2 - 4 + 8$

77. $20 - 4 \div 2 \cdot (3 - 1)^3$

78. $12 \div 3 \cdot 2^2 + (7 - 3)^2$

79. $(4 - 2) \cdot 6 \div 3 + (5 - 2)^2$

80. $18 - 2 \cdot 3 + (4 - 1)^3$

81. $100 \div (2 + 3)^2 - 8 \div 2$

By placing parentheses at various places in the expression $2 \cdot 3 + 8 \cdot 4 - 2$, it is possible to change the value of the expression. For Exercises 82 to 85, insert parentheses in the above expression so that the value is the given number.

82. 22

83. 54

84. 44

85. 66

Critical Thinking

For Exercises 86 to 89, determine whether the two expressions are equal.

86. $(2 + 3)^5$ and $2^5 + 3^5$

87. $(2 + 3)^5$ and $2^5 + 3^5$

88. $(12 \div 3)^4$ and $12^4 \div 3^4$

89. $(6 - 4)^4$ and $6^4 - 4^4$

Projects or Group Activities

90. Recall that the Associative Property of Addition states that grouping an addition in any order gives the same result.
   a. Is subtraction an associative operation? Explain your answer.
   b. Is division an associative operation? Explain your answer.

91. Evaluate **a.** $(3^4)^2$ and **b.** $3^{(4^2)}$.
   c. According to the Order of Operations Agreement, what is the value of 3^{4^2}?

SECTION

1.7 | Prime Numbers and Factoring

OBJECTIVE A   *To factor numbers*

Whole-number **factors** of a number divide that number evenly (there is no remainder).

1, 2, 3, and 6 are whole-number factors of 6 because they divide 6 evenly.

$$1)\overline{6}^{\,6} \quad 2)\overline{6}^{\,3} \quad 3)\overline{6}^{\,2} \quad 6)\overline{6}^{\,1}$$

Note that both the divisor and the quotient are factors of the dividend.

To find the factors of a number, try dividing the number by 1, 2, 3, 4, 5, ... Those numbers that divide the number evenly are its factors. Continue this process until the factors start to repeat.

> **HOW TO 1**   Find all the factors of 42.
>
> | | |
> |---|---|
> | $42 \div 1 = 42$ | 1 and 42 are factors. |
> | $42 \div 2 = 21$ | 2 and 21 are factors. |
> | $42 \div 3 = 14$ | 3 and 14 are factors. |
> | $42 \div 4$ | Will not divide evenly |
> | $42 \div 5$ | Will not divide evenly |
> | $42 \div 6 = 7$ | 6 and 7 are factors. ⎫ Factors are repeating; all the |
> | $42 \div 7 = 6$ | 7 and 6 are factors. ⎭ factors of 42 have been found. |
>
> 1, 2, 3, 6, 7, 14, 21, and 42 are the factors of 42.

The following rules are helpful in finding the factors of a number.

2 is a factor of a number if the last digit of the number is 0, 2, 4, 6, or 8.

436 ends in 6; therefore, 2 is a factor of 436. ($436 \div 2 = 218$)

3 is a factor of a number if the sum of the digits of the number is divisible by 3.

The sum of the digits of 489 is $4 + 8 + 9 = 21$. 21 is divisible by 3. Therefore, 3 is a factor of 489. ($489 \div 3 = 163$)

5 is a factor of a number if the last digit of the number is 0 or 5.

520 ends in 0; therefore, 5 is a factor of 520. ($520 \div 5 = 104$)

EXAMPLE 1

Find all the factors of 30.

Solution

$30 \div 1 = 30$
$30 \div 2 = 15$
$30 \div 3 = 10$
$30 \div 4$ • Will not divide evenly
$30 \div 5 = 6$
$30 \div 6 = 5$ • Factors are repeating.

1, 2, 3, 5, 6, 10, 15, and 30 are the factors of 30.

YOU TRY IT 1

Find all the factors of 40.

Your solution

Solution on p. S4

OBJECTIVE B   *To find the prime factorization of a number*

Point of Interest

Prime numbers are an important part of cryptology, the study of secret codes. To make it less likely that codes can be broken, cryptologists use prime numbers that have hundreds of digits.

A number is a **prime number** if its only whole-number factors are 1 and itself. 7 is prime because its only factors are 1 and 7. If a number is not prime, it is called a **composite number.** Because 6 has factors of 2 and 3, 6 is a composite number. The number 1 is not considered a prime number; therefore, it is not included in the following list of prime numbers less than 50.

$$2, 3, 5, 7, 11, 13, 17, 19, 23, 29, 31, 37, 41, 43, 47$$

The **prime factorization** of a number is the expression of the number as a product of its prime factors. In the example below, we use a "T-diagram" to find the prime factors of 60. Begin with the smallest prime number as a trial divisor, and continue with prime numbers as trial divisors until the final quotient is 1.

$$
\begin{array}{c|c}
\multicolumn{2}{c}{60} \\
\hline
2 & 30 \\
2 & 15 \\
3 & 5 \\
5 & 1 \\
\end{array}
\qquad
\begin{array}{l}
60 \div 2 = 30 \\
30 \div 2 = 15 \\
15 \div 3 = 5 \\
5 \div 5 = 1 \\
\end{array}
$$

The prime factorization of 60 is $2 \cdot 2 \cdot 3 \cdot 5$.

Finding the prime factorization of larger numbers can be more difficult. Try each prime number as a trial divisor. Stop when the square of the trial divisor is greater than the number being factored.

HOW TO 2   Find the prime factorization of 106.

$$
\begin{array}{c|c}
\multicolumn{2}{c}{106} \\
\hline
2 & 53 \\
53 & 1 \\
\end{array}
$$

• **53 cannot be divided evenly by 2, 3, 5, 7, or 11. Prime numbers greater than 11 need not be tested because 11^2 is greater than 53.**

The prime factorization of 106 is $2 \cdot 53$.

EXAMPLE 2

Find the prime factorization of 315.

Solution

$$
\begin{array}{c|c}
\multicolumn{2}{c}{315} \\
\hline
3 & 105 \\
3 & 35 \\
5 & 7 \\
7 & 1 \\
\end{array}
$$

• **$315 \div 3 = 105$**
• **$105 \div 3 = 35$**
• **$35 \div 5 = 7$**
• **$7 \div 7 = 1$**

$315 = 3 \cdot 3 \cdot 5 \cdot 7$

YOU TRY IT 2

Find the prime factorization of 44.

Your solution

EXAMPLE 3

Find the prime factorization of 201.

Solution

$$
\begin{array}{c|c}
\multicolumn{2}{c}{201} \\
\hline
3 & 67 \\
67 & 1 \\
\end{array}
$$

• **Try only 2, 3, 5, 7, and 11, because $11^2 > 67$.**

$201 = 3 \cdot 67$

YOU TRY IT 3

Find the prime factorization of 177.

Your solution

Solutions on p. S4

1.7 EXERCISES

✔ Concept Check

1. Which of the following numbers are factors of 72?
   (i) 0   **(ii)** 1   **(iii)** 9   **(iv)** 14   **(v)** 24   **(vi)** 72

2. Which of the following numbers are prime factors of 210?
   (i) 2   **(ii)** 5   **(iii)** 7   **(iv)** 11   **(v)** 30   **(vi)** 35

OBJECTIVE A   *To factor numbers*

For Exercises 3 to 42, find all the factors of the number.

3. 4   **4.** 6   **5.** 10   **6.** 20   **7.** 7

8. 12   **9.** 9   **10.** 8   **11.** 13   **12.** 17

13. 18   **14.** 24   **15.** 56   **16.** 36   **17.** 45

18. 28   **19.** 29   **20.** 33   **21.** 22   **22.** 26

23. 52   **24.** 49   **25.** 82   **26.** 37   **27.** 57

28. 69   **29.** 48   **30.** 64   **31.** 95   **32.** 46

33. 54   **34.** 50   **35.** 66   **36.** 77   **37.** 80

38. 100   **39.** 96   **40.** 85   **41.** 90   **42.** 101

43. True or false? A number can have an odd number of factors.

44. True or false? If a number has exactly four factors, then the product of those four factors must be the number.

OBJECTIVE B   *To find the prime factorization of a number*

For Exercises 45 to 88, find the prime factorization.

45. 6   **46.** 14   **47.** 17   **48.** 83

49. 24   **50.** 12   **51.** 27   **52.** 9

53. 36   **54.** 40   **55.** 19   **56.** 37

57. 90   **58.** 65   **59.** 115   **60.** 80

61. 18   **62.** 26   **63.** 28   **64.** 49

65. 31   **66.** 42   **67.** 62   **68.** 81

69. 22   **70.** 39   **71.** 101   **72.** 89

73. 66   **74.** 86   **75.** 74   **76.** 95

77. 67   **78.** 78   **79.** 55   **80.** 46

81. 120   **82.** 144   **83.** 160   **84.** 175

85. 216   **86.** 400   **87.** 625   **88.** 225

89. True or false? The prime factorization of 102 is $2 \cdot 51$.

Critical Thinking

90. All prime numbers greater than 10 end in one of four digits. What are these digits?

91. Not every number that ends in one of the digits you found in Exercise 90 is a prime number. Give examples of numbers that end in each of these digits but are not prime numbers.

92. There are three digits such that any two of them will form a two-digit prime number. What are these three digits? Give an example of a prime number that uses all three digits. Give an example of a number that uses all three digits but is not a prime number.

Projects or Group Activities

93. What is the Sieve of Eratosthenes? Use this method to find all prime numbers less than 100.

CHAPTER

1 | Summary

Key Words	Examples

The **whole numbers** are 0, 1, 2, 3, 4, 5, 6, 7, 8, 9, 10, ...
[1.1A, p. 2]

The **graph of a whole number** is shown by placing a heavy dot directly above that number on the number line. [1.1A, p. 2]

This is the graph of 4 on the number line.

$$\begin{array}{ccccccccccccc} 0 & 1 & 2 & 3 & 4 & 5 & 6 & 7 & 8 & 9 & 10 & 11 & 12 \end{array}$$

The symbol for **is less than** is $<$. The symbol for **is greater than** is $>$. These symbols are used to show the order relation between two numbers. [1.1A, p. 2]

$3 < 7$
$9 > 2$

When a whole number is written using the digits 0, 1, 2, 3, 4, 5, 6, 7, 8, and 9, it is said to be in **standard form.** The position of each digit in the number determines the digit's **place value.** The place values are used to write the expanded form of a number. [1.1B, p. 3]

The number 598,317 is in standard form. The digit 8 is in the thousands place. The number 598,317 is written in expanded form as
$500{,}000 + 90{,}000 + 8000 + 300 + 10 + 7.$

Addition is the process of finding the total of two or more numbers. The numbers being added are called **addends**. The result is the **sum.** [1.2A, p. 8]

$$\begin{array}{r} \overset{1\ \ 1\,1}{8{,}762} \\ +\ 1{,}359 \\ \hline 10{,}121 \end{array}$$

Subtraction is the process of finding the difference between two numbers. The **minuend** minus the **subtrahend** equals the **difference.** [1.3A, p. 16]

$$\begin{array}{r} 4\ \ \overset{11}{\cancel{5}}\ \overset{}{\cancel{2}},\overset{11}{\cancel{1}}\ \overset{6}{7}\ \overset{13}{\cancel{3}} \\ -\ 3\ 4{,}9\ 6\ 8 \\ \hline 1\ 7{,}2\ 0\ 5 \end{array}$$

Multiplication is repeated addition of the same number. The numbers that are multiplied are called **factors**. The result is the **product.** [1.4A, p. 25]

$$\begin{array}{r} {\scriptstyle 4\ 5} \\ 358 \\ \times\ \ 7 \\ \hline 2506 \end{array}$$

Division is used to separate objects into equal groups. The **dividend** divided by the **divisor** equals the **quotient.** [1.5A, p. 33]

For any division problem,
(quotient · divisor) + remainder = dividend. [1.5B, p. 36]

$$\begin{array}{r} 93\ \text{r3} \\ 7)\overline{\ 654} \\ -63 \\ \hline 24 \\ -21 \\ \hline 3 \end{array}$$

Check: $(7 \cdot 93) + 3 = 651 + 3 = 654$

The expression 4^3 is in **exponential notation.** The **exponent,** 3, indicates how many times 4 occurs as a factor in the multiplication. [1.6A, p. 47]

$5^4 = 5 \cdot 5 \cdot 5 \cdot 5 = 625$

Whole-number **factors** of a number divide that number evenly (there is no remainder). [1.7A, p. 53]

$18 \div 1 = 18$
$18 \div 2 = 9$
$18 \div 3 = 6$
$18 \div 4$ 4 does not divide 18 evenly.
$18 \div 5$ 5 does not divide 18 evenly.
$18 \div 6 = 3$ The factors are repeating.

The factors of 18 are 1, 2, 3, 6, 9, and 18.

A number greater than 1 is a **prime number** if its only whole-number factors are 1 and itself. If a number is not prime, it is a **composite number.** [1.7B, p. 54]

The prime numbers less than 20 are 2, 3, 5, 7, 11, 13, 17, and 19.
The composite numbers less than 20 are 4, 6, 8, 9, 10, 12, 14, 15, 16, and 18.

The **prime factorization** of a number is the expression of the number as a product of its prime factors. [1.7B, p. 54]

$$\begin{array}{r|r} & 42 \\ \hline 2 & 21 \\ 3 & 7 \\ 7 & 1 \end{array}$$

The prime factorization of 42 is $2 \cdot 3 \cdot 7$.

Essential Rules and Procedures

Examples

To round a number to a given place value: If the digit to the right of the given place value is less than 5, replace that digit and all digits to the right by zeros. If the digit to the right of the given place value is greater than or equal to 5, increase the digit in the given place value by 1, and replace all other digits to the right by zeros. [1.1D, p. 4]

36,178 rounded to the nearest thousand is 36,000.

4592 rounded to the nearest thousand is 5000.

Properties of Addition [1.2A, p. 8]

Commutative Property of Addition
Two numbers can be added in either order; the sum will be the same.

$8 + 3 = 3 + 8$

Associative Property of Addition
Grouping an addition in any order gives the same result.

$(2 + 4) + 6 = 2 + (4 + 6)$

Addition Property of Zero
Zero added to a number does not change the number.

$7 + 0 = 7$

To estimate the answer to an addition calculation: Round each number to the same place value. Perform the calculation using the rounded numbers. [1.2A, p. 10]

$$\begin{array}{r} 39,471 \\ 12,586 \end{array} \qquad \begin{array}{r} 40,000 \\ +\ 10,000 \\ \hline 50,000 \end{array}$$

50,000 is an estimate of the sum of 39,471 and 12,586.

Properties of Multiplication [1.4A, pp. 25–26]

Commutative Property of Multiplication
Two numbers can be multiplied in either order; the product will be the same.

$2 \cdot 8 = 8 \cdot 2$

Associative Property of Multiplication
Grouping numbers to be multiplied in any order gives the same result.

$(2 \cdot 4) \cdot 6 = 2 \cdot (4 \cdot 6)$

Multiplication Property of Zero
A number multiplied by zero is zero.

$3 \cdot 0 = 0$

Multiplication Property of One
Multiplying a number by 1 does not change the number.

$6 \cdot 1 = 6$

Division Properties of Zero and One [1.5A, p. 33]
Any whole number, except zero, divided by itself is 1.
Zero divided by any whole number other than zero is zero.

$3 \div 3 = 1$
$0 \div 3 = 0$

Order of Operations Agreement [1.6B, p. 48]

Step 1. Perform operations inside grouping symbols such as parentheses.

Step 2. Simplify exponential expressions.

Step 3. Do multiplication and division as they occur from left to right.

Step 4. Do addition and subtraction as they occur from left to right.

$$5^2 - 3(2 + 4) = 5^2 - 3(6)$$
$$= 25 - 3(6)$$
$$= 25 - 18$$
$$= 7$$

1 | Review Exercises

1. Simplify: $3 \cdot 2^3 \cdot 5^2$

2. Write 10,327 in expanded form.

3. Find all the factors of 18.

4. Find the sum of 5894, 6301, and 298.

5. Subtract: 4926
                  $-$ 3177

6. Divide: $7\overline{)14{,}945}$

7. Place the correct symbol, $<$ or $>$, between the two numbers: 101   87

8. Write $5 \cdot 5 \cdot 7 \cdot 7 \cdot 7 \cdot 7 \cdot 7$ in exponential notation.

9. What is 2019 multiplied by 307?

10. What is 10,134 decreased by 4725?

11. Add: 298
                 461
             $+$ 322

12. Simplify: $2^3 - 3 \cdot 2$

13. Round 45,672 to the nearest hundred.

14. Write 276,057 in words.

15. Find the quotient of 109,763 and 84.

16. Write two million eleven thousand forty-four in standard form.

17. What is 3906 divided by 8?

18. Simplify: $3^2 + 2^2 \cdot (5 - 3)$

19. Simplify: $8 \cdot (6 - 2)^2 \div 4$

20. Find the prime factorization of 72.

21. What is 3895 minus 1762?

22. Multiply: 843
                   $\times$ 27

23. Wages   Vincent Meyers, a sales assistant, earns $480 for working a 40-hour week. Last week, Vincent worked an additional 12 hours at $24 an hour. Find Vincent's total pay for last week's work.

24. Fuel Efficiency   Louis Reyes, a sales executive, drove a car 351 miles on 13 gallons of gas. Find the number of miles driven per gallon of gasoline.

25. Consumerism   A car is purchased for $29,880, with a down payment of $3000. The balance is paid in 48 equal monthly payments. Find the monthly car payment.

26. Compensation   An insurance account executive received commissions of $723, $544, $812, and $488 during a 4-week period. Find the total income from commissions for the 4 weeks.

27. Banking   You had a balance of $516 in your checking account before making deposits of $88 and $213. Find the total amount deposited, and determine your new account balance.

28. Car Payments   You have a car payment of $246 per month. What is the total of the car payments over a 12-month period?

College Enrollment   The table at the right shows the approximate numbers of males and females enrolled in U.S. colleges in 2005 and 2009. Use this information for Exercises 29 to 32.

29. In which year, 2005 or 2009, were more males enrolled in U.S. colleges?

Year	Males	Females
2005	7,455,925	10,031,550
2009	8,769,504	11,658,207

Source: National Center for Education Statistics

30. What is the difference between the number of males and the number of females enrolled in U.S. colleges in 2005?

31. Find the increase in the number of males enrolled in U.S. colleges from 2005 to 2009.

32. How many more students were enrolled in U.S. colleges in 2009 than in 2005?

CHAPTER

1 | TEST

1. Simplify: $3^3 \cdot 4^2$

2. Write 207,068 in words.

3. Subtract:
$$\begin{array}{r} 23{,}006 \\ -\ 7{,}937 \end{array}$$

4. Find all the factors of 20.

5. Multiply:
$$\begin{array}{r} 9736 \\ \times\ 704 \end{array}$$

6. Simplify: $4^2 \cdot (4 - 2) \div 8 + 5$

7. Write 906,378 in expanded form.

8. Round 74,965 to the nearest hundred.

9. Divide: $97\overline{)108{,}764}$

10. Write $3 \cdot 3 \cdot 3 \cdot 7 \cdot 7$ in exponential form.

11. Find the sum of 8756, 9094, and 37,065.

12. Find the prime factorization of 84.

13. Simplify: $16 \div 4 \cdot 2 - (7 - 5)^2$

14. Find the product of 8 and 90,763.

15. Write one million two hundred four thousand six in standard form.

16. Divide: $7\overline{)60{,}972}$

17. Place the correct symbol, < or >, between the two numbers: 21   19

18. Find the quotient of 5624 and 8.

19. Add: 25,492
      +71,306

20. Find the difference between 29,736 and 9814.

● Education   The table at the right shows the projected enrollment in public and private elementary and secondary schools for the fall of 2013 and the fall of 2016. Use this information for Exercises 21 and 22.

Year	Pre-Kindergarten through Grade 8	Grades 9 through 12
2013	41,873,000	16,000,000
2016	43,097,000	16,684,000

Source: The National Center for Education Statistics

21. Find the difference between the projected total enrollment in 2016 and in 2013.

22. In 2016, how many students are projected to be enrolled in pre-kindergarten through grade 12?

23. Farming   A farmer harvested 48,290 pounds of lemons from one grove and 23,710 pounds of lemons from another grove. The lemons were packed in boxes with 24 pounds of lemons in each box. How many boxes were needed to pack the lemons?

24. Biology   A hummingbird beats its wings approximately 52 times per second. How many times will a hummingbird beat its wings in 900 seconds (15 minutes)?

25. Traffic   A radar detector was set up on a highway to determine the average speed of motorists on a certain segment of the highway. The recorded speeds, in miles per hour, for 12 cars were 68, 73, 59, 77, 65, 52, 71, 68, 76, 64, 59, and 60. What was the average speed for these 12 cars?

Fractions

Focus on Success

Have you formed or are you part of a study group? Remember that a study group can be a great way to stay focused on succeeding in this course. You can support each other, get help and offer help on homework, and prepare for tests together. (See Homework Time, page AIM-5.)

© iStockphoto.com/Christoper Futcher

Prep Test

Are you ready to succeed in this chapter? Take the Prep Test below to find out if you are ready to learn the new material.

For Exercises 1 to 6, add, subtract, multiply, or divide.

1. 4×5

2. $2 \cdot 2 \cdot 2 \cdot 3 \cdot 5$

3. 9×1

4. $6 + 4$

5. $10 - 3$

6. $63 \div 30$

7. Which of the following numbers divide evenly into 12?
1 2 3 4 5 6 7 8 9 10 11 12

8. Simplify: $8 \times 7 + 3$

9. Complete: $8 = ? + 1$

10. Place the correct symbol, $<$ or $>$, between the two numbers.
44   48

SECTION

2.1 The Least Common Multiple and Greatest Common Factor

OBJECTIVE A   *To find the least common multiple (LCM)*

 Tips for Success

Before you begin a new chapter, you should take some time to review previously learned skills. One way to do this is to complete the Prep Test. See page 65. This test focuses on the particular skills that will be required for the new chapter.

The **multiples of a number** are the products of that number and the numbers 1, 2, 3, 4, 5, ...

$3 \times 1 = 3$
$3 \times 2 = 6$
$3 \times 3 = 9$
$3 \times 4 = 12$ The multiples of 3 are 3, 6, 9, 12, 15, ...
$3 \times 5 = 15$
.
.
.

A number that is a multiple of two or more numbers is a **common multiple** of those numbers.

The multiples of 4 are 4, 8, 12, 16, 20, 24, 28, 32, 36, ...
The multiples of 6 are 6, 12, 18, 24, 30, 36, 42, ...
Some common multiples of 4 and 6 are 12, 24, and 36.

The **least common multiple (LCM)** is the smallest common multiple of two or more numbers.

The least common multiple of 4 and 6 is 12.

Listing the multiples of each number is one way to find the LCM. Another way to find the LCM uses the prime factorization of each number.

To find the LCM of 450 and 600, find the prime factorization of each number and write the factorization of each number in a table. Circle the greatest product in each column. The LCM is the product of the circled numbers.

	2	3	5
450 =	2	(3 · 3)	(5 · 5)
600 =	(2 · 2 · 2)	3	5 · 5

• In the column headed by 5, the products are equal. Circle just one product.

The LCM is the product of the circled numbers.
The LCM = $2 \cdot 2 \cdot 2 \cdot 3 \cdot 3 \cdot 5 \cdot 5 = 1800$.

EXAMPLE 1

Find the LCM of 24, 36, and 50.

Solution

	2	3	5
24 =	(2 · 2 · 2)	3	
36 =	2 · 2	(3 · 3)	
50 =	2		(5 · 5)

The LCM = $2 \cdot 2 \cdot 2 \cdot 3 \cdot 3 \cdot 5 \cdot 5 = 1800$.

YOU TRY IT 1

Find the LCM of 12, 27, and 50.

Your solution

Solution on p. S4

OBJECTIVE B *To find the greatest common factor (GCF)*

Recall that a number that divides another number evenly is a factor of that number. The number 64 can be evenly divided by 1, 2, 4, 8, 16, 32, and 64, so the numbers 1, 2, 4, 8, 16, 32, and 64 are factors of 64.

A number that is a factor of two or more numbers is a **common factor** of those numbers.

The factors of 30 are 1, 2, 3, 5, 6, 10, 15, and 30.

The factors of 105 are 1, 3, 5, 7, 15, 21, 35, and 105.

The common factors of 30 and 105 are 1, 3, 5, and 15.

The **greatest common factor (GCF)** is the largest common factor of two or more numbers.

The greatest common factor of 30 and 105 is 15.

Listing the factors of each number is one way of finding the GCF. Another way to find the GCF is to use the prime factorization of each number.

To find the GCF of 126 and 180, find the prime factorization of each number and write the factorization of each number in a table. Circle the least product in each column that does not have a blank. The GCF is the product of the circled numbers.

	2	3	5	7
126 =	(2)	(3 · 3)		7
180 =	2 · 2	3 · 3	5	

• In the column headed by 3, the products are equal. Circle just one product. Columns 5 and 7 have a blank, so 5 and 7 are not common factors of 126 and 180. Do not circle any number in these columns.

The GCF is the product of the circled numbers.
The GCF = 2 · 3 · 3 = 18.

EXAMPLE 2

Find the GCF of 90, 168, and 420.

Solution

	2	3	5	7
90 =	(2)	3 · 3	5	
168 =	2 · 2 · 2	(3)		7
420 =	2 · 2	3	5	7

The GCF = 2 · 3 = 6.

YOU TRY IT 2

Find the GCF of 36, 60, and 72.

Your solution

EXAMPLE 3

Find the GCF of 7, 12, and 20.

Solution

	2	3	5	7
7 =				7
12 =	2 · 2	3		
20 =	2 · 2		5	

Because no numbers are circled, the GCF = 1.

YOU TRY IT 3

Find the GCF of 11, 24, and 30.

Your solution

Solutions on p. S4

2.1 EXERCISES

✔ **Concept Check**

For Exercises 1 to 4, list the first four multiples of the given number.

1. 5   **2.** 7   **3.** 10   **4.** 15

5. List the first ten multiples of 6 and the first ten multiples of 8. What are the common multiples of 6 and 8 in the lists? What is the least common multiple of 6 and 8?

For Exercises 6 to 9, list the factors of the given number.

6. 12   **7.** 20   **8.** 23   **9.** 28

10. List the factors of 18 and the factors of 24. What are the common factors of 18 and 24? What is the greatest common factor of 18 and 24?

OBJECTIVE A   *To find the least common multiple (LCM)*

For Exercises 11 to 40, find the LCM.

11. 5, 8   **12.** 3, 6   **13.** 3, 8   **14.** 2, 5   **15.** 4, 6

16. 6, 8   **17.** 8, 12   **18.** 12, 16   **19.** 5, 12   **20.** 3, 16

21. 8, 14   **22.** 4, 10   **23.** 8, 32   **24.** 7, 21   **25.** 9, 36

26. 14, 42   **27.** 44, 60   **28.** 120, 160   **29.** 102, 184   **30.** 123, 234

31. 4, 8, 12   **32.** 5, 10, 15   **33.** 3, 5, 10   **34.** 2, 5, 8   **35.** 3, 8, 12

36. 5, 12, 18   **37.** 9, 36, 64   **38.** 18, 54, 63   **39.** 3, 7, 20   **40.** 4, 9, 35

41. 🔖 True or false? If two numbers have no common factors, then the LCM of the two numbers is their product.

42. 🔖 True or false? If one number is a multiple of a second number, then the LCM of the two numbers is the second number.

OBJECTIVE B   *To find the greatest common factor (GCF)*

For Exercises 43 to 72, find the GCF.

43. 3, 5   **44.** 5, 7   **45.** 6, 9   **46.** 18, 24   **47.** 15, 25

48. 14, 49   **49.** 25, 100   **50.** 16, 80   **51.** 32, 51   **52.** 21, 44

53. 12, 80   **54.** 8, 36   **55.** 16, 140   **56.** 48, 144   **57.** 44, 96

58. 18, 32   **59.** 3, 5, 11   **60.** 6, 8, 10   **61.** 7, 14, 49   **62.** 6, 15, 36

63. 10, 15, 20   **64.** 12, 18, 20   **65.** 24, 40, 72   **66.** 3, 17, 51   **67.** 17, 31, 81

68. 14, 42, 84   **69.** 25, 125, 625 **70.** 12, 68, 92   **71.** 32, 56, 72   **72.** 24, 36, 48

73. 🔲 True or false? If two numbers have a GCF of 1, then the LCM of the two numbers is their product.

74. 🔲 True or false? If the LCM of two numbers is one of the two numbers, then the GCF of the numbers is the other of the two numbers.

Critical Thinking

75. Work Schedules   Joe Salvo, a lifeguard, works 3 days and then has a day off. Joe's friend Raya works 5 days and then has a day off. How many days after Joe and Raya have a day off together will they have another day off together?

76. ◣ Find the LCM of each of the following pairs of prime numbers: 2 and 3, 5 and 7, and 11 and 19. Based on these examples, what is the LCM of two prime numbers?

77. ◣ Find the GCF of each of the following pairs of prime numbers: 3 and 5, 7 and 11, and 29 and 43. Based on these examples, what is the GCF of two prime numbers?

Projects or Group Activities

78. Using the pattern for the first two triangles shown below, determine the center number of the last triangle.

79. Two numbers are called *coprime* if the GCF of the two numbers is 1. Determine whether each pair of numbers is coprime.
    a. 48, 50   **b.** 25, 36   **c.** 22, 27   **d.** 71, 73

2.2　Introduction to Fractions

OBJECTIVE A　*To write a fraction that represents part of a whole*

Take Note

The *fraction bar* separates the numerator from the denominator. The *numerator* is the part of the fraction that appears above the fraction bar. The *denominator* is the part of the fraction that appears below the fraction bar.

Point of Interest

The fraction bar was first used in 1050 by al-Hassar. It is also called a vinculum.

A **fraction** can represent the number of equal parts of a whole.

The shaded portion of the circle is represented by the fraction $\frac{4}{7}$. Four of the seven equal parts of the circle (that is, four-sevenths of it) are shaded.

Each part of a fraction has a name.

$$\text{Fraction bar} \rightarrow \frac{4}{7} \begin{array}{l} \leftarrow \textbf{Numerator} \\ \leftarrow \textbf{Denominator} \end{array}$$

A **proper fraction** is a fraction less than 1. The numerator of a proper fraction is smaller than the denominator. The shaded portion of the circle can be represented by the proper fraction $\frac{3}{4}$.

A **mixed number** is a number greater than 1 with a whole-number part and a fractional part. The shaded portion of the circles can be represented by the mixed number $2\frac{1}{4}$.

An **improper fraction** is a fraction greater than or equal to 1. The numerator of an improper fraction is greater than or equal to the denominator. The shaded portion of the circles can be represented by the improper fraction $\frac{9}{4}$. The shaded portion of the square can be represented by $\frac{4}{4}$.

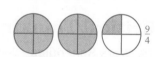

EXAMPLE 1

Express the shaded portion of the circles as a mixed number.

Solution　　$3\frac{2}{5}$

YOU TRY IT 1

Express the shaded portion of the circles as a mixed number.

Your solution

EXAMPLE 2

Express the shaded portion of the circles as an improper fraction.

Solution　　$\frac{17}{5}$

YOU TRY IT 2

Express the shaded portion of the circles as an improper fraction.

Your solution

Solutions on p. S4

To write an improper fraction as a mixed number or a whole number, and a mixed number as an improper fraction

Point of Interest

Archimedes (c. 287–212 B.C.) is the person who calculated that $\pi \approx 3\frac{1}{7}$. He actually showed that $3\frac{10}{71} < \pi < 3\frac{1}{7}$. The approximation $3\frac{10}{71}$ is more accurate but more difficult to use.

Note from the diagram that the mixed number $2\frac{3}{5}$ and the improper fraction $\frac{13}{5}$ both represent the shaded portion of the circles, so $2\frac{3}{5} = \frac{13}{5}$.

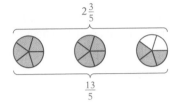

An improper fraction can be written as a mixed number or a whole number.

HOW TO 1 Write $\frac{13}{5}$ as a mixed number.

Divide the numerator by the denominator.	To write the fractional part of the mixed number, write the remainder over the divisor.	Write the answer.
$\begin{array}{r} 2 \\ 5{\overline{\smash{)}\,13}} \\ -10 \\ \hline 3 \end{array}$	$2\frac{3}{5}$ $\begin{array}{r} 5{\overline{\smash{)}\,13}} \\ -10 \\ \hline 3 \end{array}$	$\frac{13}{5} = 2\frac{3}{5}$

To write a mixed number as an improper fraction, multiply the denominator of the fractional part by the whole-number part. The sum of this product and the numerator of the fractional part is the numerator of the improper fraction. The denominator remains the same.

HOW TO 2 Write $7\frac{3}{8}$ as an improper fraction.

$$7\frac{3}{8} = \frac{(8 \times 7) + 3}{8} = \frac{56 + 3}{8} = \frac{59}{8} \qquad 7\frac{3}{8} = \frac{59}{8}$$

EXAMPLE 3

Write $\frac{21}{4}$ as a mixed number.

Solution

$\begin{array}{r} 5 \\ 4{\overline{\smash{)}\,21}} \\ -20 \\ \hline 1 \end{array}$ $\qquad \frac{21}{4} = 5\frac{1}{4}$

YOU TRY IT 3

Write $\frac{22}{5}$ as a mixed number.

Your solution

EXAMPLE 4

Write $\frac{18}{6}$ as a whole number.

Solution $\frac{18}{6} = 18 \div 6 = 3$

YOU TRY IT 4

Write $\frac{28}{7}$ as a whole number.

Your solution

EXAMPLE 5

Write $21\frac{3}{4}$ as an improper fraction.

Solution $21\frac{3}{4} = \frac{84 + 3}{4} = \frac{87}{4}$

YOU TRY IT 5

Write $14\frac{5}{8}$ as an improper fraction.

Your solution

Solutions on pp. S4–S5

2.2 EXERCISES

✔ Concept Check

For Exercises 1 to 4, identify the fraction as a proper fraction, an improper fraction, or a mixed number. State whether the fraction is less than 1, equal to 1, or greater than 1.

1. $\dfrac{12}{7}$ 2. $5\dfrac{2}{11}$ 3. $\dfrac{29}{40}$ 4. $\dfrac{13}{13}$

OBJECTIVE A   *To write a fraction that represents part of a whole*

For Exercises 5 to 8, express the shaded portion of the circle as a fraction.

5.   6.   7.   8.

For Exercises 9 to 14, express the shaded portion of the circles as a mixed number.

9.   10.

11.   12.

13.    14.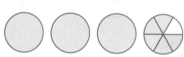

For Exercises 15 to 20, express the shaded portion of the circles as an improper fraction.

15.   16.

17. 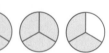   18.

19.    20.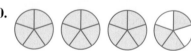

21. Shade $1\dfrac{2}{5}$ of   22. Shade $1\dfrac{3}{4}$ of

23. Shade $\dfrac{6}{5}$ of   24. Shade $\dfrac{7}{3}$ of

25. 📝 True or false? The fractional part of a mixed number is an improper fraction.

OBJECTIVE B   *To write an improper fraction as a mixed number or a whole number, and a mixed number as an improper fraction*

For Exercises 26 to 49, write the improper fraction as a mixed number or a whole number.

26. $\dfrac{11}{4}$ **27.** $\dfrac{16}{3}$ **28.** $\dfrac{20}{4}$ **29.** $\dfrac{18}{9}$ **30.** $\dfrac{9}{8}$ **31.** $\dfrac{13}{4}$

32. $\dfrac{23}{10}$ **33.** $\dfrac{29}{2}$ **34.** $\dfrac{48}{16}$ **35.** $\dfrac{51}{3}$ **36.** $\dfrac{8}{7}$ **37.** $\dfrac{16}{9}$

38. $\dfrac{7}{3}$ **39.** $\dfrac{9}{5}$ **40.** $\dfrac{16}{1}$ **41.** $\dfrac{23}{1}$ **42.** $\dfrac{17}{8}$ **43.** $\dfrac{31}{16}$

44. $\dfrac{12}{5}$ **45.** $\dfrac{19}{3}$ **46.** $\dfrac{9}{9}$ **47.** $\dfrac{40}{8}$ **48.** $\dfrac{72}{8}$ **49.** $\dfrac{3}{3}$

For Exercises 50 to 73, write the mixed number as an improper fraction.

50. $2\dfrac{1}{3}$ **51.** $4\dfrac{2}{3}$ **52.** $6\dfrac{1}{2}$ **53.** $8\dfrac{2}{3}$ **54.** $6\dfrac{5}{6}$ **55.** $7\dfrac{3}{8}$

56. $9\dfrac{1}{4}$ **57.** $6\dfrac{1}{4}$ **58.** $10\dfrac{1}{2}$ **59.** $15\dfrac{1}{8}$ **60.** $8\dfrac{1}{9}$ **61.** $3\dfrac{5}{12}$

62. $5\dfrac{3}{11}$ **63.** $3\dfrac{7}{9}$ **64.** $2\dfrac{5}{8}$ **65.** $12\dfrac{2}{3}$ **66.** $1\dfrac{5}{8}$ **67.** $5\dfrac{3}{7}$

68. $11\dfrac{1}{9}$ **69.** $12\dfrac{3}{5}$ **70.** $3\dfrac{3}{8}$ **71.** $4\dfrac{5}{9}$ **72.** $6\dfrac{7}{13}$ **73.** $8\dfrac{5}{14}$

74. True or false? If an improper fraction is equivalent to 1, then the numerator and the denominator are the same number.

Critical Thinking

75. Name three situations in which fractions are used. Provide an example of a fraction that is used in each situation.

Projects or Group Activities

76. Using a denominator of 5, write improper fractions that represent the numbers 1, 2, 3, and 4.

77. Using a denominator of 8, write an improper fraction that represents a number greater than 2 but less than 3. *Hint*: There is more than one answer.

2.3 Writing Equivalent Fractions

OBJECTIVE A   *To find equivalent fractions by raising to higher terms*

Equal fractions with different denominators are called **equivalent fractions.**

$\frac{4}{6}$ is equivalent to $\frac{2}{3}$.

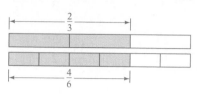

Remember that the Multiplication Property of One states that the product of a number and 1 is the number. This is true for fractions as well as whole numbers. This property can be used to write equivalent fractions.

$$\frac{2}{3} \times 1 = \frac{2}{3} \times \frac{1}{1} = \frac{2 \cdot 1}{3 \cdot 1} = \frac{2}{3}$$

$$\frac{2}{3} \times 1 = \frac{2}{3} \times \boxed{\frac{2}{2}} = \frac{2 \cdot 2}{3 \cdot 2} = \frac{4}{6} \qquad \frac{4}{6} \text{ is equivalent to } \frac{2}{3}.$$

$$\frac{2}{3} \times 1 = \frac{2}{3} \times \boxed{\frac{4}{4}} = \frac{2 \cdot 4}{3 \cdot 4} = \frac{8}{12} \qquad \frac{8}{12} \text{ is equivalent to } \frac{2}{3}.$$

$\frac{2}{3}$ was rewritten as the equivalent fractions $\frac{4}{6}$ and $\frac{8}{12}$.

HOW TO 1   Write a fraction that is equivalent to $\frac{5}{8}$ and has a denominator of 32.

$32 \div 8 = 4$

$\dfrac{5}{8} = \dfrac{5 \cdot 4}{8 \cdot 4} = \dfrac{20}{32}$

$\frac{20}{32}$ is equivalent to $\frac{5}{8}$.

- Divide the larger denominator by the smaller.
- Multiply the numerator and denominator of the given fraction by the quotient (4).

EXAMPLE 1

Write $\frac{2}{3}$ as an equivalent fraction that has a denominator of 42.

Solution $42 \div 3 = 14, \dfrac{2}{3} = \dfrac{2 \cdot 14}{3 \cdot 14} = \dfrac{28}{42}$

$\frac{28}{42}$ is equivalent to $\frac{2}{3}$.

YOU TRY IT 1

Write $\frac{3}{5}$ as an equivalent fraction that has a denominator of 45.

Your solution

EXAMPLE 2

Write 4 as a fraction that has a denominator of 12.

Solution   Write 4 as $\frac{4}{1}$.

$12 \div 1 = 12, 4 = \dfrac{4 \cdot 12}{1 \cdot 12} = \dfrac{48}{12}$

$\frac{48}{12}$ is equivalent to 4.

YOU TRY IT 2

Write 6 as a fraction that has a denominator of 18.

Your solution

Solutions on p. S5

OBJECTIVE B *To write a fraction in simplest form*

Writing the **simplest form of a fraction** means writing it so that the numerator and denominator have no common factors other than 1.

The fractions $\frac{4}{6}$ and $\frac{2}{3}$ are equivalent fractions.

$\frac{4}{6}$ has been written in simplest form as $\frac{2}{3}$.

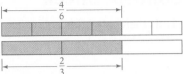

The Multiplication Property of One can be used to write fractions in simplest form. Write the numerator and denominator of the given fraction as a product of factors. Write factors common to both the numerator and denominator as an improper fraction equivalent to 1.

$$\frac{4}{6} = \frac{2 \cdot 2}{2 \cdot 3} = \boxed{\frac{2}{2}} \cdot \frac{2}{3} = \boxed{\frac{2}{2}} \cdot \frac{2}{3} = 1 \cdot \frac{2}{3} = \frac{2}{3}$$

The process of eliminating common factors is displayed with slashes through the common factors as shown at the right.

To write a fraction in simplest form, eliminate the common factors.

An improper fraction can be changed to a mixed number.

$$\frac{4}{6} = \frac{\overset{1}{2} \cdot 2}{2 \cdot 3} = \frac{2}{3}$$

$$\frac{18}{30} = \frac{\overset{1}{2} \cdot \overset{1}{3} \cdot 3}{2 \cdot 3 \cdot 5} = \frac{3}{5}$$

$$\frac{22}{6} = \frac{\overset{1}{2} \cdot 11}{2 \cdot 3} = \frac{11}{3} = 3\frac{2}{3}$$

EXAMPLE 3

Write $\frac{15}{40}$ in simplest form.

Solution
$$\frac{15}{40} = \frac{3 \cdot \overset{1}{5}}{2 \cdot 2 \cdot 2 \cdot 5} = \frac{3}{8}$$

YOU TRY IT 3

Write $\frac{16}{24}$ in simplest form.

Your solution

EXAMPLE 4

Write $\frac{6}{42}$ in simplest form.

Solution
$$\frac{6}{42} = \frac{\overset{1}{2} \cdot \overset{1}{3}}{2 \cdot 3 \cdot 7} = \frac{1}{7}$$

YOU TRY IT 4

Write $\frac{8}{56}$ in simplest form.

Your solution

EXAMPLE 5

Write $\frac{8}{9}$ in simplest form.

Solution
$$\frac{8}{9} = \frac{2 \cdot 2 \cdot 2}{3 \cdot 3} = \frac{8}{9}$$

$\frac{8}{9}$ is already in simplest form because there are no common factors in the numerator and denominator.

YOU TRY IT 5

Write $\frac{15}{32}$ in simplest form.

Your solution

EXAMPLE 6

Write $\frac{30}{12}$ in simplest form.

Solution
$$\frac{30}{12} = \frac{\overset{1}{2} \cdot \overset{1}{3} \cdot 5}{2 \cdot 2 \cdot 3} = \frac{5}{2} = 2\frac{1}{2}$$

YOU TRY IT 6

Write $\frac{48}{36}$ in simplest form.

Your solution

Solutions on p. S5

2.3 EXERCISES

✔ Concept Check

1. Is there a fraction equivalent to $\frac{3}{5}$ with a denominator of 7? Explain.

2. If a fraction is in simplest form, what is the GCF of the numerator and denominator of the fraction?

OBJECTIVE A   *To find equivalent fractions by raising to higher terms*

For Exercises 3 to 37, write an equivalent fraction with the given denominator.

3. $\dfrac{1}{2} = \dfrac{}{10}$

4. $\dfrac{1}{4} = \dfrac{}{16}$

5. $\dfrac{3}{16} = \dfrac{}{48}$

6. $\dfrac{5}{9} = \dfrac{}{81}$

7. $\dfrac{3}{8} = \dfrac{}{32}$

8. $\dfrac{7}{11} = \dfrac{}{33}$

9. $\dfrac{3}{17} = \dfrac{}{51}$

10. $\dfrac{7}{10} = \dfrac{}{90}$

11. $\dfrac{3}{4} = \dfrac{}{16}$

12. $\dfrac{5}{8} = \dfrac{}{32}$

13. $3 = \dfrac{}{9}$

14. $5 = \dfrac{}{25}$

15. $\dfrac{1}{3} = \dfrac{}{60}$

16. $\dfrac{1}{16} = \dfrac{}{48}$

17. $\dfrac{11}{15} = \dfrac{}{60}$

18. $\dfrac{3}{50} = \dfrac{}{300}$

19. $\dfrac{2}{3} = \dfrac{}{18}$

20. $\dfrac{5}{9} = \dfrac{}{36}$

21. $\dfrac{5}{7} = \dfrac{}{49}$

22. $\dfrac{7}{8} = \dfrac{}{32}$

23. $\dfrac{5}{9} = \dfrac{}{18}$

24. $\dfrac{11}{12} = \dfrac{}{36}$

25. $7 = \dfrac{}{3}$

26. $9 = \dfrac{}{4}$

27. $\dfrac{7}{9} = \dfrac{}{45}$

28. $\dfrac{5}{6} = \dfrac{}{42}$

29. $\dfrac{15}{16} = \dfrac{}{64}$

30. $\dfrac{11}{18} = \dfrac{}{54}$

31. $\dfrac{3}{14} = \dfrac{}{98}$

32. $\dfrac{5}{6} = \dfrac{}{144}$

33. $\dfrac{5}{8} = \dfrac{}{48}$

34. $\dfrac{7}{12} = \dfrac{}{96}$

35. $\dfrac{5}{14} = \dfrac{}{42}$

36. $\dfrac{2}{3} = \dfrac{}{42}$

37. $\dfrac{17}{24} = \dfrac{}{144}$

38. 📝 When you multiply the numerator and denominator of a fraction by the same number, you are actually multiplying the fraction by the number _____.

OBJECTIVE B   *To write a fraction in simplest form*

For Exercises 39 to 73, write the fraction in simplest form.

39. $\dfrac{4}{12}$

40. $\dfrac{8}{22}$

41. $\dfrac{22}{44}$

42. $\dfrac{2}{14}$

43. $\dfrac{2}{12}$

44. $\dfrac{50}{75}$　　　**45.** $\dfrac{40}{36}$　　　**46.** $\dfrac{12}{8}$　　　**47.** $\dfrac{0}{30}$　　　**48.** $\dfrac{10}{10}$

49. $\dfrac{9}{22}$　　　**50.** $\dfrac{14}{35}$　　　**51.** $\dfrac{75}{25}$　　　**52.** $\dfrac{8}{60}$　　　**53.** $\dfrac{16}{84}$

54. $\dfrac{20}{44}$　　　**55.** $\dfrac{12}{35}$　　　**56.** $\dfrac{8}{36}$　　　**57.** $\dfrac{28}{44}$　　　**58.** $\dfrac{12}{16}$

59. $\dfrac{16}{12}$　　　**60.** $\dfrac{24}{18}$　　　**61.** $\dfrac{24}{40}$　　　**62.** $\dfrac{44}{60}$　　　**63.** $\dfrac{8}{88}$

64. $\dfrac{9}{90}$　　　**65.** $\dfrac{144}{36}$　　　**66.** $\dfrac{140}{297}$　　　**67.** $\dfrac{48}{144}$　　　**68.** $\dfrac{32}{120}$

69. $\dfrac{60}{100}$　　　**70.** $\dfrac{33}{110}$　　　**71.** $\dfrac{36}{16}$　　　**72.** $\dfrac{80}{45}$　　　**73.** $\dfrac{32}{160}$

74. Suppose the denominator of a fraction is a multiple of the numerator. When the fraction is written in simplest form, what number is its numerator?

Critical Thinking

75. Make a list of five different fractions that are equivalent to $\frac{2}{3}$.

76. Show that $\frac{15}{24} = \frac{5}{8}$ by using a diagram.

Projects or Group Activities

77. Geography　a. What fraction of the states in the United States of America have names that begin with the letter M?
b. What fraction of the states have names that begin and end with a vowel?

SECTION

2.4 Addition of Fractions and Mixed Numbers

OBJECTIVE A *To add fractions with the same denominator*

Addition of Fractions with the Same Denominator

To add fractions with the same denominator, add the numerators and place the sum over the common denominator.

EXAMPLES

1. $\dfrac{2}{7} + \dfrac{3}{7} = \dfrac{2+3}{7} = \dfrac{5}{7}$

2. $\dfrac{1}{8} + \dfrac{5}{8} = \dfrac{1+5}{8} = \dfrac{6}{8} = \dfrac{3}{4}$

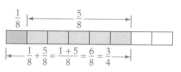

📋 **Take Note**

In Example 2 at the right, note that the answer is reduced to simplest form. Always write your answer in simplest form.

EXAMPLE 1

Add: $\dfrac{5}{18} + \dfrac{7}{18}$

Solution

$\dfrac{5}{18} + \dfrac{7}{18} = \dfrac{5+7}{18} = \dfrac{12}{18}$

$= \dfrac{2}{3}$

• The denominators are the same. Add the numerators. Place the sum over the common denominator.
• Write the answer in simplest form.

YOU TRY IT 1

Add: $\dfrac{3}{8} + \dfrac{7}{8}$

Your solution

Solution on p. S5

OBJECTIVE B *To add fractions with different denominators*

Addition of Fractions with Different Denominators

To add fractions with different denominators, first rewrite the fractions as equivalent fractions with a common denominator. Then add the numerators and place the sum over the common denominator. The LCM of the denominators of the fractions is the **least common denominator (LCD).**

EXAMPLE

Add: $\dfrac{1}{2} + \dfrac{1}{3}$

The LCM of the denominators 2 and 3 is 6.

$\dfrac{1}{2} + \dfrac{1}{3} = \dfrac{3}{6} + \dfrac{2}{6}$

$= \dfrac{3+2}{6} = \dfrac{5}{6}$

• Write equivalent fractions with 6 as the denominator.

• Add the numerators.

📱 **Integrating Technology**

Some scientific calculators have a fraction key, $a^{b/c}$. It is used to perform operations on fractions. To use this key to simplify the expression at the right, enter

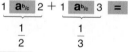

$\dfrac{1}{2}$ $\dfrac{1}{3}$

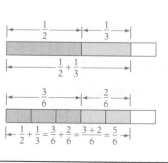

EXAMPLE 2

Add: $\dfrac{5}{8} + \dfrac{7}{9}$

Solution

Write equivalent fractions using 72 (the LCM of the denominators) as the common denominator. Then add.

$$\dfrac{5}{8} + \dfrac{7}{9} = \dfrac{45}{72} + \dfrac{56}{72} = \dfrac{45+56}{72} = \dfrac{101}{72} = 1\dfrac{29}{72}$$

YOU TRY IT 2

Add: $\dfrac{7}{9} + \dfrac{11}{15}$

Your solution

EXAMPLE 3

Find $\dfrac{7}{12}$ more than $\dfrac{3}{8}$.

Solution

Write equivalent fractions using 24 (the LCM of the denominators) as the common denominator. Then add.

$$\dfrac{3}{8} + \dfrac{7}{12} = \dfrac{9}{24} + \dfrac{14}{24} = \dfrac{9+14}{24} = \dfrac{23}{24}$$

YOU TRY IT 3

Find the sum of $\dfrac{5}{12}$ and $\dfrac{9}{16}$.

Your solution

EXAMPLE 4

Add: $\dfrac{2}{3} + \dfrac{3}{5} + \dfrac{5}{6}$

Solution

Write equivalent fractions using 30 (the LCM of the denominators) as the common denominator. Then add.

$$\dfrac{2}{3} + \dfrac{3}{5} + \dfrac{5}{6} = \dfrac{20}{30} + \dfrac{18}{30} + \dfrac{25}{30} = \dfrac{20+18+25}{30}$$

$$= \dfrac{63}{30} = 2\dfrac{3}{30} = 2\dfrac{1}{10}$$

YOU TRY IT 4

Add: $\dfrac{3}{4} + \dfrac{4}{5} + \dfrac{5}{8}$

Your solution

Solutions on p. S5

OBJECTIVE C   *To add whole numbers, mixed numbers, and fractions*

The sum of a whole number and a fraction is a mixed number.

📋 **Take Note**

The procedure at the right illustrates why $2 + \dfrac{2}{3} = 2\dfrac{2}{3}$.

You do not need to show these steps when adding a whole number and a fraction. Here are two more examples:

$7 + \dfrac{1}{5} = 7\dfrac{1}{5}$

$6 + \dfrac{3}{4} = 6\dfrac{3}{4}$

HOW TO 1   Add: $2 + \dfrac{2}{3}$

$$2 + \dfrac{2}{3} = \dfrac{6}{3} + \dfrac{2}{3} = \dfrac{8}{3} = 2\dfrac{2}{3}$$

To add a whole number and a mixed number, write the fraction and then add the whole numbers.

HOW TO 2   Add: $7\dfrac{2}{5} + 4$

Write the fraction.
$$7\dfrac{2}{5}$$
$$\underline{+\ 4\phantom{\dfrac{2}{5}}}$$
$$\dfrac{2}{5}$$

Add the whole numbers.
$$7\dfrac{2}{5}$$
$$\underline{+\ 4\phantom{\dfrac{2}{5}}}$$
$$11\dfrac{2}{5}$$

To add two mixed numbers, add the fractional parts and then add the whole numbers. Remember to reduce the sum to simplest form.

Integrating Technology

Use the fraction key on a calculator to enter mixed numbers. For the example at the right, enter

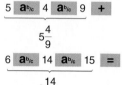

HOW TO 3   What is $6\frac{14}{15}$ added to $5\frac{4}{9}$?

The LCM of the denominators 9 and 15 is 45.

Add the fractional parts.

$$
\begin{array}{r}
5\dfrac{4}{9} = 5\dfrac{20}{45} \\[2mm]
+6\dfrac{14}{15} = 6\dfrac{42}{45} \\[1mm]
\hline
\dfrac{62}{45}
\end{array}
$$

Add the whole numbers.

$$
\begin{array}{r}
5\dfrac{4}{9} = 5\dfrac{20}{45} \\[2mm]
+6\dfrac{14}{15} = 6\dfrac{42}{45} \\[1mm]
\hline
11\dfrac{62}{45} = 11 + \dfrac{62}{45} = 11 + 1\dfrac{17}{45} = 12\dfrac{17}{45}
\end{array}
$$

APPLY THE CONCEPT

A pastry chef is making a blueberry cake that requires $1\frac{1}{3}$ cups of flour for the streusel topping and $1\frac{1}{4}$ cups of flour for the cake. To find the total amount of flour the chef needs, add $1\frac{1}{3}$ and $1\frac{1}{4}$.

$$
1\frac{1}{3} + 1\frac{1}{4} = 1\frac{4}{12} + 1\frac{3}{12} = 2\frac{7}{12}
$$

The chef needs $2\frac{7}{12}$ cups of flour.

EXAMPLE 5

Add: $5 + \dfrac{3}{8}$

Solution $5 + \dfrac{3}{8} = 5\dfrac{3}{8}$

YOU TRY IT 5

What is 7 added to $\dfrac{6}{11}$?

Your solution

EXAMPLE 6

Find 17 increased by $3\frac{3}{8}$.

Solution $17 + 3\dfrac{3}{8} = 20\dfrac{3}{8}$

YOU TRY IT 6

Find the sum of 29 and $17\frac{5}{12}$.

Your solution

EXAMPLE 7

Add: $5\dfrac{2}{3} + 11\dfrac{5}{6} + 12\dfrac{7}{9}$

Solution

$$
5\frac{2}{3} = 5\frac{12}{18} \quad \bullet \text{ LCD} = 18
$$

$$
11\frac{5}{6} = 11\frac{15}{18}
$$

$$
+ 12\frac{7}{9} = 12\frac{14}{18}
$$

$$
28\frac{41}{18} = 30\frac{5}{18}
$$

YOU TRY IT 7

Add: $7\dfrac{4}{5} + 6\dfrac{7}{10} + 13\dfrac{11}{15}$

Your solution

OBJECTIVE D   *To solve application problems*

EXAMPLE 8

The lengths of the luff, leech, and foot of the jib for a sailboat are shown at the right. Find the perimeter of the sail. (Perimeter is the distance around an object.)

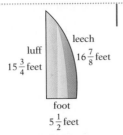

luff $15\frac{3}{4}$ feet

leech $16\frac{7}{8}$ feet

foot $5\frac{1}{2}$ feet

Strategy

To find the perimeter, add the lengths of the luff, leech, and foot $(15\frac{3}{4}, 16\frac{7}{8}, \text{and } 5\frac{1}{2})$.

Solution

$$15\frac{3}{4} + 16\frac{7}{8} + 5\frac{1}{2} = 15\frac{6}{8} + 16\frac{7}{8} + 5\frac{4}{8}$$

$$= 36\frac{17}{8} = 38\frac{1}{8}$$

The perimeter of the sail is $38\frac{1}{8}$ feet.

YOU TRY IT 8

On Monday, you spent $4\frac{1}{2}$ hours in class, $3\frac{3}{4}$ hours studying, and $1\frac{1}{3}$ hours driving. Find the total number of hours spent on these three activities.

Your strategy

Your solution

EXAMPLE 9

This week, Barbara Walsh worked 4 hours on Tuesday, $2\frac{1}{3}$ hours on Wednesday, and $5\frac{2}{3}$ hours on Friday at a part-time job. Barbara is paid $9 an hour. How much did she earn this week?

Strategy

To find how much Barbara earned:
• Find the total number of hours worked.
• Multiply the total number of hours worked by the hourly wage (9).

Solution

$$\begin{array}{r} 4 \\ 2\frac{1}{3} \\ + 5\frac{2}{3} \\ \hline 11\frac{3}{3} = 12 \text{ hours worked} \end{array} \qquad \begin{array}{r} 12 \\ \times\ 9 \\ \hline 108 \end{array}$$

Barbara earned $108 this week.

YOU TRY IT 9

Jeff Sapone, a carpenter, worked $1\frac{2}{3}$ hours of overtime on Monday, $3\frac{1}{3}$ hours of overtime on Tuesday, and 2 hours of overtime on Wednesday. At an overtime hourly rate of $36, find Jeff's overtime pay for the 3 days.

Your strategy

Your solution

Solutions on pp. S5–S6

2.4 EXERCISES

✔ Concept Check

For Exercises 1 and 2, replace the question marks to make a true statement.

1. $\dfrac{2}{9} + \dfrac{5}{9} = \dfrac{?+?}{9} = \dfrac{?}{9}$

2. $\dfrac{1}{8} + \dfrac{3}{8} = \dfrac{?+?}{8} = \dfrac{?}{8} = ?$

For Exercises 3 to 6, find the LCD of the fractions.

3. $\dfrac{1}{4}, \dfrac{3}{8}$

4. $\dfrac{2}{3}, \dfrac{3}{4}$

5. $\dfrac{5}{6}, \dfrac{4}{9}$

6. $\dfrac{1}{2}, \dfrac{3}{5}, \dfrac{3}{14}$

OBJECTIVE A   *To add fractions with the same denominator*

For Exercises 7 to 22, add.

7. $\dfrac{2}{7} + \dfrac{1}{7}$

8. $\dfrac{3}{11} + \dfrac{5}{11}$

9. $\dfrac{2}{9} + \dfrac{4}{9}$

10. $\dfrac{5}{8} + \dfrac{1}{8}$

11. $\dfrac{3}{14} + \dfrac{5}{14}$

12. $\dfrac{3}{20} + \dfrac{9}{20}$

13. $\dfrac{1}{2} + \dfrac{1}{2}$

14. $\dfrac{1}{3} + \dfrac{2}{3}$

15. $\dfrac{8}{11} + \dfrac{7}{11}$

16. $\dfrac{9}{13} + \dfrac{7}{13}$

17. $\dfrac{8}{5} + \dfrac{9}{5}$

18. $\dfrac{5}{3} + \dfrac{7}{3}$

19. $\dfrac{3}{8} + \dfrac{7}{8} + \dfrac{1}{8}$

20. $\dfrac{5}{12} + \dfrac{7}{12} + \dfrac{1}{12}$

21. $\dfrac{4}{15} + \dfrac{7}{15} + \dfrac{11}{15}$

22. $\dfrac{5}{7} + \dfrac{4}{7} + \dfrac{5}{7}$

23. Find the sum of $\frac{5}{12}$, $\frac{1}{12}$, and $\frac{11}{12}$.

24. Find the total of $\frac{5}{8}$, $\frac{3}{8}$, and $\frac{7}{8}$.

For Exercises 25 to 28, each statement concerns a pair of fractions that have the same denominator. State whether the sum of the fractions is a proper fraction, the number 1, a mixed number, or a whole number other than 1.

25. The sum of the numerators is a multiple of the denominator.

26. The sum of the numerators is one more than the denominator.

27. The sum of the numerators is the denominator.

28. The sum of the numerators is smaller than the denominator.

OBJECTIVE B   *To add fractions with different denominators*

For Exercises 29 to 48, add.

29. $\dfrac{1}{2} + \dfrac{2}{3}$

30. $\dfrac{2}{3} + \dfrac{1}{4}$

31. $\dfrac{3}{14} + \dfrac{5}{7}$

32. $\dfrac{3}{5} + \dfrac{7}{10}$

33. $\dfrac{8}{15} + \dfrac{7}{20}$

34. $\dfrac{1}{6} + \dfrac{7}{9}$

35. $\dfrac{3}{8} + \dfrac{9}{14}$

36. $\dfrac{5}{12} + \dfrac{5}{16}$

37. $\dfrac{3}{20} + \dfrac{7}{30}$

38. $\dfrac{5}{12} + \dfrac{7}{30}$

39. $\dfrac{1}{3} + \dfrac{5}{6} + \dfrac{7}{9}$

40. $\dfrac{2}{3} + \dfrac{5}{6} + \dfrac{7}{12}$

41. $\dfrac{5}{6} + \dfrac{1}{12} + \dfrac{5}{16}$

42. $\dfrac{2}{9} + \dfrac{7}{15} + \dfrac{4}{21}$

43. $\dfrac{2}{3} + \dfrac{1}{5} + \dfrac{7}{12}$

44. $\dfrac{3}{4} + \dfrac{4}{5} + \dfrac{7}{12}$

45. $\dfrac{2}{3} + \dfrac{3}{5} + \dfrac{7}{8}$

46. $\dfrac{3}{10} + \dfrac{14}{15} + \dfrac{9}{25}$

47. $\dfrac{2}{3} + \dfrac{5}{8} + \dfrac{7}{9}$

48. $\dfrac{1}{3} + \dfrac{2}{9} + \dfrac{7}{8}$

49. What is $\frac{3}{8}$ added to $\frac{3}{5}$?

50. What is $\frac{5}{9}$ added to $\frac{7}{12}$?

51. Find the sum of $\frac{3}{8}$, $\frac{5}{6}$, and $\frac{7}{12}$.

52. Find the total of $\frac{1}{2}$, $\frac{5}{8}$, and $\frac{7}{9}$.

53. 🔖 Which statement describes a pair of fractions for which the least common denominator is the product of the denominators?
   (i) The denominator of one fraction is a multiple of the denominator of the second fraction.
   (ii) The denominators of the two fractions have no common factors.

OBJECTIVE C *To add whole numbers, mixed numbers, and fractions*

For Exercises 54 to 75, add.

54. $2\dfrac{2}{5}$
$+\ 3\dfrac{3}{10}$

55. $4\dfrac{1}{2}$
$+\ 5\dfrac{7}{12}$

56. $3\dfrac{3}{8}$
$+\ 2\dfrac{5}{16}$

57. 4
$+\ 5\dfrac{2}{7}$

58. $6\dfrac{8}{9}$
$+\ 12$

59. $7\dfrac{5}{12} + 2\dfrac{9}{16}$

60. $9\dfrac{1}{2} + 3\dfrac{3}{11}$

61. $6 + 2\dfrac{3}{13}$

62. $8\dfrac{21}{40} + 6$

63. $8\dfrac{29}{30} + 7\dfrac{11}{40}$

64. $17\dfrac{5}{16} + 3\dfrac{11}{24}$

65. $17\dfrac{3}{8} + 7\dfrac{7}{20}$

66. $14\dfrac{7}{12} + 29\dfrac{13}{21}$

67. $5\dfrac{7}{8} + 27\dfrac{5}{12}$

68. $7\dfrac{5}{6} + 3\dfrac{5}{9}$

69. $7\dfrac{5}{9} + 2\dfrac{7}{12}$

70. $3\dfrac{1}{2} + 2\dfrac{3}{4} + 1\dfrac{5}{6}$

71. $2\dfrac{1}{2} + 3\dfrac{2}{3} + 4\dfrac{1}{4}$

72. $3\dfrac{1}{3} + 7\dfrac{1}{5} + 2\dfrac{1}{7}$

73. $3\dfrac{1}{2} + 3\dfrac{1}{5} + 8\dfrac{1}{9}$

74. $6\dfrac{5}{9} + 6\dfrac{5}{12} + 2\dfrac{5}{18}$

75. $2\dfrac{3}{8} + 4\dfrac{7}{12} + 3\dfrac{5}{16}$

76. Carpentry For the bookcase shown at the right, what is the distance from the top of the bottom shelf to the top of the next shelf?

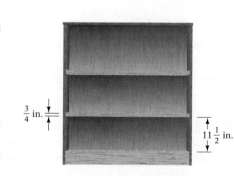

$\dfrac{3}{4}$ in.

$11\dfrac{1}{2}$ in.

77. Building Maintenance A pole $6\dfrac{3}{8}$ feet long is used to change light bulbs in ceiling fixtures. The pole comes with an extension that is $3\dfrac{1}{2}$ feet long. What is the length of the pole with the extension in place?

78. Find the sum of $2\frac{4}{9}$ and $5\frac{7}{12}$.

79. Find $5\frac{5}{6}$ more than $3\frac{3}{8}$.

80. What is $4\frac{3}{4}$ added to $9\frac{1}{3}$?

81. What is $4\frac{8}{9}$ added to $9\frac{1}{6}$?

82. Find the total of 2, $4\frac{5}{8}$, and $2\frac{2}{9}$.

83. Find the total of $1\frac{5}{8}$, 3, and $7\frac{7}{24}$.

For Exercises 84 and 85, state whether the given sum can be a whole number. Answer *yes* or *no*.

84. The sum of two mixed numbers

85. The sum of a mixed number and a whole number

OBJECTIVE D   *To solve application problems*

86. Mechanics   Find the length of the shaft.

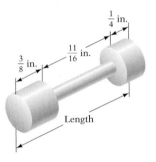

Length

87. Mechanics   Find the length of the shaft.

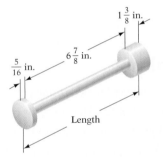

Length

88. Carpentry   A table 30 inches high has a top that is $1\frac{1}{8}$ inches thick. Find the total thickness of the table top after a $\frac{3}{16}$-inch veneer is applied.

89.   For the table pictured at the right, what does the sum $30 + 1\frac{1}{8} + \frac{3}{16}$ represent?

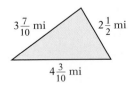

Veneer

$\frac{3}{16}$ in.

$1\frac{1}{8}$ in.

30 in.

90. Wages   You are working a part-time job that pays $11 an hour. You worked 5, $3\frac{3}{4}$, $2\frac{1}{3}$, $1\frac{1}{4}$, and $7\frac{2}{3}$ hours during the last five days.

  a. Find the total number of hours you worked during the last five days.
  b. Find your total wages for the five days.

91. Sports   The course of a yachting race is in the shape of a triangle with sides that measure $4\frac{3}{10}$ miles, $3\frac{7}{10}$ miles, and $2\frac{1}{2}$ miles. Find the total length of the course.

$3\frac{7}{10}$ mi $2\frac{1}{2}$ mi

$4\frac{3}{10}$ mi

Construction   The size of an interior door frame is determined by the width of the wall into which it is installed. The width of the wall is determined by the width of the stud in the wall and the thickness of the sheets of drywall installed on each side of the wall. A 2×4 stud is $3\frac{5}{8}$ inches thick. A 2×6 stud is $5\frac{5}{8}$ inches thick. Use this information for Exercises 92 to 94.

92. Find the thickness of a wall constructed with 2×4 studs and drywall that is $\frac{1}{2}$ inch thick.

93. Find the thickness of a wall constructed with 2×6 studs and drywall that is $\frac{1}{2}$ inch thick.

94. A fire wall is a physical barrier in a building designed to limit the spread of fire. Suppose a fire wall is built between the garage and the kitchen of a house. Find the width of the fire wall if it is constructed using 2×4 studs and drywall that is $\frac{5}{8}$ inch thick.

95. **Construction**   Two pieces of wood must be bolted together. One piece of wood is $\frac{1}{2}$ inch thick. The second piece is $\frac{5}{8}$ inch thick. A washer will be placed on each of the outer side of the top piece of wood. The washer is $\frac{1}{16}$ inch thick. The nut is $\frac{3}{16}$ inch thick. Find the minimum length of bolt needed to bolt the two pieces of wood together.

Critical Thinking

96. 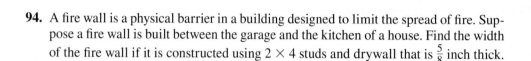 A survey was conducted to determine people's favorite color from among blue, green, red, purple, and other. The surveyor claims that $\frac{1}{3}$ of the people responded blue, $\frac{1}{6}$ responded green, $\frac{1}{8}$ responded red, $\frac{1}{12}$ responded purple, and $\frac{2}{5}$ responded some other color. Is this possible? Explain your answer.

Projects or Group Activities

A **unit fraction** is a fraction with numerator 1 and denominator greater than 1. For instance, $\frac{1}{5}$ and $\frac{1}{12}$ are unit fractions.

97. List the three largest unit fractions.

98. 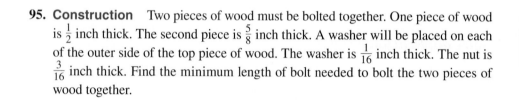 Is there a smallest unit fraction? Explain.

Early Egyptians expressed nonunit fractions as the sums of unit fractions. For instance, $\frac{3}{10}$ would be represented as $\frac{1}{5} + \frac{1}{10}$ because $\frac{3}{10} = \frac{1}{5} + \frac{1}{10}$. For Exercises 99 to 101, represent the given fraction as the sum of two unit fractions.

99. $\dfrac{7}{12}$ 100. $\dfrac{11}{24}$ 101. $\dfrac{5}{12}$

SECTION

2.5 Subtraction of Fractions and Mixed Numbers

OBJECTIVE A   *To subtract fractions with the same denominator*

Subtraction of Fractions with the Same Denominator

To subtract fractions with the same denominator, subtract the numerators and place the difference over the common denominator.

EXAMPLE

$$\frac{6}{7} - \frac{2}{7} = \frac{6 - 2}{7} = \frac{4}{7}$$

EXAMPLE 1

Subtract: $\dfrac{11}{18} - \dfrac{7}{18}$

Solution

$$\frac{11}{18} - \frac{7}{18} = \frac{11 - 7}{18}$$

• The denominators are the same. Subtract the numerators.

$$= \frac{4}{18}$$

• Place the difference over the common denominator.

$$= \frac{2}{9}$$

• Write the answer in simplest form.

YOU TRY IT 1

Find the difference between $\dfrac{16}{27}$ and $\dfrac{7}{27}$.

Your solution

Solution on p. S6

OBJECTIVE B   *To subtract fractions with different denominators*

Subtraction of Fractions with Different Denominators

To subtract fractions with different denominators, first rewrite the fractions as equivalent fractions with a common denominator. Then subtract the numerators and place the difference over the common denominator.

EXAMPLE

Subtract: $\dfrac{5}{6} - \dfrac{1}{4}$

The LCD of the denominators 6 and 4 is 12.

$$\frac{5}{6} - \frac{1}{4} = \frac{10}{12} - \frac{3}{12}$$

• Rewrite each fraction as an equivalent fraction with 12 as the denominator.

$$= \frac{10 - 3}{12} = \frac{7}{12}$$

• Subtract the numerators and place the difference over the common denominator.

EXAMPLE 2

Subtract: $\dfrac{11}{16} - \dfrac{5}{12}$

Solution

The LCD of the denominators 16 and 12 is 48. Write equivalent fractions using 48 as the common denominator. Then subtract the fractions.

$$\dfrac{11}{16} - \dfrac{5}{12} = \dfrac{33}{48} - \dfrac{20}{48} = \dfrac{33-20}{48} = \dfrac{13}{48}$$

YOU TRY IT 2

Subtract: $\dfrac{13}{18} - \dfrac{7}{24}$

Your solution

EXAMPLE 3

Find the difference between $\frac{7}{8}$ and $\frac{5}{12}$.

Solution

The LCD of the denominators 8 and 12 is 24. Write equivalent fractions using 24 as the common denominator. Then subtract the fractions.

$$\dfrac{7}{8} - \dfrac{5}{12} = \dfrac{21}{24} - \dfrac{10}{24} = \dfrac{21-10}{24} = \dfrac{11}{24}$$

YOU TRY IT 3

Find $\frac{5}{6}$ less than $\frac{8}{9}$.

Your solution

Solutions on p. S6

OBJECTIVE C   *To subtract whole numbers, mixed numbers, and fractions*

To subtract mixed numbers without borrowing, subtract the fractional parts and then subtract the whole numbers.

HOW TO 1   Subtract: $5\dfrac{5}{6} - 2\dfrac{3}{4}$

Subtract the fractional parts.

$$5\dfrac{5}{6} = 5\dfrac{10}{12}$$
$$-2\dfrac{3}{4} = 2\dfrac{9}{12}$$
$$\overline{\qquad \dfrac{1}{12}}$$

• The LCD of the denominators 6 and 4 is 12.

Subtract the whole numbers.

$$5\dfrac{5}{6} = 5\dfrac{10}{12}$$
$$-2\dfrac{3}{4} = 2\dfrac{9}{12}$$
$$\overline{\qquad 3\dfrac{1}{12}}$$

The difference is $3\frac{1}{12}$.

Subtraction of mixed numbers sometimes involves borrowing.

HOW TO 2   Subtract: $7\dfrac{1}{6} - 2\dfrac{5}{8}$

Write equivalent fractions using the LCD.

Borrow 1 from 7. Add the 1 to $\dfrac{4}{24}$. Write $1\dfrac{4}{24}$ as $\dfrac{28}{24}$.

Subtract the mixed numbers.

$$7\dfrac{1}{6} = 7\dfrac{4}{24}$$
$$-2\dfrac{5}{8} = 2\dfrac{15}{24}$$

$$7\dfrac{1}{6} = \overset{6}{7}1\dfrac{4}{24} = 6\dfrac{28}{24}$$
$$-2\dfrac{5}{8} = \quad 2\dfrac{15}{24} = 2\dfrac{15}{24}$$

$$7\dfrac{1}{6} = 6\dfrac{28}{24}$$
$$-2\dfrac{5}{8} = 2\dfrac{15}{24}$$
$$\quad\quad\quad 4\dfrac{13}{24}$$

The difference is $4\dfrac{13}{24}$.

HOW TO 3   Subtract: $5 - 2\dfrac{5}{8}$

Borrow 1 from 5.

Write 1 as a fraction so that the fractions have the same denominators.

Subtract the mixed numbers.

$$5 \quad = \overset{4}{5}1$$
$$-2\dfrac{5}{8} = 2\dfrac{5}{8}$$

$$5 \quad = 4\dfrac{8}{8}$$
$$-2\dfrac{5}{8} = 2\dfrac{5}{8}$$

$$5 \quad = 4\dfrac{8}{8}$$
$$-2\dfrac{5}{8} = 2\dfrac{5}{8}$$
$$\quad\quad\quad 2\dfrac{3}{8}$$

The difference is $2\dfrac{3}{8}$.

APPLY THE CONCEPT

The inseam of a pant leg is $30\dfrac{1}{2}$ inches long. What is the length of the inseam after a tailor cuts $\dfrac{3}{4}$ inch from the pant leg?

To find the length of the inseam, subtract $\dfrac{3}{4}$ from $30\dfrac{1}{2}$.

$$30\dfrac{1}{2} - \dfrac{3}{4} = 30\dfrac{2}{4} - \dfrac{3}{4} = 29\dfrac{6}{4} - \dfrac{3}{4} = 29\dfrac{3}{4}$$

The length of the inseam is $29\dfrac{3}{4}$ inches.

EXAMPLE 4

Find $11\frac{5}{12}$ decreased by $2\frac{11}{16}$.

Solution

$$11\frac{5}{12} = 11\frac{20}{48} = 10\frac{68}{48} \quad \bullet \text{ LCD} = 48$$

$$-2\frac{11}{16} = \quad 2\frac{33}{48} = \quad 2\frac{33}{48}$$

$$8\frac{35}{48}$$

YOU TRY IT 4

What is $21\frac{7}{9}$ minus $7\frac{11}{12}$?

Your solution

EXAMPLE 5

Subtract: $9 - 4\frac{3}{11}$

Solution

$$9 \quad = 8\frac{11}{11} \quad \bullet \text{ LCD} = 11$$

$$-4\frac{3}{11} = 4\frac{3}{11}$$

$$4\frac{8}{11}$$

YOU TRY IT 5

Subtract: $8 - 2\frac{4}{13}$

Your solution

Solutions on p. S6

OBJECTIVE D *To solve application problems*

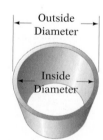

Outside Diameter

Inside Diameter

HOW TO 4 The outside diameter of a bushing is $3\frac{3}{8}$ inches, and the wall thickness is $\frac{1}{4}$ inch. Find the inside diameter of the bushing.

$$\frac{1}{4} + \frac{1}{4} = \frac{2}{4} = \frac{1}{2} \qquad \bullet \text{ Add } \frac{1}{4} \text{ and } \frac{1}{4} \text{ to find the total thickness of the two walls.}$$

$$3\frac{3}{8} = 3\frac{3}{8} = 2\frac{11}{8} \qquad \bullet \text{ Subtract the total thickness of the two walls from the outside}$$
$$\text{diameter to find the inside diameter.}$$

$$-\frac{1}{2} = \frac{4}{8} = \quad \frac{4}{8}$$

$$2\frac{7}{8}$$

The inside diameter of the bushing is $2\frac{7}{8}$ inches.

EXAMPLE 6

A $2\frac{2}{3}$-inch piece is cut from a $6\frac{5}{8}$-inch board. How much of the board is left?

Strategy

To find the length remaining, subtract the length of the piece cut from the total length of the board.

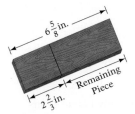

$6\frac{5}{8}$ in.

Remaining Piece

$2\frac{2}{3}$ in.

Solution

$$6\frac{5}{8} = 6\frac{15}{24} = 5\frac{39}{24}$$
$$-2\frac{2}{3} = 2\frac{16}{24} = 2\frac{16}{24}$$
$$\overline{\phantom{-2\frac{2}{3}=2\frac{16}{24}=}3\frac{23}{24}}$$

$3\frac{23}{24}$ inches of the board are left.

YOU TRY IT 6

A flight from New York to Los Angeles takes $5\frac{1}{2}$ hours. After the plane has been in the air for $2\frac{3}{4}$ hours, how much flight time remains?

Your strategy

Your solution

EXAMPLE 7

Two painters are staining a house. In one day, one painter stained $\frac{1}{3}$ of the house and the other stained $\frac{1}{4}$ of the house. How much of the job remains to be done?

Strategy

To find how much of the job remains:
- Find the total amount of the house already stained $\left(\frac{1}{3} + \frac{1}{4}\right)$.
- Subtract the amount already stained from 1, which represents the complete job.

Solution

$$\frac{1}{3} = \frac{4}{12} \qquad 1 = \frac{12}{12}$$
$$+\frac{1}{4} = \frac{3}{12} \qquad -\frac{7}{12} = \frac{7}{12}$$
$$\overline{\phantom{+\frac{1}{4}=}\frac{7}{12}} \qquad \overline{\phantom{-\frac{7}{12}=}\frac{5}{12}}$$

$\frac{5}{12}$ of the house remains to be stained.

YOU TRY IT 7

A patient is put on a diet to lose 24 pounds in 3 months. The patient lost $7\frac{1}{2}$ pounds the first month and $5\frac{3}{4}$ pounds the second month. How much weight must be lost during the third month to achieve the goal?

Your strategy

Your solution

Solutions on p. S6

2.5 EXERCISES

✔ Concept Check

For Exercises 1 and 2, replace each question mark to make a true statement.

1. $\dfrac{5}{11} - \dfrac{3}{11} = \dfrac{? - ?}{11} = \dfrac{?}{11}$

2. $\dfrac{7}{9} - \dfrac{4}{9} = \dfrac{? - ?}{9} = \dfrac{?}{9} = ?$

For Exercises 3 and 4, answer the question without doing any calculations.

3. If $\dfrac{11}{18} - \dfrac{7}{12} = \dfrac{1}{36}$, what is the sum of $\dfrac{1}{36}$ and $\dfrac{7}{12}$?

4. If $\dfrac{9}{16} + \dfrac{1}{3} = \dfrac{43}{48}$, what is the difference between $\dfrac{43}{48}$ and $\dfrac{9}{16}$?

OBJECTIVE A   *To subtract fractions with the same denominator*

For Exercises 5 to 14, subtract.

5. $\dfrac{9}{17} - \dfrac{7}{17}$ 6. $\dfrac{11}{15} - \dfrac{3}{15}$ 7. $\dfrac{11}{12} - \dfrac{7}{12}$ 8. $\dfrac{13}{15} - \dfrac{4}{15}$ 9. $\dfrac{9}{20} - \dfrac{7}{20}$

10. $\dfrac{48}{55} - \dfrac{13}{55}$ 11. $\dfrac{42}{65} - \dfrac{17}{65}$ 12. $\dfrac{11}{24} - \dfrac{5}{24}$ 13. $\dfrac{23}{30} - \dfrac{13}{30}$ 14. $\dfrac{17}{42} - \dfrac{5}{42}$

15. What is $\dfrac{5}{14}$ less than $\dfrac{13}{14}$?   16. Find the difference between $\dfrac{7}{8}$ and $\dfrac{5}{8}$.

17. Find $\dfrac{17}{24}$ decreased by $\dfrac{11}{24}$.   18. What is $\dfrac{19}{30}$ minus $\dfrac{11}{30}$?

For Exercises 19 and 20, each statement describes the difference between a pair of fractions that have the same denominator. State whether the difference of the fractions will need to be rewritten in order to be in simplest form. Answer *yes* or *no*.

19. The difference between the numerators is a factor of the denominator.

20. The difference between the numerators is 1.

OBJECTIVE B   *To subtract fractions with different denominators*

For Exercises 21 to 30, subtract.

21. $\dfrac{2}{3} - \dfrac{1}{6}$ 22. $\dfrac{7}{8} - \dfrac{5}{16}$ 23. $\dfrac{5}{8} - \dfrac{2}{7}$ 24. $\dfrac{5}{6} - \dfrac{3}{7}$ 25. $\dfrac{5}{7} - \dfrac{3}{14}$

26. $\dfrac{5}{9} - \dfrac{7}{15}$ 27. $\dfrac{8}{15} - \dfrac{7}{20}$ 28. $\dfrac{7}{9} - \dfrac{1}{6}$ 29. $\dfrac{9}{16} - \dfrac{17}{32}$ 30. $\dfrac{29}{60} - \dfrac{3}{40}$

31. What is $\frac{3}{5}$ less than $\frac{11}{12}$?

32. What is $\frac{5}{9}$ less than $\frac{11}{15}$?

33. Find the difference between $\frac{11}{24}$ and $\frac{7}{18}$.

34. Find the difference between $\frac{9}{14}$ and $\frac{5}{42}$.

35. Find $\frac{11}{12}$ decreased by $\frac{11}{15}$.

36. Find $\frac{17}{20}$ decreased by $\frac{7}{15}$.

37. What is $\frac{13}{20}$ minus $\frac{1}{6}$?

38. What is $\frac{5}{6}$ minus $\frac{7}{9}$?

39. Which statement describes a pair of fractions for which the least common denominator is one of the denominators?
   (i) The denominator of one fraction is a factor of the denominator of the second fraction.
   (ii) The denominators of the two fractions have no common factors.

OBJECTIVE C *To subtract whole numbers, mixed numbers, and fractions*

For Exercises 40 to 54, subtract.

40. $5\frac{7}{12}$
$-2\frac{5}{12}$

41. $16\frac{11}{15}$
$-11\frac{8}{15}$

42. $6\frac{1}{3}$
-2

43. $5\frac{7}{8}$
-1

44. 10
$-6\frac{1}{3}$

45. 3
$-2\frac{5}{21}$

46. $6\frac{2}{5}$
$-4\frac{4}{5}$

47. $16\frac{3}{8}$
$-10\frac{7}{8}$

48. $16\frac{2}{5}$
$-8\frac{4}{9}$

49. $23\frac{7}{8}$
$-16\frac{2}{3}$

50. 17
$-7\frac{8}{13}$

51. 6
$-4\frac{3}{5}$

52. $23\frac{1}{6}$
$-15\frac{3}{8}$

53. $40\frac{4}{9}$
$-24\frac{5}{6}$

54. $12\frac{5}{18}$
$-11\frac{11}{27}$

55. Interior Design   An interior decorator places a picture hook on a wall $29\frac{1}{2}$ inches down from the ceiling. If the support wire for the picture is $7\frac{3}{4}$ inches from the top of the picture as shown at the right, what is the distance from the ceiling to the top of the picture?

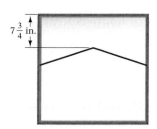

56. Storage Space   A laser printer $19\frac{3}{8}$ inches tall is placed on a shelf that is $23\frac{1}{4}$ inches below another shelf. Find the distance between the top of the printer and the bottom of the higher shelf.

57. What is $7\frac{3}{5}$ less than $23\frac{3}{20}$?

58. Find the difference between $12\frac{3}{8}$ and $7\frac{5}{12}$.

59. What is $10\frac{5}{9}$ minus $5\frac{11}{15}$?

60. Find $6\frac{1}{3}$ decreased by $3\frac{3}{5}$.

61. ✏️ Can the difference between a whole number and a mixed number ever be a whole number?

OBJECTIVE D   *To solve application problems*

62. Mechanics   Find the missing dimension.

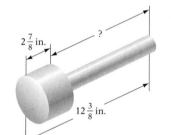

63. Mechanics   Find the missing dimension.

64. ⬤ **Sports**   In the Kentucky Derby the horses run $1\frac{1}{4}$ miles. In the Belmont Stakes they run $1\frac{1}{2}$ miles, and in the Preakness Stakes they run $1\frac{3}{16}$ miles. How much farther do the horses run in the Kentucky Derby than in the Preakness Stakes? How much farther do they run in the Belmont Stakes than in the Preakness Stakes?

65. Carpentry   The standard height of a desk is $29\frac{1}{2}$ inches. A writer is building a desk that is $28\frac{3}{4}$ inches high. How much shorter is this desk than a desk of standard height?

66. **Fundraising**   A 12-mile walkathon has three checkpoints. The first checkpoint is $3\frac{3}{8}$ miles from the starting point. The second checkpoint is $4\frac{1}{3}$ miles from the first.
    a.   How many miles is it from the starting point to the second checkpoint?
    b.   How many miles is it from the second checkpoint to the finish line?

67. **Hiking**   Two hikers plan a 3-day, $27\frac{1}{2}$-mile backpack trip carrying a total of 80 pounds. The hikers plan to travel $7\frac{3}{8}$ miles the first day and $10\frac{1}{3}$ miles the second day.
    a.   How many total miles do the hikers plan to travel the first two days?
    b.   How many miles will be left to travel on the third day?

For Exercises 68 and 69, refer to Exercise 67. Describe what each difference represents.

68. $27\frac{1}{2} - 7\frac{3}{8}$

69. $10\frac{1}{3} - 7\frac{3}{8}$

70. **Health**   A patient with high blood pressure who weighs 225 pounds is put on a diet to lose 25 pounds in 3 months. The patient loses $8\frac{3}{4}$ pounds the first month and $11\frac{5}{8}$ pounds the second month. How much weight must be lost during the third month for the goal to be achieved?

71. **Sports**   A wrestler is entered in the 172-pound weight class in the conference finals coming up in 3 weeks. The wrestler needs to lose $12\frac{3}{4}$ pounds. The wrestler loses $5\frac{1}{4}$ pounds the first week and $4\frac{1}{4}$ pounds the second week.
    a. Without doing the calculations, determine whether the wrestler can reach his weight class by losing less in the third week than in the second week.
    b. How many pounds must be lost in the third week to reach the desired weight?

72. **Construction**   Find the difference in thickness between a fire wall constructed with 2 × 6 studs and drywall that is $\frac{1}{2}$ inch thick and a fire wall constructed with 2 × 4 studs and drywall that is $\frac{5}{8}$ inch thick. See Exercises 92 to 94 on page 86.

73. **Finances**   If $\frac{4}{15}$ of an electrician's income is spent on housing, what fraction of the electrician's income is not spent on housing?

Critical Thinking

74. Fill in the square to produce a true statement: $5\frac{1}{3} - \boxed{} = 2\frac{1}{2}$

75. Fill in the square to produce a true statement: $\boxed{} - 4\frac{1}{2} = 1\frac{5}{8}$

Projects or Group Activities

76. Fill in the blank squares at the right so that the sum of the numbers is the same along any row, column, or diagonal. The resulting square is called a magic square.

		$\frac{3}{4}$
1	$\frac{5}{8}$	
$\frac{1}{2}$		$\frac{7}{8}$

✔ CHECK YOUR PROGRESS: CHAPTER 2

For Exercises 1 to 4, find the LCM of the numbers.

1. 12, 18   **2.** 6, 9, 18   **3.** 2, 5, 7   **4.** 28, 36

For Exercises 5 to 8, find the GCF of the numbers.

5. 18, 24   **6.** 27, 54   **7.** 3, 6, 14   **8.** 30, 70, 105

For Exercises 9 to 12, write the fraction in simplest form.

9. $\dfrac{36}{45}$ **10.** $\dfrac{17}{51}$ **11.** $\dfrac{25}{36}$ **12.** $\dfrac{36}{4}$

For Exercises 13 to 28, add or subtract.

13. $\dfrac{2}{9} + \dfrac{4}{9}$ **14.** $\dfrac{17}{24} - \dfrac{5}{24}$ **15.** $\dfrac{7}{9} - \dfrac{7}{18}$ **16.** $\dfrac{7}{20} + \dfrac{1}{4}$

17. $\dfrac{5}{6} + \dfrac{11}{16}$ **18.** $\dfrac{3}{4} - \dfrac{9}{26}$ **19.** $\dfrac{2}{3} - \dfrac{3}{16}$ **20.** $\dfrac{3}{5} + \dfrac{1}{4}$

21. $2\dfrac{1}{10} + 7\dfrac{1}{15}$ **22.** $11\dfrac{4}{9} + 7\dfrac{1}{6}$ **23.** $7\dfrac{6}{7} - 1\dfrac{1}{2}$ **24.** $3\dfrac{13}{28} - 1\dfrac{1}{8}$

25. $5\dfrac{8}{9} + 7\dfrac{5}{6}$ **26.** $9\dfrac{3}{4} + 7\dfrac{3}{10}$ **27.** $9 - 5\dfrac{3}{4}$ **28.** $8\dfrac{1}{4} - 5\dfrac{5}{6}$

SECTION

2.6

Multiplication of Fractions and Mixed Numbers

OBJECTIVE A   *To multiply fractions*

★ **Tips for Success**

Before the class meeting in which your professor begins a new section, you should read each objective statement for that section. Next, browse through the material in each objective. The purpose of browsing through the material is to prepare your brain to accept and organize the new information when it is presented to you. See *AIM for Success* at the front of the book.

Multiplication of Fractions

The product of two fractions is the product of the numerators over the product of the denominators.

EXAMPLE

Multiply: $\dfrac{2}{3} \times \dfrac{4}{5}$

$\dfrac{2}{3} \times \dfrac{4}{5} = \dfrac{2 \cdot 4}{3 \cdot 5} = \dfrac{8}{15}$ • Multiply the numerators.
• Multiply the denominators.

The product $\dfrac{2}{3} \times \dfrac{4}{5}$ can be read "$\dfrac{2}{3}$ times $\dfrac{4}{5}$" or "$\dfrac{2}{3}$ of $\dfrac{4}{5}$." Reading the times sign as "of" is useful in application problems.

$\dfrac{4}{5}$ of the bar is shaded.

Shade $\dfrac{2}{3}$ of the $\dfrac{4}{5}$ already shaded.

$\dfrac{8}{15}$ of the bar is then shaded dark yellow.

$\dfrac{2}{3}$ of $\dfrac{4}{5} = \dfrac{2}{3} \times \dfrac{4}{5} = \dfrac{8}{15}$

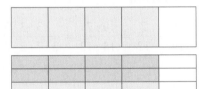

After multiplying two fractions, write the product in simplest form.

HOW TO 1   Multiply: $\dfrac{3}{4} \times \dfrac{14}{15}$

$\dfrac{3}{4} \times \dfrac{14}{15} = \dfrac{3 \cdot 14}{4 \cdot 15}$ • Multiply the numerators.
• Multiply the denominators.

$= \dfrac{3 \cdot 2 \cdot 7}{2 \cdot 2 \cdot 3 \cdot 5}$ • Write the prime factorization of each number.

$= \dfrac{\overset{1}{\cancel{3}} \cdot \overset{1}{\cancel{2}} \cdot 7}{2 \cdot 2 \cdot \underset{1}{\cancel{3}} \cdot 5} = \dfrac{7}{10}$ • Eliminate the common factors. Then multiply the remaining factors in the numerator and denominator.

This example could also be worked by using the GCF.

$\dfrac{3}{4} \times \dfrac{14}{15} = \dfrac{42}{60}$ • Multiply the numerators.
• Multiply the denominators.

$= \dfrac{6 \cdot 7}{6 \cdot 10}$ • The GCF of 42 and 60 is 6. Factor 6 from 42 and 60.

$= \dfrac{\overset{1}{\cancel{6}} \cdot 7}{\underset{1}{\cancel{6}} \cdot 10} = \dfrac{7}{10}$ • Eliminate the GCF.

EXAMPLE 1

Multiply: $\dfrac{4}{15} \times \dfrac{5}{28}$

Solution

$$\dfrac{4}{15} \times \dfrac{5}{28} = \dfrac{4 \cdot 5}{15 \cdot 28} = \dfrac{\overset{1}{\cancel{2}} \cdot \overset{1}{\cancel{2}} \cdot \overset{1}{\cancel{5}}}{3 \cdot \underset{1}{\cancel{5}} \cdot \underset{1}{\cancel{2}} \cdot \underset{1}{\cancel{2}} \cdot 7} = \dfrac{1}{21}$$

YOU TRY IT 1

Multiply: $\dfrac{4}{21} \times \dfrac{7}{44}$

Your solution

EXAMPLE 2

Find the product of $\dfrac{5}{8}$ and $\dfrac{7}{9}$.

Solution

$$\dfrac{5}{8} \times \dfrac{7}{9} = \dfrac{5 \cdot 7}{8 \cdot 9} = \dfrac{5 \cdot 7}{2 \cdot 2 \cdot 2 \cdot 3 \cdot 3} = \dfrac{35}{72}$$

YOU TRY IT 2

Find the product of $\dfrac{7}{12}$ and $\dfrac{5}{6}$.

Your solution

EXAMPLE 3

What is $\dfrac{9}{14}$ times $\dfrac{7}{12}$?

Solution

$$\dfrac{9}{14} \times \dfrac{7}{12} = \dfrac{9 \cdot 7}{14 \cdot 12} = \dfrac{3 \cdot \overset{1}{\cancel{3}} \cdot \overset{1}{\cancel{7}}}{2 \cdot \underset{1}{\cancel{7}} \cdot 2 \cdot 2 \cdot \underset{1}{\cancel{3}}} = \dfrac{3}{8}$$

YOU TRY IT 3

What is $\dfrac{5}{16}$ times $\dfrac{12}{25}$?

Your solution

Solutions on pp. S6–S7

OBJECTIVE B   *To multiply whole numbers, mixed numbers, and fractions*

When one or more of the factors in a product is a mixed number, write each mixed number as an improper fraction before multiplying.

HOW TO 2   Multiply: $2\dfrac{2}{3} \times 4\dfrac{1}{4}$

Write each mixed number as an improper fraction; then multiply the fractions.

$$2\dfrac{2}{3} \times 4\dfrac{1}{4} = \dfrac{8}{3} \times \dfrac{17}{4}$$

$$= \dfrac{8 \cdot 17}{3 \cdot 4} = \dfrac{\overset{1}{\cancel{2}} \cdot \overset{1}{\cancel{2}} \cdot 2 \cdot 17}{3 \cdot \underset{1}{\cancel{2}} \cdot \underset{1}{\cancel{2}}} = \dfrac{34}{3} = 11\dfrac{1}{3}$$

To multiply a whole number by a fraction or a mixed number, write the whole number as a fraction with a denominator of 1.

HOW TO 3   Multiply: $3\dfrac{3}{8} \times 4$

Write the mixed number as an improper fraction. Write 4 with a denominator of 1. Then multiply the fractions.

$$3\dfrac{3}{8} \times 4 = \dfrac{27}{8} \times \dfrac{4}{1}$$

$$= \dfrac{27 \cdot 4}{8 \cdot 1} = \dfrac{3 \cdot 3 \cdot 3 \cdot \overset{1}{\cancel{2}} \cdot \overset{1}{\cancel{2}}}{2 \cdot \underset{1}{\cancel{2}} \cdot \underset{1}{\cancel{2}}} = \dfrac{27}{2} = 13\dfrac{1}{2}$$

APPLY THE CONCEPT

A hexagonal paving stone measures $5\frac{3}{4}$ inches on each side. Find the total distance around the paving stone.

To find the total distance around the paving stone, multiply $5\frac{3}{4}$ by the number of sides, 6.

$$5\frac{3}{4} \times 6 = \frac{23}{4} \times \frac{6}{1} = \frac{23 \cdot 6}{4 \cdot 1} = \frac{23 \cdot \overset{1}{2} \cdot 3}{2 \cdot 2 \cdot 1} = \frac{69}{2} = 34\frac{1}{2}$$

The total distance around the paving stone is $34\frac{1}{2}$ inches.

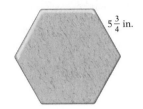

$5\frac{3}{4}$ in.

EXAMPLE 4

Multiply: $4\frac{5}{6} \times \frac{12}{13}$

Solution

$$4\frac{5}{6} \times \frac{12}{13} = \frac{29}{6} \times \frac{12}{13} = \frac{29 \cdot 12}{6 \cdot 13}$$

$$= \frac{29 \cdot \overset{1}{2} \cdot 2 \cdot \overset{1}{3}}{\underset{1}{2} \cdot \underset{1}{3} \cdot 13} = \frac{58}{13} = 4\frac{6}{13}$$

YOU TRY IT 4

Multiply: $5\frac{2}{5} \times \frac{5}{9}$

Your solution

EXAMPLE 5

Find $5\frac{2}{3}$ times $4\frac{1}{2}$.

Solution

$$5\frac{2}{3} \times 4\frac{1}{2} = \frac{17}{3} \times \frac{9}{2} = \frac{17 \cdot 9}{3 \cdot 2}$$

$$= \frac{17 \cdot \overset{1}{3} \cdot 3}{\underset{1}{3} \cdot 2} = \frac{51}{2} = 25\frac{1}{2}$$

YOU TRY IT 5

Find the product of $3\frac{2}{5}$ and $6\frac{1}{4}$.

Your solution

Solutions on p. S7

OBJECTIVE C   *To solve application problems*

Length (ft)	Weight (lb/ft)
$6\frac{1}{2}$	$\frac{3}{8}$
$8\frac{5}{8}$	$1\frac{1}{4}$
$10\frac{3}{4}$	$2\frac{1}{2}$
$12\frac{7}{12}$	$4\frac{1}{3}$

The table at the left lists the lengths of several steel rods and their corresponding weights per foot. The weight per foot is measured in pounds per foot of rod and is abbreviated as lb/ft.

HOW TO 4   Find the weight of the steel rod that is $10\frac{3}{4}$ feet long.

Strategy

To find the weight of the steel rod, multiply its length by its weight per foot.

Solution

$$10\frac{3}{4} \times 2\frac{1}{2} = \frac{43}{4} \times \frac{5}{2} = \frac{43 \cdot 5}{4 \cdot 2} = \frac{215}{8} = 26\frac{7}{8}$$

The weight of the $10\frac{3}{4}$-foot rod is $26\frac{7}{8}$ pounds.

EXAMPLE 6

An electrician earns $206 for each day worked. What are the electrician's earnings for working $4\frac{1}{2}$ days?

Strategy

To find the electrician's total earnings, multiply the daily earnings (206) by the number of days worked $\left(4\frac{1}{2}\right)$.

Solution

$$206 \times 4\frac{1}{2} = \frac{206}{1} \times \frac{9}{2}$$

$$= \frac{206 \cdot 9}{1 \cdot 2}$$

$$= 927$$

The electrician's earnings are $927.

YOU TRY IT 6

Over the last 10 years, a house increased in value by $2\frac{1}{2}$ times. The price of the house 10 years ago was $170,000. What is the value of the house today?

Your strategy

Your solution

EXAMPLE 7

The total value of a small office building and the land on which it is built is $290,000. The value of the land is $\frac{1}{4}$ the total value. What is the dollar value of the building?

Strategy

To find the dollar value of the building:

• Find the value of the land $\left(\frac{1}{4} \times 290,000\right)$.

• Subtract the value of the land from the total value (290,000).

Solution

$$\frac{1}{4} \times 290,000 = \frac{290,000}{4}$$

$$= 72,500 \quad \bullet \text{ Value of the land}$$

$$290,000 - 72,500 = 217,500$$

The dollar value of the building is $217,500.

YOU TRY IT 7

A paint company bought a drying chamber and an air compressor for spray painting. The total cost of the two items was $160,000. The drying chamber's cost was $\frac{4}{5}$ of the total cost. What was the cost of the air compressor?

Your strategy

Your solution

Solutions on p. S7

2.6 EXERCISES

✔ Concept Check

For Exercises 1 and 2, replace each question mark to make a true statement.

1. $\dfrac{5}{9} \times \dfrac{2}{3} = \dfrac{5 \cdot ?}{? \cdot 3} = ?$

2. $\dfrac{6}{9} \times 4 = \dfrac{6 \cdot ?}{7 \cdot ?} = \dfrac{?}{?} = ?$

3. 🖋 Is the product of two proper fractions always a proper fraction?

4. 🖋 Is the product of a proper fraction and a whole number less than the whole number or greater than the whole number?

OBJECTIVE A   *To multiply fractions*

For Exercises 5 to 36, multiply.

5. $\dfrac{2}{3} \times \dfrac{7}{8}$

6. $\dfrac{1}{2} \times \dfrac{2}{3}$

7. $\dfrac{5}{16} \times \dfrac{7}{15}$

8. $\dfrac{3}{8} \times \dfrac{6}{7}$

9. $\dfrac{1}{6} \times \dfrac{1}{8}$

10. $\dfrac{2}{5} \times \dfrac{5}{6}$

11. $\dfrac{11}{12} \times \dfrac{6}{7}$

12. $\dfrac{11}{12} \times \dfrac{3}{5}$

13. $\dfrac{8}{9} \times \dfrac{27}{4}$

14. $\dfrac{3}{5} \times \dfrac{3}{10}$

15. $\dfrac{5}{6} \times \dfrac{1}{2}$

16. $\dfrac{3}{8} \times \dfrac{5}{12}$

17. $\dfrac{16}{9} \times \dfrac{27}{8}$

18. $\dfrac{5}{8} \times \dfrac{16}{15}$

19. $\dfrac{3}{2} \times \dfrac{4}{9}$

20. $\dfrac{5}{3} \times \dfrac{3}{7}$

21. $\dfrac{7}{8} \times \dfrac{3}{14}$

22. $\dfrac{2}{9} \times \dfrac{4}{5}$

23. $\dfrac{7}{10} \times \dfrac{3}{8}$

24. $\dfrac{5}{12} \times \dfrac{6}{7}$

25. $\dfrac{15}{8} \times \dfrac{16}{3}$

26. $\dfrac{5}{6} \times \dfrac{4}{15}$

27. $\dfrac{1}{2} \times \dfrac{2}{15}$

28. $\dfrac{3}{8} \times \dfrac{5}{16}$

29. $\dfrac{5}{7} \times \dfrac{14}{15}$

30. $\dfrac{3}{8} \times \dfrac{36}{41}$

31. $\dfrac{5}{12} \times \dfrac{42}{65}$

32. $\dfrac{16}{33} \times \dfrac{55}{72}$

33. $\dfrac{12}{5} \times \dfrac{5}{3}$

34. $\dfrac{17}{9} \times \dfrac{81}{17}$

35. $\dfrac{10}{21} \times \dfrac{14}{15}$

36. $\dfrac{19}{64} \times \dfrac{48}{95}$

37. 🖋 Give an example of a proper and an improper fraction whose product is 1.

38. Multiply $\frac{7}{12}$ and $\frac{15}{42}$.

39. Multiply $\frac{32}{9}$ and $\frac{3}{8}$.

40. Find the product of $\frac{5}{9}$ and $\frac{3}{20}$.

41. Find the product of $\frac{7}{3}$ and $\frac{15}{14}$.

42. What is $\frac{1}{2}$ times $\frac{8}{15}$?

43. What is $\frac{3}{8}$ times $\frac{12}{17}$?

OBJECTIVE B   *To multiply whole numbers, mixed numbers, and fractions*

For Exercises 44 to 71, multiply.

44. $4 \times \frac{3}{8}$

45. $14 \times \frac{5}{7}$

46. $\frac{2}{3} \times 6$

47. $\frac{5}{12} \times 40$

48. $\frac{1}{3} \times 1\frac{1}{3}$

49. $\frac{2}{5} \times 2\frac{1}{2}$

50. $1\frac{7}{8} \times \frac{4}{15}$

51. $2\frac{1}{5} \times \frac{5}{22}$

52. $4 \times 2\frac{1}{2}$

53. $9 \times 3\frac{1}{3}$

54. $2\frac{1}{7} \times 3$

55. $5\frac{1}{4} \times 8$

56. $3\frac{2}{3} \times 5$

57. $4\frac{2}{9} \times 3$

58. $\frac{1}{2} \times 3\frac{3}{7}$

59. $\frac{3}{8} \times 4\frac{4}{5}$

60. $6\frac{1}{8} \times \frac{4}{7}$

61. $5\frac{1}{3} \times \frac{5}{16}$

62. $\frac{3}{8} \times 4\frac{1}{2}$

63. $\frac{5}{7} \times 2\frac{1}{3}$

64. $0 \times 2\frac{2}{3}$

65. $6\frac{1}{8} \times 0$

66. $2\frac{5}{8} \times 3\frac{2}{5}$

67. $5\frac{3}{16} \times 5\frac{1}{3}$

68. $5\frac{1}{5} \times 3\frac{1}{13}$

69. $3\frac{3}{4} \times 2\frac{3}{20}$

70. $12\frac{3}{5} \times 1\frac{3}{7}$

71. $6\frac{1}{2} \times 1\frac{3}{13}$

72. Computer Graphics   A drawing software program allows an artist to scale (reduce or enlarge) a drawing on the computer screen. If the current height of a drawing on the screen is $4\frac{3}{8}$ inches, what is the height after the artist scales the drawing to $\frac{4}{5}$ of its current height?

73. Geometry   The distance around a square, called its perimeter, is 4 times the length of one side. Find the distance around the square patio slab shown at the right.

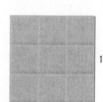

$13\frac{1}{2}$ feet

74. ⟨⟩ True or false? If the product of a whole number and a fraction is a whole number, then the denominator of the fraction is a factor of the original whole number.

75. Multiply $2\frac{1}{2}$ and $3\frac{3}{5}$.

76. Multiply $4\frac{3}{8}$ and $3\frac{3}{5}$.

77. Find the product of $2\frac{1}{8}$ and $\frac{5}{17}$.

78. Find the product of $12\frac{2}{5}$ and $3\frac{7}{31}$.

79. What is $1\frac{3}{8}$ times $2\frac{1}{5}$?

80. What is $3\frac{1}{8}$ times $2\frac{4}{7}$?

OBJECTIVE C *To solve application problems*

⟨⟩ For Exercises 81 and 82, give your answer without actually doing a calculation.

81. Read Exercise 83. Will the requested cost be greater than or less than $12?

82. Read Exercise 85. Will the requested length be greater than or less than 4 feet?

83. Consumerism Salmon costs $4 per pound. Find the cost of $2\frac{3}{4}$ pounds of salmon.

84. Exercise Maria Rivera can walk $3\frac{1}{2}$ miles in 1 hour. At this rate, how far can Maria walk in $\frac{1}{3}$ hour?

85. Carpentry A board that costs $6 is $9\frac{1}{4}$ feet long. One-third of the board is cut off. What is the length of the piece cut off?

86. Geometry The perimeter of a square is equal to four times the length of a side of the square. Find the perimeter of a square whose side measures $16\frac{3}{4}$ inches.

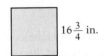

87. Geometry To find the area of a square, multiply the length of one side of the square times itself. What is the area of a square whose side measures $5\frac{1}{4}$ feet? The area of the square will be in square feet.

88. Geometry The area of a rectangle is equal to the product of the length of the rectangle times its width. Find the area of a rectangle that has a length of $4\frac{2}{5}$ miles and a width of $3\frac{3}{10}$ miles. The area will be in square miles.

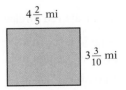

89. ● **Biofuels** See the news clipping at the right. About how many acres of corn planted in the United States each year are turned into ethanol?

Measurement For Exercises 90 to 92, use the table on page 99 that shows the lengths of steel rods and their corresponding weights per foot.

90. Find the weight of the $6\frac{1}{2}$-foot steel rod.

91. Find the weight of the $12\frac{7}{12}$-foot steel rod.

92. Find the total weight of the $8\frac{5}{8}$-foot and the $10\frac{3}{4}$-foot steel rods.

93. **Sewing** The Booster Club is making 22 capes for the members of the high school marching band. Each cape is made from $1\frac{3}{8}$ yards of material at a cost of \$12 per yard. Find the total cost of the material.

94. **Construction** On an architectural drawing of a kitchen, the front face of the cabinet below the sink is $23\frac{1}{2}$ inches from the back wall. Before the cabinet is installed, a plumber must install a drain in the floor halfway between the wall and the front face of the cabinet. Find the required distance from the wall to the center of the drain.

Critical Thinking

95. The product of 1 and a number is $\frac{1}{2}$. Find the number.

96. ◣ **Time** Our calendar is based on the solar year, which is $365\frac{1}{4}$ days. Use this fact to explain leap years.

97. Which of the labeled points on the number line at the right could be the graph of the product of B and C?

0 A B C 1 D   2   E   3

Projects or Group Activities

98. Fill in the red circles at the right with the fractions $\frac{1}{6}$, $\frac{5}{18}$, $\frac{4}{9}$, $\frac{5}{9}$, $\frac{2}{3}$, $\frac{3}{4}$, $1\frac{1}{9}$, $1\frac{1}{2}$, and $2\frac{1}{4}$ so that the product of any row is equal to $\frac{5}{18}$. (*Note:* More than one answer is possible.)

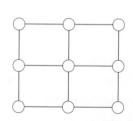

In the NEWS!

Fields of Energy

About two-fifths of the approximately 90 million acres of corn planted each year in the United States is used to produce ethanol. The majority of new cars can run on E10, a fuel consisting of 10% ethanol.
Source: guardian.co.uk

© iStockphoto.com/Janice Richard

2.7   Division of Fractions and Mixed Numbers

OBJECTIVE A   *To divide fractions*

The **reciprocal of a fraction** is the fraction with the numerator and denominator interchanged.

The reciprocal of $\frac{2}{3}$ is $\frac{3}{2}$.

The process of interchanging the numerator and denominator is called **inverting a fraction.**

To find the reciprocal of a whole number, first write the whole number as a fraction with a denominator of 1. Then find the reciprocal of the fraction.

The reciprocal of 5 is $\frac{1}{5}$. $\left(\text{Think } 5 = \frac{5}{1}.\right)$

Reciprocals are used to rewrite division problems as related multiplication problems. Look at the following two problems:

$$8 \div 2 = 4 \qquad\qquad 8 \times \frac{1}{2} = 4$$

8 divided by 2 is **4.**   8 times the reciprocal of 2 is **4.**

"Divided by" means the same as "times the reciprocal of." Thus "÷ 2" can be replaced with "$\times \frac{1}{2}$," and the answer will be the same. Fractions are divided by making this replacement.

| **HOW TO 1** | Divide: $\dfrac{2}{3} \div \dfrac{3}{4}$ |

$$\frac{2}{3} \div \frac{3}{4} = \frac{2}{3} \times \frac{4}{3} = \frac{2 \cdot 4}{3 \cdot 3} = \frac{2 \cdot 2 \cdot 2}{3 \cdot 3} = \frac{8}{9}$$

• Multiply the first fraction by the reciprocal of the second fraction.

EXAMPLE 1

Divide: $\dfrac{5}{8} \div \dfrac{4}{9}$

Solution

$$\frac{5}{8} \div \frac{4}{9} = \frac{5}{8} \times \frac{9}{4} = \frac{5 \cdot 9}{8 \cdot 4}$$

$$= \frac{5 \cdot 3 \cdot 3}{2 \cdot 2 \cdot 2 \cdot 2 \cdot 2} = \frac{45}{32} = 1\frac{13}{32}$$

YOU TRY IT 1

Divide: $\dfrac{3}{7} \div \dfrac{2}{3}$

Your solution

EXAMPLE 2

Divide: $\dfrac{3}{5} \div \dfrac{12}{25}$

Solution

$$\frac{3}{5} \div \frac{12}{25} = \frac{3}{5} \times \frac{25}{12} = \frac{3 \cdot 25}{5 \cdot 12}$$

$$= \frac{\overset{1}{\cancel{3}} \cdot \overset{1}{\cancel{5}} \cdot 5}{\underset{1}{\cancel{5}} \cdot 2 \cdot 2 \cdot \underset{1}{\cancel{3}}} = \frac{5}{4} = 1\frac{1}{4}$$

YOU TRY IT 2

Divide: $\dfrac{3}{4} \div \dfrac{9}{10}$

Your solution

Solutions on p. S7

OBJECTIVE B *To divide whole numbers, mixed numbers, and fractions*

To divide a fraction and a whole number, first write the whole number as a fraction with a denominator of 1.

HOW TO 2 Divide: $\dfrac{3}{7} \div 5$

$$\dfrac{3}{7} \div \boxed{5} = \dfrac{3}{7} \div \boxed{\dfrac{5}{1}} = \dfrac{3}{7} \times \dfrac{1}{5} = \dfrac{3 \cdot 1}{7 \cdot 5} = \dfrac{3}{35}$$

• Write 5 with a denominator of 1. Then divide the fractions.

When a number in a quotient is a mixed number, write the mixed number as an improper fraction before dividing.

HOW TO 3 Divide: $1\dfrac{13}{15} \div 4\dfrac{4}{5}$

Write the mixed numbers as improper fractions. Then divide the fractions.

$$1\dfrac{13}{15} \div 4\dfrac{4}{5} = \dfrac{28}{15} \div \dfrac{24}{5} = \dfrac{28}{15} \times \dfrac{5}{24} = \dfrac{28 \cdot 5}{15 \cdot 24} = \dfrac{\overset{1}{2} \cdot \overset{1}{2} \cdot 7 \cdot \overset{1}{5}}{3 \cdot \underset{1}{5} \cdot \underset{1}{2} \cdot \underset{1}{2} \cdot 2 \cdot 3} = \dfrac{7}{18}$$

EXAMPLE 3

Divide $\dfrac{4}{9}$ by 6.

Solution

$$\dfrac{4}{9} \div 6 = \dfrac{4}{9} \div \dfrac{6}{1} = \dfrac{4}{9} \times \dfrac{1}{6}$$

$$= \dfrac{4 \cdot 1}{9 \cdot 6} = \dfrac{\overset{1}{2} \cdot 2}{3 \cdot 3 \cdot 2 \cdot 3} = \dfrac{2}{27}$$

YOU TRY IT 3

Divide $\dfrac{5}{7}$ by 6.

Your solution

EXAMPLE 4

Find the quotient of $\dfrac{3}{8}$ and $2\dfrac{1}{10}$.

Solution

$$\dfrac{3}{8} \div 2\dfrac{1}{10} = \dfrac{3}{8} \div \dfrac{21}{10} = \dfrac{3}{8} \times \dfrac{10}{21}$$

$$= \dfrac{3 \cdot 10}{8 \cdot 21} = \dfrac{\overset{1}{3} \cdot \overset{1}{2} \cdot 5}{2 \cdot 2 \cdot 2 \cdot \underset{1}{3} \cdot 7} = \dfrac{5}{28}$$

YOU TRY IT 4

Find the quotient of $12\dfrac{3}{5}$ and 7.

Your solution

EXAMPLE 5

Divide: $2\dfrac{3}{4} \div 1\dfrac{5}{7}$

Solution

$$2\dfrac{3}{4} \div 1\dfrac{5}{7} = \dfrac{11}{4} \div \dfrac{12}{7} = \dfrac{11}{4} \times \dfrac{7}{12} = \dfrac{11 \cdot 7}{4 \cdot 12}$$

$$= \dfrac{11 \cdot 7}{2 \cdot 2 \cdot 2 \cdot 2 \cdot 3} = \dfrac{77}{48} = 1\dfrac{29}{48}$$

YOU TRY IT 5

Divide: $3\dfrac{2}{3} \div 2\dfrac{2}{5}$

Your solution

Solutions on p. S7

EXAMPLE 6

Divide: $1\dfrac{13}{15} \div 4\dfrac{1}{5}$

Solution

$1\dfrac{13}{15} \div 4\dfrac{1}{5} = \dfrac{28}{15} \div \dfrac{21}{5} = \dfrac{28}{15} \times \dfrac{5}{21} = \dfrac{28 \cdot 5}{15 \cdot 21}$

$\qquad = \dfrac{2 \cdot 2 \cdot \overset{1}{\cancel{7}} \cdot \overset{1}{\cancel{5}}}{3 \cdot \underset{1}{\cancel{5}} \cdot 3 \cdot \underset{1}{\cancel{7}}} = \dfrac{4}{9}$

YOU TRY IT 6

Divide: $2\dfrac{5}{6} \div 8\dfrac{1}{2}$

Your solution

EXAMPLE 7

Divide: $4\dfrac{3}{8} \div 7$

Solution

$4\dfrac{3}{8} \div 7 = \dfrac{35}{8} \div \dfrac{7}{1} = \dfrac{35}{8} \times \dfrac{1}{7}$

$\qquad = \dfrac{35 \cdot 1}{8 \cdot 7} = \dfrac{5 \cdot \overset{1}{\cancel{7}}}{2 \cdot 2 \cdot 2 \cdot \underset{1}{\cancel{7}}} = \dfrac{5}{8}$

YOU TRY IT 7

Divide: $6\dfrac{2}{5} \div 4$

Your solution

Solutions on p. S7

Solutions on p. S7

OBJECTIVE C   *To solve application problems*

EXAMPLE 8

A car used $15\dfrac{1}{2}$ gallons of gasoline on a 310-mile trip. How many miles can this car travel on 1 gallon of gasoline?

Strategy

To find the number of miles, divide the number of miles traveled by the number of gallons of gasoline used.

Solution

$310 \div 15\dfrac{1}{2} = \dfrac{310}{1} \div \dfrac{31}{2}$

$\qquad = \dfrac{310}{1} \times \dfrac{2}{31} = \dfrac{310 \cdot 2}{1 \cdot 31}$

$\qquad = \dfrac{2 \cdot 5 \cdot \overset{1}{\cancel{31}} \cdot 2}{1 \cdot \underset{1}{\cancel{31}}} = \dfrac{20}{1} = 20$

The car travels 20 miles on 1 gallon of gasoline.

YOU TRY IT 8

A factory worker can assemble a product in $7\dfrac{1}{2}$ minutes. How many products can the worker assemble in 1 hour?

Your strategy

Your solution

Solution on p. S8

Solution on p. S8

EXAMPLE 9

A 12-foot board is cut into pieces $2\frac{1}{4}$ feet long for use as bookshelves. What is the length of the remaining piece after as many shelves as possible have been cut?

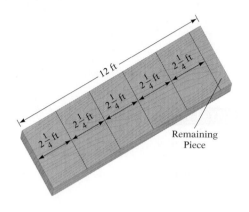

Strategy

To find the length of the remaining piece:

• Divide the total length of the board (12) by the length of each shelf $\left(2\frac{1}{4}\right)$. This will give you the number of shelves cut, with a certain fraction of a shelf left over.
• Multiply the fractional part of the result in step 1 by the length of one shelf to determine the length of the remaining piece.

Solution

$$12 \div 2\frac{1}{4} = \frac{12}{1} \div \frac{9}{4} = \frac{12}{1} \times \frac{4}{9}$$

$$= \frac{12 \cdot 4}{1 \cdot 9} = \frac{16}{3} = 5\frac{1}{3}$$

There are 5 pieces that are each $2\frac{1}{4}$ feet long.

There is 1 piece that is $\frac{1}{3}$ of $2\frac{1}{4}$ feet long.

$$\frac{1}{3} \times 2\frac{1}{4} = \frac{1}{3} \times \frac{9}{4} = \frac{1 \cdot 9}{3 \cdot 4} = \frac{3}{4}$$

The length of the piece remaining is $\frac{3}{4}$ foot.

A 16-foot board is cut into pieces $3\frac{1}{3}$ feet long for shelves for a bookcase. What is the length of the remaining piece after as many shelves as possible have been cut?

Your strategy

Your solution

Solution on p. S8

2.7 EXERCISES

✔ Concept Check

For Exercises 1 to 4, find the reciprocal of the given number.

1. $\dfrac{3}{7}$ **2.** 7   **3.** $\dfrac{4}{5}$ **4.** $\dfrac{1}{6}$

5. Replace the question marks to make a true statement.

$$\frac{3}{8} \div \frac{4}{9} = \frac{3}{8} \times \frac{?}{?} = ?$$

6. Is the quotient of two proper fractions always a proper fraction?

OBJECTIVE A   *To divide fractions*

For Exercises 7 to 34, divide.

7. $\dfrac{1}{3} \div \dfrac{2}{5}$ **8.** $\dfrac{3}{7} \div \dfrac{3}{2}$ **9.** $\dfrac{3}{7} \div \dfrac{3}{7}$ **10.** $0 \div \dfrac{1}{2}$

11. $0 \div \dfrac{3}{4}$ **12.** $\dfrac{16}{33} \div \dfrac{4}{11}$ **13.** $\dfrac{5}{24} \div \dfrac{15}{36}$ **14.** $\dfrac{11}{15} \div \dfrac{1}{12}$

15. $\dfrac{1}{9} \div \dfrac{2}{3}$ **16.** $\dfrac{10}{21} \div \dfrac{5}{7}$ **17.** $\dfrac{2}{5} \div \dfrac{4}{7}$ **18.** $\dfrac{3}{8} \div \dfrac{5}{12}$

19. $\dfrac{1}{2} \div \dfrac{1}{4}$ **20.** $\dfrac{1}{3} \div \dfrac{1}{9}$ **21.** $\dfrac{1}{5} \div \dfrac{1}{10}$ **22.** $\dfrac{4}{15} \div \dfrac{2}{5}$

23. $\dfrac{7}{15} \div \dfrac{14}{5}$ **24.** $\dfrac{5}{8} \div \dfrac{15}{2}$ **25.** $\dfrac{14}{3} \div \dfrac{7}{9}$ **26.** $\dfrac{7}{4} \div \dfrac{9}{2}$

27. $\dfrac{5}{9} \div \dfrac{25}{3}$ **28.** $\dfrac{5}{16} \div \dfrac{3}{8}$ **29.** $\dfrac{2}{3} \div \dfrac{1}{3}$ **30.** $\dfrac{4}{9} \div \dfrac{1}{9}$

31. $\dfrac{5}{7} \div \dfrac{2}{7}$ **32.** $\dfrac{5}{6} \div \dfrac{1}{9}$ **33.** $\dfrac{2}{3} \div \dfrac{2}{9}$ **34.** $\dfrac{5}{12} \div \dfrac{5}{6}$

35. Divide $\dfrac{7}{8}$ by $\dfrac{3}{4}$.   **36.** Divide $\dfrac{7}{12}$ by $\dfrac{3}{4}$.

37. Find the quotient of $\dfrac{5}{7}$ and $\dfrac{3}{14}$.   **38.** Find the quotient of $\dfrac{6}{11}$ and $\dfrac{9}{32}$.

39. 🖎 True or false? If a fraction has a numerator of 1, then the reciprocal of the fraction is a whole number.   **40.** 🖎 True or false? The reciprocal of an improper fraction that is not equal to 1 is a proper fraction.

OBJECTIVE B   *To divide whole numbers, mixed numbers, and fractions*

For Exercises 41 to 79, divide.

41. $4 \div \dfrac{2}{3}$

42. $\dfrac{2}{3} \div 4$

43. $\dfrac{3}{2} \div 3$

44. $3 \div \dfrac{3}{2}$

45. $\dfrac{5}{6} \div 25$

46. $22 \div \dfrac{3}{11}$

47. $6 \div 3\dfrac{1}{3}$

48. $5\dfrac{1}{2} \div 11$

49. $6\dfrac{1}{2} \div \dfrac{1}{2}$

50. $\dfrac{3}{8} \div 2\dfrac{1}{4}$

51. $8\dfrac{1}{4} \div 2\dfrac{3}{4}$

52. $3\dfrac{5}{9} \div 32$

53. $4\dfrac{1}{5} \div 21$

54. $6\dfrac{8}{9} \div \dfrac{31}{36}$

55. $\dfrac{11}{12} \div 2\dfrac{1}{3}$

56. $\dfrac{7}{8} \div 3\dfrac{1}{4}$

57. $35 \div \dfrac{7}{24}$

58. $\dfrac{3}{8} \div 2\dfrac{3}{4}$

59. $\dfrac{11}{18} \div 2\dfrac{2}{9}$

60. $\dfrac{21}{40} \div 3\dfrac{3}{10}$

61. $2\dfrac{1}{16} \div 2\dfrac{1}{2}$

62. $7\dfrac{3}{5} \div 1\dfrac{7}{12}$

63. $1\dfrac{2}{3} \div \dfrac{3}{8}$

64. $16 \div \dfrac{2}{3}$

65. $1\dfrac{5}{8} \div 4$

66. $13\dfrac{3}{8} \div \dfrac{1}{4}$

67. $16 \div 1\dfrac{1}{2}$

68. $9 \div \dfrac{7}{8}$

69. $1\dfrac{1}{3} \div 5\dfrac{8}{9}$

70. $13\dfrac{2}{3} \div 0$

71. $82\dfrac{3}{5} \div 19\dfrac{1}{10}$

72. $45\dfrac{3}{5} \div 15$

73. $102 \div 1\dfrac{1}{2}$

74. $0 \div 3\dfrac{1}{2}$

75. $8\dfrac{2}{7} \div 1$

76. $6\dfrac{9}{16} \div 1\dfrac{3}{32}$

77. $8\dfrac{8}{9} \div 2\dfrac{13}{18}$

78. $10\dfrac{1}{5} \div 1\dfrac{7}{10}$

79. $7\dfrac{3}{8} \div 1\dfrac{27}{32}$

80. Divide $7\dfrac{7}{9}$ by $5\dfrac{5}{6}$.

81. Divide $2\dfrac{3}{4}$ by $1\dfrac{23}{32}$.

82. Find the quotient of $8\dfrac{1}{4}$ and $1\dfrac{5}{11}$.

83. Find the quotient of $\dfrac{14}{17}$ and $3\dfrac{1}{9}$.

84. True or false? The reciprocal of a mixed number is an improper fraction.

85. True or false? A fraction divided by its reciprocal is 1.

OBJECTIVE C   *To solve application problems*

For Exercises 86 and 87, give your answer without actually doing a calculation.

86. Read Exercise 88. Will the requested number of boxes be greater than or less than 600?

87. Read Exercise 89. Will the requested number of servings be greater than or less than 16?

88. Consumerism   Individual cereal boxes contain $\dfrac{3}{4}$ ounce of cereal. How many boxes can be filled with 600 ounces of cereal?

89. Consumerism   A box of Post's Great Grains cereal costing $4 contains 16 ounces of cereal. How many $1\dfrac{1}{3}$-ounce servings are in this box?

90. Gemology   A $\dfrac{5}{8}$-karat diamond was purchased for $1200. What would a similar diamond weighing 1 karat cost?

91. Real Estate   The Inverness Investor Group bought $8\dfrac{1}{3}$ acres of land for $200,000. What was the cost of each acre?

92. Fuel Efficiency   A car used $12\dfrac{1}{2}$ gallons of gasoline on a 275-mile trip. How many miles can the car travel on 1 gallon of gasoline?

93. Mechanics   A nut moves $\dfrac{5}{32}$ inch for each turn. Find the number of turns it will take for the nut to move $1\dfrac{7}{8}$ inches.

94. Real Estate The Hammond Company purchased $9\frac{3}{4}$ acres of land for a housing project. One and one-half acres were set aside for a park.

   a. How many acres are available for housing?

   b. How many $\frac{1}{4}$-acre parcels of land can be sold after the land for the park is set aside?

95. The Food Industry A chef purchased a roast that weighed $10\frac{3}{4}$ pounds. After the fat was trimmed and the bone removed, the roast weighed $9\frac{1}{3}$ pounds.

   a. What was the total weight of the fat and bone?

   b. How many $\frac{1}{3}$-pound servings can be cut from the trimmed roast?

96. Carpentry A 15-foot board is cut into pieces $3\frac{1}{2}$ feet long for a bookcase. What is the length of the piece remaining after as many shelves as possible have been cut?

97. Construction The railing of a stairway extends onto a landing. The distance between the end posts of the railing on the landing is $22\frac{3}{4}$ inches. Five posts are to be inserted, evenly spaced, between the end posts. Each post has a square base that measures $1\frac{1}{4}$ inches. Find the distance between each pair of posts.

98. Construction The railing of a stairway extends onto a landing. The distance between the end posts of the railing on the landing is $42\frac{1}{2}$ inches. Ten posts are to be inserted, evenly spaced, between the end posts. Each post has a square base that measures $1\frac{1}{2}$ inches. Find the distance between each pair of posts.

Critical Thinking

For Exercises 99 to 106, fill in the box to make a true statement.

99. $\frac{2}{3} - \square = \frac{1}{6}$ **100.** $\square - \frac{5}{8} = \frac{5}{24}$ **101.** $\square + \frac{3}{5} = 1\frac{1}{10}$ **102.** $\frac{5}{9} + \square = \frac{13}{18}$

103. $\frac{3}{4} \cdot \square = \frac{1}{2}$ **104.** $\square \cdot \frac{2}{3} = 1\frac{3}{4}$ **105.** $\square \div \frac{3}{4} = \frac{8}{9}$ **106.** $\frac{3}{4} \div \square = \frac{2}{3}$

107. Finances A bank recommends that the maximum monthly payment for a home be $\frac{1}{3}$ of the owner's total monthly income. Your monthly income is $4500. What would the bank recommend as your maximum monthly house payment?

108. ● **Sports**   Researchers at Oregon State University studied the effect of grass height on the distance a struck golf ball would roll on the grass putting surface of a golf course green. For the study, plots of grass were mowed to a height of $\frac{3}{20}$ inch. This is higher than the more common heights of $\frac{1}{10}$ inch or $\frac{1}{8}$ inch used in professional golf tournaments. How much higher than the standard heights did the researchers mow the grass?

109. Board Games   A wooden travel game board has hinges that allow the board to be folded in half. If the dimensions of the open board are 14 inches by 14 inches by $\frac{7}{8}$ inch, what are the dimensions of the board when it is closed?

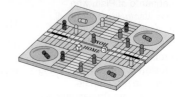

110. Maps   On a map, two cities are $4\frac{5}{8}$ inches apart. If $\frac{3}{8}$ inch on the map represents 60 miles, what is the number of miles between the two cities?

111. Publishing   A page of type in a certain textbook is $7\frac{1}{2}$ inches wide. If the page is divided into three equal columns, with $\frac{3}{8}$ inch between columns, how wide is each column?

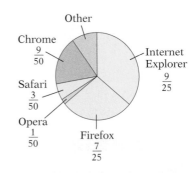

$\leftarrow\!\!-\, 7\frac{1}{2}$ in. $-\!\!\rightarrow$

$\frac{3}{8}$ $\frac{3}{8}$

Projects or Group Activities

● **Browser Usage**   The graph at the right, based on data from W3Counter, shows the market share of several Internet browsers. Use this graph for Exercises 112 to 115.

112. What total fraction of the market is represented by Internet Explorer, Firefox, and Chrome?

Other

Chrome
$\frac{9}{50}$

Safari
$\frac{3}{50}$

Opera
$\frac{1}{50}$

Internet Explorer
$\frac{9}{25}$

Firefox
$\frac{7}{25}$

113. How many times more people use Safari than use Opera?

114. In 2011, there were approximately 2 billion people worldwide using the Internet. According to the graph, approximately how many people were using the Chrome browser?

115. What fraction of the world browser market do the unnamed browsers represent?

2.8 Order, Exponents, and the Order of Operations Agreement

OBJECTIVE A   *To identify the order relation between two fractions*

 Point of Interest

Leonardo of Pisa, who was also called Fibonacci (c. 1175–1250), is credited with bringing the Hindu-Arabic number system to the Western world and promoting its use in place of the cumbersome Roman numeral system.

He was also influential in promoting the idea of the fraction bar. His notation, however, was very different from the notation we use today.

For instance, he wrote $\dfrac{3}{4}\dfrac{5}{7}$ to mean $\dfrac{5}{7} + \dfrac{3}{7 \cdot 4}$, which equals $\dfrac{23}{28}$.

Recall that whole numbers can be graphed as points on the number line. Fractions can also be graphed as points on the number line.

The graph of $\frac{3}{4}$ on the number line

The number line can be used to determine the order relation between two fractions. A fraction that appears to the left of a given fraction is less than the given fraction. A fraction that appears to the right of a given fraction is greater than the given fraction.

$$\frac{1}{8} < \frac{3}{8} \qquad \frac{6}{8} > \frac{3}{8}$$

To find the order relation between two fractions with the same denominator, compare the numerators. The fraction that has the smaller numerator is the smaller fraction. When the denominators are different, begin by writing equivalent fractions with a common denominator; then compare the numerators.

HOW TO 1   Find the order relation between $\frac{11}{18}$ and $\frac{5}{8}$.

The LCD of the fractions is 72.

$$\frac{11}{18} = \frac{44}{72} \leftarrow \text{Smaller numerator}$$

$$\frac{5}{8} = \frac{45}{72} \leftarrow \text{Larger numerator}$$

$$\frac{11}{18} < \frac{5}{8} \quad \text{or} \quad \frac{5}{8} > \frac{11}{18}$$

EXAMPLE 1

Place the correct symbol, $<$ or $>$, between the two numbers.

$$\frac{5}{12} \qquad \frac{7}{18}$$

Solution

$$\frac{5}{12} = \frac{15}{36} \qquad \frac{7}{18} = \frac{14}{36}$$

$$\frac{5}{12} > \frac{7}{18}$$

YOU TRY IT 1

Place the correct symbol, $<$ or $>$, between the two numbers.

$$\frac{9}{14} \qquad \frac{13}{21}$$

Your solution

Solution on p. S8

OBJECTIVE B *To use the Order of Operations Agreement to simplify expressions*

Recall that repeated multiplication of the same number is written using an exponent.

$$\left(\frac{2}{3}\right)^4 = \frac{2}{3} \cdot \frac{2}{3} \cdot \frac{2}{3} \cdot \frac{2}{3} = \frac{2 \cdot 2 \cdot 2 \cdot 2}{3 \cdot 3 \cdot 3 \cdot 3} = \frac{16}{81}$$

The exponent 4 indicates the number of times to multiply $\frac{2}{3}$. The expression $\left(\frac{2}{3}\right)^4$ is an **exponential expression.**

The Order of Operations Agreement is used to simplify expressions containing parentheses, exponents, multiplication, division, addition, or subtraction.

Order of Operations Agreement

Step 1. Perform operations inside grouping symbols such as parentheses and fraction bars.

Step 2. Simplify exponential expressions.

Step 3. Do multiplications and divisions as they occur from left to right.

Step 4. Do additions and subtractions as they occur from left to right.

EXAMPLES

1. $\dfrac{1}{2} \cdot \left(\dfrac{4}{5} - \dfrac{1}{5}\right) = \dfrac{1}{2} \cdot \left(\dfrac{3}{5}\right)$ • Perform operations inside grouping symbols. [Step 1]

$\qquad\qquad = \dfrac{3}{10}$ • Multiply. [Step 3]

2. $\dfrac{2}{3} \cdot \left(\dfrac{3}{5}\right)^2 = \dfrac{2}{3} \cdot \dfrac{9}{25}$ • Simplify exponential expressions. [Step 2]

$\qquad\qquad = \dfrac{6}{25}$ • Multiply. [Step 3]

3. $\dfrac{1}{4} \div \dfrac{2}{5} \cdot \dfrac{2}{3} = \dfrac{1}{4} \cdot \dfrac{5}{2} \cdot \dfrac{2}{3}$ • Do multiplications and divisions from left to right. [Step 3]

$\qquad\qquad = \dfrac{5}{8} \cdot \dfrac{2}{3}$

$\qquad\qquad = \dfrac{5}{12}$

4. $\dfrac{3}{4} - \dfrac{2}{3} \cdot \dfrac{1}{2} = \dfrac{3}{4} - \dfrac{1}{3}$ • Do multiplications and divisions from left to right. [Step 3]

$\qquad\qquad = \dfrac{5}{12}$ • Do additions and subtractions from left to right. [Step 4]

HOW TO 2 Simplify: $\dfrac{14}{15} - \left(\dfrac{1}{2}\right)^2 \times \left(\dfrac{2}{3} + \dfrac{4}{5}\right)$

$\dfrac{14}{15} - \left(\dfrac{1}{2}\right)^2 \times \underbrace{\left(\dfrac{2}{3} + \dfrac{4}{5}\right)}$

1. Perform operations in parentheses.

$\dfrac{14}{15} - \underbrace{\left(\dfrac{1}{2}\right)^2} \times \dfrac{22}{15}$

2. Simplify exponential expressions.

$\dfrac{14}{15} - \underbrace{\dfrac{1}{4} \times \dfrac{22}{15}}$

3. Do multiplications and divisions as they occur from left to right.

$\underbrace{\dfrac{14}{15} - \dfrac{11}{30}}$

4. Do additions and subtractions as they occur from left to right.

$\dfrac{17}{30}$

One or more of the steps of the Order of Operations Agreement may not be needed to simplify an expression. In that case, proceed to the next step in the Order of Operations Agreement.

EXAMPLE 2

Simplify: $\left(\dfrac{3}{4}\right)^2 \div \left(\dfrac{3}{8} - \dfrac{1}{12}\right)$

Solution

$\left(\dfrac{3}{4}\right)^2 \div \left(\dfrac{3}{8} - \dfrac{1}{12}\right) = \left(\dfrac{3}{4}\right)^2 \div \left(\dfrac{7}{24}\right)$

$\qquad = \dfrac{9}{16} \div \dfrac{7}{24}$

$\qquad = \dfrac{9}{16} \cdot \dfrac{24}{7}$

$\qquad = \dfrac{27}{14}$

$\qquad = 1\dfrac{13}{14}$

YOU TRY IT 2

Simplify: $\left(\dfrac{1}{13}\right)^2 \cdot \left(\dfrac{1}{4} + \dfrac{1}{6}\right) \div \dfrac{5}{13}$

Your solution

Solution on p. S8

2.8 EXERCISES

✔ Concept Check

For Exercises 1 to 3, determine whether the shaded portion of the first figure is less than, equal to, or greater than the shaded portion of the second figure.

1.

2.

3.

4. Which expression below is equivalent to $\frac{3}{4} - \frac{1}{4} \cdot \frac{2}{3}$?

(i) $\left(\frac{3}{4} - \frac{1}{4} \right) \cdot \frac{2}{3}$

(ii) $\frac{3}{4} - \left(\frac{1}{4} \cdot \frac{2}{3} \right)$

OBJECTIVE A *To identify the order relation between two fractions*

For Exercises 5 to 16, place the correct symbol, $<$ or $>$, between the two numbers.

5. $\frac{11}{40} \quad \frac{19}{40}$

6. $\frac{92}{103} \quad \frac{19}{103}$

7. $\frac{2}{3} \quad \frac{5}{7}$

8. $\frac{2}{5} \quad \frac{3}{8}$

9. $\frac{5}{8} \quad \frac{7}{12}$

10. $\frac{11}{16} \quad \frac{17}{24}$

11. $\frac{7}{9} \quad \frac{11}{12}$

12. $\frac{5}{12} \quad \frac{7}{15}$

13. $\frac{13}{14} \quad \frac{19}{21}$

14. $\frac{13}{18} \quad \frac{7}{12}$

15. $\frac{7}{24} \quad \frac{11}{30}$

16. $\frac{13}{36} \quad \frac{19}{48}$

17. ✎ Without writing the fractions $\frac{4}{5}$ and $\frac{1}{7}$ with a common denominator, decide which fraction is larger.

OBJECTIVE B *To use the Order of Operations Agreement to simplify expressions*

For Exercises 18 to 55, simplify.

18. $\left(\dfrac{3}{8}\right)^2$

19. $\left(\dfrac{5}{12}\right)^2$

20. $\left(\dfrac{2}{9}\right)^3$

21. $\left(\dfrac{1}{2}\right) \cdot \left(\dfrac{2}{3}\right)^2$

22. $\left(\dfrac{2}{3}\right) \cdot \left(\dfrac{1}{2}\right)^4$

23. $\left(\dfrac{1}{3}\right)^2 \cdot \left(\dfrac{3}{5}\right)^3$

24. $\left(\dfrac{2}{5}\right)^3 \cdot \left(\dfrac{5}{7}\right)^2$

25. $\left(\dfrac{5}{9}\right)^3 \cdot \left(\dfrac{18}{25}\right)^2$

26. $\dfrac{1}{2} - \dfrac{1}{3} + \dfrac{2}{3}$

27. $\dfrac{2}{5} + \dfrac{3}{10} - \dfrac{2}{3}$

28. $\dfrac{1}{3} \div \dfrac{1}{2} + \dfrac{3}{4}$

29. $\dfrac{3}{7} \cdot \dfrac{14}{15} + \dfrac{4}{5}$

30. $\dfrac{7}{9} - \dfrac{2}{3} \cdot \dfrac{4}{5}$

31. $\dfrac{5}{8} + \dfrac{1}{8} \cdot \dfrac{2}{3}$

32. $\dfrac{3}{4} \cdot \dfrac{4}{5} - \dfrac{1}{2} \cdot \dfrac{2}{3}$

33. $\dfrac{5}{6} \div \dfrac{2}{3} - \dfrac{3}{4} \cdot \dfrac{1}{2}$

34. $\dfrac{1}{3} + \dfrac{3}{5} \cdot \dfrac{4}{9} - \dfrac{1}{2}$

35. $\dfrac{7}{8} - \dfrac{2}{3} \cdot \dfrac{1}{2} + \dfrac{5}{6}$

36. $\dfrac{8}{9} - \dfrac{3}{4} \div \dfrac{9}{10} + \dfrac{4}{9}$

37. $\dfrac{5}{6} + \dfrac{1}{2} \div \dfrac{3}{4} - \dfrac{5}{8}$

38. $\left(\dfrac{3}{4}\right)^2 - \dfrac{5}{12}$

39. $\left(\dfrac{3}{5}\right)^3 - \dfrac{3}{25}$

40. $\dfrac{5}{6} \cdot \left(\dfrac{2}{3} - \dfrac{1}{6}\right) + \dfrac{7}{18}$

41. $\dfrac{3}{4} \cdot \left(\dfrac{11}{12} - \dfrac{7}{8}\right) + \dfrac{5}{16}$

42. $\dfrac{7}{12} - \left(\dfrac{2}{3}\right)^2 + \dfrac{5}{8}$

43. $\dfrac{11}{16} - \left(\dfrac{3}{4}\right)^2 + \dfrac{7}{12}$

44. $\dfrac{3}{4} \cdot \left(\dfrac{4}{9}\right)^2 + \dfrac{1}{2}$

45. $\dfrac{9}{10} \cdot \left(\dfrac{2}{3}\right)^3 + \dfrac{2}{3}$

46. $\left(\dfrac{1}{2} + \dfrac{3}{4}\right) \div \dfrac{5}{8}$

47. $\left(\dfrac{2}{3} + \dfrac{5}{6}\right) \div \dfrac{5}{9}$

48. $\dfrac{3}{8} \div \left(\dfrac{5}{12} + \dfrac{3}{8}\right)$

49. $\dfrac{7}{12} \div \left(\dfrac{2}{3} + \dfrac{5}{9}\right)$

50. $\left(\dfrac{3}{8}\right)^2 \div \left(\dfrac{3}{7} + \dfrac{3}{14}\right)$

51. $\left(\dfrac{5}{6}\right)^2 \div \left(\dfrac{5}{12} + \dfrac{2}{3}\right)$

52. $\dfrac{2}{5} \div \dfrac{3}{8} \cdot \dfrac{4}{5}$

53. $\left(\dfrac{1}{6} + \dfrac{1}{2}\right)^2 + \dfrac{2}{3}$

54. $\left(\dfrac{7}{8} - \dfrac{1}{2}\right)^2 - \dfrac{1}{16}$

55. $\dfrac{5}{6} + \left(\dfrac{3}{4} - \dfrac{1}{2}\right)^2$

56. Insert parentheses into the expression $\dfrac{2}{9} \cdot \dfrac{5}{6} + \dfrac{3}{4} \div \dfrac{3}{5}$ so that **a.** the first operation to be performed is addition and **b.** the first operation to be performed is division.

Critical Thinking

57. **The Food Industry** The table at the right shows the results of a survey that asked fast-food patrons their criteria for choosing where to go for fast food. For example, 3 out of every 25 people surveyed said that speed of service was most important in choosing a fast-food restaurant.
  a. According to the survey, do more people choose a fast-food restaurant on the basis of location or quality of the food?
  b. Which criterion was cited by the most people?

Fast-Food Patrons' Top Criteria for Choosing Fast-Food Restaurants	
Food quality	$\dfrac{1}{4}$
Location	$\dfrac{13}{50}$
Menu	$\dfrac{4}{25}$
Price	$\dfrac{2}{25}$
Speed	$\dfrac{3}{25}$
Other	$\dfrac{13}{100}$

Source: Maritz Marketing Research, Inc.

Projects or Group Activities

For Exercises 58 to 60, insert parentheses into the expression $\dfrac{7}{8} + \dfrac{2}{3} \cdot \dfrac{1}{2} + \dfrac{5}{6}$ so the value of the expression is the given number.

58. $1\dfrac{55}{72}$

59. $1\dfrac{29}{48}$

60. $2\dfrac{1}{24}$

CHAPTER

2   Summary

Key Words

Examples

A number that is a multiple of two or more numbers is a **common multiple** of those numbers. The **least common multiple (LCM)** of two or more numbers is the smallest common multiple of the numbers. [2.1A, p. 66]

12, 24, 36, 48, . . . are common multiples of 4 and 6.
The LCM of 4 and 6 is 12.

A number that is a factor of two or more numbers is a **common factor** of those numbers. The **greatest common factor (GCF)** of two or more numbers is the largest common factor of the numbers. [2.1B, p. 67]

The common factors of 12 and 16 are 1, 2, and 4.
The GCF of 12 and 16 is 4.

A **fraction** can represent the number of equal parts of a whole. In a fraction, the **fraction bar** separates the **numerator** and the **denominator.** [2.2A, p. 70]

In the fraction $\frac{3}{4}$, the numerator is 3 and the denominator is 4.

In a **proper fraction,** the numerator is smaller than the denominator; a proper fraction is a number less than 1. In an **improper fraction,** the numerator is greater than or equal to the denominator; an improper fraction is a number greater than or equal to 1. A **mixed number** is a number greater than 1 with a whole-number part and a fractional part. [2.2A, p. 70]

$\frac{2}{5}$ is proper fraction.

$\frac{7}{6}$ is an improper fraction.

$4\frac{1}{10}$ is a mixed number; 4 is the whole-number part and $\frac{1}{10}$ is the fractional part.

Equal fractions with different denominators are called **equivalent fractions.** [2.3A, p. 74]

$\frac{3}{4}$ and $\frac{6}{8}$ are equivalent fractions.

A fraction is in **simplest form** when the numerator and denominator have no common factors other than 1. [2.3B, p. 75]

The fraction $\frac{11}{12}$ is in simplest form.

The **reciprocal** of a fraction is the fraction with the numerator and denominator interchanged. [2.7A, p. 105]

The reciprocal of $\frac{3}{8}$ is $\frac{8}{3}$.
The reciprocal of 5 is $\frac{1}{5}$.

Essential Rules and Procedures

Examples

To find the LCM of two or more numbers, find the prime factorization of each number and write the factorization of each number in a table. Circle the greatest product in each column. The LCM is the product of the circled numbers. [2.1A, p. 66]

$$12 = \begin{array}{|c|c|} \hline 2 & 3 \\ \hline \boxed{2 \cdot 2} & 3 \\ \hline 2 & \boxed{3 \cdot 3} \\ \hline \end{array}$$

$18 =$

The LCM of 12 and 18 is $2 \cdot 2 \cdot 3 \cdot 3 = 36$.

To find the GCF of two or more numbers, find the prime factorization of each number and write the factorization of each number in a table. Circle the least product in each column that does not have a blank. The GCF is the product of the circled numbers. [2.1B, p. 67]

	2	3
12 =	2 · 2	③
18 =	②	3 · 3

The GCF of 12 and 18 is $2 \cdot 3 = 6$.

To write an improper fraction as a mixed number or a whole number, divide the numerator by the denominator. [2.2B, p. 71]

$$\frac{29}{6} = 29 \div 6 = 4\frac{5}{6}$$

To write a mixed number as an improper fraction, multiply the denominator of the fractional part of the mixed number by the whole-number part. Add this product and the numerator of the fractional part. The sum is the numerator of the improper fraction. The denominator remains the same. [2.2B, p. 71]

$$3\frac{2}{5} = \frac{5 \times 3 + 2}{5} = \frac{17}{5}$$

To find equivalent fractions by raising to higher terms, multiply the numerator and denominator of the fraction by the same number. [2.3A, p. 74]

$$\frac{3}{4} = \frac{3 \cdot 5}{4 \cdot 5} = \frac{15}{20}$$

$\frac{3}{4}$ and $\frac{15}{20}$ are equivalent fractions.

To write a fraction in simplest form, write the prime factorization of the numerator and denominator of the fraction; then eliminate the common factors. [2.3B, p. 75]

$$\frac{30}{45} = \frac{2 \cdot \overset{1}{\cancel{3}} \cdot \overset{1}{\cancel{5}}}{\underset{1}{\cancel{3}} \cdot 3 \cdot \underset{1}{\cancel{5}}} = \frac{2}{3}$$

To add fractions with the same denominator, add the numerators and place the sum over the common denominator. [2.4A, p. 78]

$$\frac{5}{12} + \frac{11}{12} = \frac{16}{12} = 1\frac{4}{12} = 1\frac{1}{3}$$

To add fractions with different denominators, first rewrite the fractions as equivalent fractions with a common denominator. (The least common denominator is the LCM of the denominators of the fractions.) Then add the fractions. [2.4B, p. 78]

$$\frac{1}{4} + \frac{2}{5} = \frac{5}{20} + \frac{8}{20} = \frac{13}{20}$$

To subtract fractions with the same denominator, subtract the numerators and place the difference over the common denominator. [2.5A, p. 87]

$$\frac{9}{16} - \frac{5}{16} = \frac{4}{16} = \frac{1}{4}$$

To subtract fractions with different denominators, first rewrite the fractions as equivalent fractions with a common denominator. (The least common denominator is the LCM of the denominators of the fractions.) Then subtract the fractions. [2.5B, p. 87]

$$\frac{2}{3} - \frac{7}{16} = \frac{32}{48} - \frac{21}{48} = \frac{11}{48}$$

To multiply two fractions, multiply the numerators; this is the numerator of the product. Multiply the denominators; this is the denominator of the product. [2.6A, p. 97]

$$\frac{3}{4} \cdot \frac{2}{9} = \frac{3 \cdot 2}{4 \cdot 9} = \frac{\overset{1}{\cancel{3}} \cdot \overset{1}{\cancel{2}}}{2 \cdot 2 \cdot \underset{1}{\cancel{3}} \cdot \underset{1}{\cancel{3}}} = \frac{1}{6}$$

To divide two fractions, multiply the first fraction by the reciprocal of the second fraction. [2.7A, p. 105]

$$\frac{8}{15} \div \frac{4}{5} = \frac{8}{15} \cdot \frac{5}{4} = \frac{8 \cdot 5}{15 \cdot 4}$$

$$= \frac{\overset{1}{\cancel{2}} \cdot \overset{1}{\cancel{2}} \cdot 2 \cdot \overset{1}{\cancel{5}}}{3 \cdot \underset{1}{\cancel{5}} \cdot \underset{1}{\cancel{2}} \cdot \underset{1}{\cancel{2}}} = \frac{2}{3}$$

To find the order relation between two fractions with the same denominator, compare the numerators. The fraction that has the smaller numerator is the smaller fraction. [2.8A, p. 114]

$$\frac{17}{25} \leftarrow \text{Smaller numerator}$$

$$\frac{19}{25} \leftarrow \text{Larger numerator}$$

$$\frac{17}{25} < \frac{19}{25}$$

To find the order relation between two fractions with different denominators, first rewrite the fractions with a common denominator. The fraction that has the smaller numerator is the smaller fraction. [2.8A, p. 114]

$$\frac{3}{5} = \frac{24}{40} \qquad \frac{5}{8} = \frac{25}{40}$$

$$\frac{24}{40} < \frac{25}{40}$$

$$\frac{3}{5} < \frac{5}{8}$$

Order of Operations Agreement [2.8B, p. 115]

Step 1. Perform operations inside grouping symbols.
Step 2. Simplify exponential expressions.
Step 3. Do multiplications and divisions as they occur from left to right.
Step 4. Do additions and subtractions as they occur from left to right.

$$\left(\frac{1}{3}\right)^2 + \left(\frac{5}{6} - \frac{7}{12}\right) \cdot (4)$$

$$= \left(\frac{1}{3}\right)^2 + \left(\frac{1}{4}\right) \cdot (4)$$

$$= \frac{1}{9} + \left(\frac{1}{4}\right) \cdot (4)$$

$$= \frac{1}{9} + 1 = 1\frac{1}{9}$$

CHAPTER

2   Review Exercises

1. Write $\frac{30}{45}$ in simplest form.

2. Simplify: $\left(\frac{3}{4}\right)^3 \cdot \frac{20}{27} - \frac{1}{8}$

3. Express the shaded portion of the circles as an improper fraction.

4. Write an equivalent fraction with the given denominator.

$$\frac{8}{11} = \frac{}{44}$$

5. Place the correct symbol, $<$ or $>$, between the two numbers.

$$\frac{11}{18} \qquad \frac{17}{24}$$

6. Subtract:

$$18\frac{1}{6}$$
$$-3\frac{5}{7}$$
$$\overline{}$$

7. Simplify: $\frac{2}{7}\left(\frac{5}{8} - \frac{1}{3}\right) \div \frac{3}{5}$

8. Multiply: $2\frac{1}{3} \times 3\frac{7}{8}$

9. Divide: $1\frac{1}{3} \div \frac{2}{3}$

10. Find $\frac{17}{24}$ decreased by $\frac{3}{16}$.

11. Divide: $8\frac{2}{3} \div 2\frac{3}{5}$

12. Find the GCF of 20 and 48.

13. Write an equivalent fraction with the given denominator.

$$\frac{2}{3} = \frac{}{36}$$

14. What is $\frac{15}{28}$ divided by $\frac{5}{7}$?

15. Find the total of $\frac{2}{3}$, $\frac{5}{6}$, and $\frac{2}{9}$.

16. Multiply: $2\frac{1}{4} \times 7\frac{1}{3}$

17. Find the LCM of 18 and 12.

18. Write $\frac{16}{44}$ in simplest form.

19. Add: $\dfrac{3}{8} + \dfrac{5}{8} + \dfrac{1}{8}$

20. What is $\dfrac{11}{50}$ multiplied by $\dfrac{25}{44}$?

21. Add: $4\dfrac{4}{9} + 2\dfrac{1}{6} + 11\dfrac{17}{27}$

22. Find the GCF of 15 and 25.

23. Write $\dfrac{17}{5}$ as a mixed number.

24. Simplify: $\left(\dfrac{4}{5} - \dfrac{2}{3}\right)^2 \div \dfrac{4}{15}$

25. Add: $\dfrac{3}{8} + 1\dfrac{2}{3} + 3\dfrac{5}{6}$

26. Find the LCM of 18 and 27.

27. Subtract: $\dfrac{11}{18} - \dfrac{5}{18}$

28. Write $2\dfrac{5}{7}$ as an improper fraction.

29. Divide: $\dfrac{5}{6} \div \dfrac{5}{12}$

30. Multiply: $\dfrac{5}{12} \times \dfrac{4}{25}$

31. Subtract: $\begin{aligned} &16 \\ -\,&5\dfrac{7}{8} \\ \hline \end{aligned}$

32. Express the shaded portion of the circles as a mixed number.

33. Meteorology   During 3 months of the rainy season, $5\dfrac{7}{8}$, $6\dfrac{2}{3}$, and $8\dfrac{3}{4}$ inches of rain fell. Find the total rainfall for the 3 months.

34. Real Estate   A home building contractor bought $4\dfrac{2}{3}$ acres of land for \$168,000. What was the cost of each acre?

35. Sports   A 15-mile race has three checkpoints. The first checkpoint is $4\dfrac{1}{2}$ miles from the starting point. The second checkpoint is $5\dfrac{3}{4}$ miles from the first checkpoint. How many miles is the second checkpoint from the finish line?

36. Fuel Efficiency   A compact car gets 36 miles on each gallon of gasoline. How many miles can the car travel on $6\dfrac{3}{4}$ gallons of gasoline?

CHAPTER

2 | TEST

1. Multiply: $\dfrac{9}{11} \times \dfrac{44}{81}$

2. Find the GCF of 24 and 80.

3. Divide: $\dfrac{5}{9} \div \dfrac{7}{18}$

4. Simplify: $\left(\dfrac{3}{4}\right)^2 \div \left(\dfrac{2}{3} + \dfrac{5}{6}\right) - \dfrac{1}{12}$

5. Write $9\frac{4}{5}$ as an improper fraction.

6. What is $5\frac{2}{3}$ multiplied by $1\frac{7}{17}$?

7. Write $\dfrac{40}{64}$ in simplest form.

8. Place the correct symbol, $<$ or $>$, between the two numbers.
$$\dfrac{3}{8} \qquad \dfrac{5}{12}$$

9. Simplify: $\left(\dfrac{1}{4}\right)^3 \div \left(\dfrac{1}{8}\right)^2 - \dfrac{1}{6}$

10. Find the LCM of 24 and 40.

11. Subtract: $\dfrac{17}{24} - \dfrac{11}{24}$

12. Write $\dfrac{18}{5}$ as a mixed number.

13. Find the quotient of $6\frac{2}{3}$ and $3\frac{1}{6}$.

14. Write an equivalent fraction with the given denominator.
$$\dfrac{5}{8} = \dfrac{}{72}$$

15. Add: $\dfrac{5}{6}$
$\dfrac{7}{9}$
$+\dfrac{1}{15}$

16. Subtract: $23\dfrac{1}{8}$
$-9\dfrac{9}{44}$

17. What is $\dfrac{9}{16}$ minus $\dfrac{5}{12}$?

18. Simplify: $\left(\dfrac{2}{3}\right)^4 \cdot \dfrac{27}{32} + \dfrac{1}{32}$

19. Add: $\dfrac{7}{12} + \dfrac{11}{12} + \dfrac{5}{12}$

20. What is $12\dfrac{5}{12}$ more than $9\dfrac{17}{20}$?

21. Express the shaded portion of the circles as an improper fraction.

22. Compensation An electrician earns $240 for each day worked. What is the total of the electrician's earnings for working $3\dfrac{1}{2}$ days?

23. Real Estate Grant Miura bought $7\dfrac{1}{4}$ acres of land for a housing project. One and three-fourths acres were set aside for a park, and the remaining land was developed into $\dfrac{1}{2}$-acre lots. How many lots were available for sale?

24. Architecture A scale of $\dfrac{1}{2}$ inch to 1 foot is used to draw the plans for a house. The scale measurements for three walls are given in the table at the right. Complete the table to determine the actual wall lengths for the three walls A, B, and C.

Wall	Scale	Actual Wall Length
A	$6\dfrac{1}{4}$ in.	?
B	9 in.	?
C	$7\dfrac{7}{8}$ in.	?

25. Meteorology In 3 successive months, the rainfall measured $11\dfrac{1}{2}$ inches, $7\dfrac{5}{8}$ inches, and $2\dfrac{1}{3}$ inches. Find the total rainfall for the 3 months.

Cumulative Review Exercises

1. Round 290,496 to the nearest thousand.

2. Subtract: $\begin{array}{r} 390,047 \\ -\ \ 98,769 \\ \hline \end{array}$

3. Find the product of 926 and 79.

4. Divide: $57\overline{)30,792}$

5. Simplify: $4 \cdot (6 - 3) \div 6 - 1$

6. Find the prime factorization of 44.

7. Find the LCM of 30 and 42.

8. Find the GCF of 60 and 80.

9. Write $7\frac{2}{3}$ as an improper fraction.

10. Write $\frac{25}{4}$ as a mixed number.

11. Write an equivalent fraction with the given denominator.

$$\frac{5}{16} = \frac{}{48}$$

12. Write $\frac{24}{60}$ in simplest form.

13. What is $\frac{9}{16}$ more than $\frac{7}{12}$?

14. Add: $\begin{array}{r} 3\frac{7}{8} \\ 7\frac{5}{12} \\ +\ 2\frac{15}{16} \\ \hline \end{array}$

15. Find $\frac{3}{8}$ less than $\frac{11}{12}$.

16. Subtract: $\begin{array}{r} 5\frac{1}{6} \\ -3\frac{7}{18} \\ \hline \end{array}$

17. Multiply: $\dfrac{3}{8} \times \dfrac{14}{15}$

18. Multiply: $3\dfrac{1}{8} \times 2\dfrac{2}{5}$

19. Divide: $\dfrac{7}{16} \div \dfrac{5}{12}$

20. Find the quotient of $6\dfrac{1}{8}$ and $2\dfrac{1}{3}$.

21. Simplify: $\left(\dfrac{1}{2}\right)^3 \cdot \dfrac{8}{9}$

22. Simplify: $\left(\dfrac{1}{2} + \dfrac{1}{3}\right) \div \left(\dfrac{2}{5}\right)^2$

23. Banking   Molly O'Brien had $1359 in a checking account. During the week, Molly wrote checks for $128, $54, and $315. Find the amount in the checking account at the end of the week.

24. Entertainment   The tickets for a movie were $10 for an adult and $4 for a student. Find the total income from the sale of 87 adult tickets and 135 student tickets.

25. Measurement   Find the total weight of three packages that weigh $1\dfrac{1}{2}$ pounds, $7\dfrac{7}{8}$ pounds, and $2\dfrac{2}{3}$ pounds.

26. Carpentry   A board $2\dfrac{5}{8}$ feet long is cut from a board $7\dfrac{1}{3}$ feet long. What is the length of the remaining piece?

27. Fuel Efficiency   A car travels 27 miles on each gallon of gasoline. How many miles can the car travel on $8\dfrac{1}{3}$ gallons of gasoline?

28. Real Estate   Jimmy Santos purchased $10\dfrac{1}{3}$ acres of land to build a housing development. Jimmy donated 2 acres for a park. How many $\dfrac{1}{3}$-acre parcels can be sold from the remaining land?

Decimals

OBJECTIVES

SECTION 3.1
A To write decimals in standard form and in words
B To round a decimal to a given place value
C To compare decimals

SECTION 3.2
A To add decimals
B To solve application problems

SECTION 3.3
A To subtract decimals
B To solve application problems

SECTION 3.4
A To multiply decimals
B To solve application problems

SECTION 3.5
A To divide decimals
B To solve application problems

SECTION 3.6
A To convert fractions to decimals
B To convert decimals to fractions
C To compare a fraction and a decimal

Focus on Success

Do you have trouble with word problems? Word problems show the variety of ways in which math can be used. The solution of every word problem can be broken down into two steps: Strategy and Solution. The Strategy consists of reading the problem, writing down what is known and unknown, and devising a plan to find the unknown. The Solution often consists of performing a calculation and checking the solution. (See Word Problems, page AIM–10).

Prep Test

Are you ready to succeed in this chapter? Take the Prep Test below to find out if you are ready to learn the new material.

1. Express the shaded portion of the rectangle as a fraction.

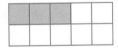

2. Round 36,852 to the nearest hundred.

3. Write 4791 in words.

4. Write six thousand eight hundred forty-two in standard form.

For Exercises 5 to 8, add, subtract, multiply, or divide.

5. $37 + 8892 + 465$

6. $2403 - 765$

7. 844×91

8. $23\overline{)6412}$

3.1   Introduction to Decimals

OBJECTIVE A   *To write decimals in standard form and in words*

 Take Note

In decimal notation, the part of the number that appears to the left of the decimal point is the **whole-number part.** The part of the number that appears to the right of the decimal point is the **decimal part.** The **decimal point** separates the whole-number part from the decimal part.

The price tag on a sweater reads $61.88. The number 61.88 is in **decimal notation.** A number written in decimal notation is often called simply a **decimal.**

A number written in decimal notation has three parts.

61	.	88
Whole-number part	**Decimal point**	**Decimal part**

The decimal part of the number represents a number less than 1. For example, $.88 is less than $1. The decimal point (.) separates the whole-number part from the decimal part.

The position of a digit in a decimal determines the digit's place value. The place-value chart is extended to the right to show the place values of digits to the right of a decimal point.

 Point of Interest

The decimal point did not make its appearance until the early 1600s. The original notation used subscripts with circles around them after each digit: 0 for ones, 1 for tenths (called "primes"), 2 for hundredths (called "seconds"), 3 for thousandths ("thirds"), and so on. For example, 1.375 would have been written

1   3   7   5
⓪   ①   ②   ③

In the decimal 458.302719, the position of the digit 7 determines that its place value is ten-thousandths.

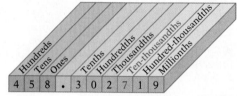

To write a decimal in words, write the decimal part of the number as though it were a whole number, and then name the place value of the last digit.

0.9684   Nine thousand six hundred eighty-four ten-thousandths

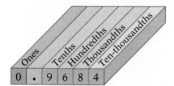

The decimal point in a decimal is read as "and."

372.516   Three hundred seventy-two and five hundred sixteen thousandths

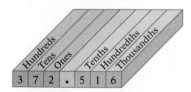

To write a decimal in standard form when it is written in words, write the whole-number part, replace the word *and* with a decimal point, and write the decimal part so that the last digit is in the given place-value position.

Four and twenty-three <u>hundredths</u>
3 is in the hundredths place.   4.2<u>3</u>

When writing a decimal in standard form, you may need to insert zeros after the decimal point so that the last digit is in the given place-value position.

Ninety-one and eight <u>thousandths</u>

8 is in the thousandths place.

Insert two zeros so that the 8 is in the thousandths place.

91.00<u>8</u>

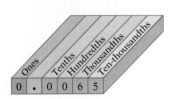

Sixty-five <u>ten-thousandths</u>

5 is in the ten-thousandths place.

Insert two zeros so that the 5 is in the ten-thousandths place.

0.006<u>5</u>

EXAMPLE 1

Name the place value of the digit 8 in the number 45.687.

Solution

The digit 8 is in the hundredths place.

YOU TRY IT 1

Name the place value of the digit 4 in the number 907.1342.

Your solution

EXAMPLE 2

Write 293.50816 in words.

Solution

Two hundred ninety-three and fifty thousand eight hundred sixteen hundred-thousandths

---

YOU TRY IT 2

Write 55.6083 in words.

Your solution

EXAMPLE 3

Write twenty-three and two hundred forty-seven millionths in standard form.

Solution

23.000247   • **7 is in the millionths place.**

YOU TRY IT 3

Write eight hundred six and four hundred ninety-one hundred-thousandths in standard form.

Your solution

Solutions on p. S8

OBJECTIVE B   *To round a decimal to a given place value*

Tips for Success

Have you considered joining a study group? Getting together regularly with other students in the class to go over material and quiz each other can be very beneficial. See *AIM for Success* at the front of the book.

In general, rounding decimals is similar to rounding whole numbers except that the digits to the right of the given place value are dropped instead of being replaced by zeros.

If the digit to the right of the given place value is less than 5, that digit and all digits to the right are dropped.	Round 6.9237 to the nearest hundredth.

 ┌─ Given place value (hundredths)

6.9237

└─ 3 < 5   Drop the digits 3 and 7.

6.9237 rounded to the nearest hundredth is 6.92.

If the digit to the right of the given place value is greater than or equal to 5, increase the digit in the given place value by 1, and drop all digits to its right.	Round 12.385 to the nearest tenth.

 ┌─ Given place value (tenths)

12.385

└─ 8 > 5   Increase 3 by 1 and drop all digits to the right of 3.

12.385 rounded to the nearest tenth is 12.4.

 Take Note

In HOW TO 1 at the right, the zero in the given place value is not dropped. This indicates that the number is rounded to the nearest thousandth. If we dropped the zero and wrote 0.47, it would indicate that the number was rounded to the nearest hundredth.

HOW TO 1   Round 0.46972 to the nearest thousandth.

 ┌─ Given place value (thousandths)

0.46972

└─ 7 > 5   Round up by adding 1 to the 9 (9 + 1 = 10). Carry the 1 to the hundredths place (6 + 1 = 7).

0.46972 rounded to the nearest thousandth is 0.470.

EXAMPLE 4

Round 0.9375 to the nearest thousandth.

Solution

 ┌─ Given place value

0.9375

└─ 5 = 5

0.9375 rounded to the nearest thousandth is 0.938.

YOU TRY IT 4

Round 3.675849 to the nearest ten-thousandth.

Your solution

EXAMPLE 5

Round 2.5963 to the nearest hundredth.

Solution

 ┌─ Given place value

2.5963

└─ 6 > 5

2.5963 rounded to the nearest hundredth is 2.60.

YOU TRY IT 5

Round 48.907 to the nearest tenth.

Your solution

Solutions on p. S8

Round 72.416 to the nearest whole number.

Solution

— Given place value

72.416

└─ 4 < 5

72.416 rounded to the nearest whole number is 72.

Round 31.8652 to the nearest whole number.

Your solution

Solution on p. S8

OBJECTIVE C   *To compare decimals*

Point of Interest

The idea that all fractions should be represented using decimals was first suggested in 1585 in Simon Stevin's publication *De Thiende*. Stevin claimed that such a system would make calculations much easier for merchants and scientists.

There is a relationship between numbers written in decimal notation and fractions.

7 tenths	59 hundredths	19 thousandths	27 ten-thousandths
$0.7 = \dfrac{7}{10}$	$0.59 = \dfrac{59}{100}$	$0.019 = \dfrac{19}{1000}$	$0.0027 = \dfrac{27}{10,000}$

This relationship can be used to compare two decimals.

HOW TO 2   Place the correct symbol, < or >, between the numbers.
0.037   0.04

	0.037	0.04
Write the numbers as fractions.	$\dfrac{37}{1000}$	$\dfrac{4}{100}$
Write the fractions with a common denominator.	$\dfrac{37}{1000}$	$\dfrac{40}{1000}$
Compare the fractions.	$\dfrac{37}{1000} <$	$\dfrac{40}{1000}$

$0.037 \; < \; 0.04$

Place the correct symbol, < or >, between the numbers.
0.02   0.0135

Solution

0.02		0.0135	
$\dfrac{2}{100}$		$\dfrac{135}{10,000}$	• **Write the numbers as fractions.**
$\dfrac{200}{10,000}$		$\dfrac{135}{10,000}$	• **Write the fractions with a common denominator.**
$\dfrac{200}{10,000}$	$>$	$\dfrac{135}{10,000}$	• **Compare the fractions.**

$0.02 \; > \; 0.0135$

Place the correct symbol, < or >, between the numbers.
0.15   0.107

Your solution

Solution on p. S8

3.1 EXERCISES

✔ Concept Check

For Exercises 1 to 4, name the place value of the digit 5.

1. 76.31587   **2.** 291.508   **3.** 432.09157   **4.** 0.0000853

For Exercises 5 to 7, write the fraction as a decimal.

5. $\dfrac{3}{10}$ **6.** $\dfrac{87}{100}$ **7.** $\dfrac{853}{1000}$

For Exercises 8 to 10, write the decimal as a fraction.

8. 0.1   **9.** 0.59   **10.** 0.601

OBJECTIVE A   *To write decimals in standard form and in words*

For Exercises 11 to 19, write the number in words.

11. 0.37   **12.** 25.6   **13.** 9.4

14. 1.004   **15.** 0.0053   **16.** 41.108

17. 0.045   **18.** 3.157   **19.** 26.04

For Exercises 20 to 27, write the number in standard form.

20. Six hundred seventy-two thousandths

21. Three and eight hundred six ten-thousandths

22. Nine and four hundred seven ten-thousandths

23. Four hundred seven and three hundredths

24. Six hundred twelve and seven hundred four thousandths

25. Two hundred forty-six and twenty-four thousandths

26. Two thousand sixty-seven and nine thousand two ten-thousandths

27. Seventy-three and two thousand six hundred eighty-four hundred-thousandths

28. Suppose the first nonzero digit to the right of the decimal point in a decimal number is in the hundredths place. If the number has three consecutive nonzero digits to the right of the decimal point, and all other digits are zero, what place value names the number?

OBJECTIVE B   *To round a decimal to a given place value*

For Exercises 29 to 46, round the number to the given place value.

29. 6.249   Tenths

30. 5.398   Tenths

31. 21.007   Tenths

32. 30.0092   Tenths

33. 18.40937   Hundredths

34. 413.5972   Hundredths

35. 72.4983   Hundredths

36. 6.061745   Thousandths

37. 936.2905   Thousandths

38. 96.8027   Whole number

39. 47.3192   Whole number

40. 5439.83   Whole number

41. 7014.96   Whole number

42. 0.023591   Ten-thousandths

43. 2.975268   Hundred-thousandths

44. 57.964   Tenths

45. 699.723   Whole number

46. 20.99693   Hundredths

47. **Measurement**   A nickel weighs about 0.1763668 ounce. Find the weight of a nickel to the nearest hundredth of an ounce.

48. **Science**   The weight of a gallon of water varies as the temperature of the water changes. At 212°F, a gallon of water weighs 7.9957 pounds. What is the weight of this gallon of water to the nearest tenth of a pound?

49. **Sports**   Runners in the Boston Marathon run a distance of 26.21875 miles. To the nearest tenth of a mile, find the distance that an entrant who completes the Boston Marathon runs.

For Exercises 50 and 51, give an example of a decimal number that satisfies the given condition.

50. The number rounded to the nearest hundredth is equal to the number rounded to the nearest thousandth.

51. The number rounded to the nearest tenth is greater than the number rounded to the nearest hundredth.

OBJECTIVE C   *To compare decimals*

Place the correct symbol, $<$ or $>$, between the two numbers.

52. 0.107   0.124

53. 0.278   0.203

54. 0.004   0.003

55. 0.045   0.038

56. 0.045   0.1

57. 0.037   0.13

58. 0.078   0.0095

59. 0.031   0.00987

60. 0.00765   0.0997

61. 0.02883   0.0305

62. 0.1008   0.09673

63. 0.0072   0.0008294

Critical Thinking

64. Indicate which digits of the number, if any, need not be entered on a calculator.
   a. 1.500   **b.** 0.908   **c.** 60.07   **d.** 0.0032

65. Find a number between each pair of numbers.
   a. Between 0.1 and 0.2
   b. Between 1 and 1.1
   c. Between 0 and 0.005

Projects or Group Activities

66. The time it takes a computer to add two numbers and the time it takes some atomic events in physics to occur are small fractions of a second. Find the meaning of a *nanosecond* and a *picosecond*. Tell which is the shorter period of time. Give examples of events that occur in nanoseconds and in picoseconds.

SECTION

3.2 | Addition of Decimals

OBJECTIVE A | *To add decimals*

To add decimals, write the numbers so that the decimal points are on a vertical line. As shown in the place value chart below, this keeps like place values in the same column. Add as for whole numbers, and write the decimal point in the sum directly below the decimal points in the addends.

HOW TO 1 Add: $0.237 + 4.9 + 27.32$

Note that by placing the decimal points on a vertical line, we make sure that digits of the same place value are added.
$0.237 + 4.9 + 27.32 = 32.457$

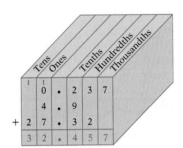

EXAMPLE 1

Find the sum of 42.3, 162.903, and 65.0729.

Solution

$$\begin{array}{r} \overset{1\ 1\ 1}{42.3} \\ 162.903 \\ +\ \ 65.0729 \\ \hline 270.2759 \end{array}$$

• Place the decimal points on a vertical line.

YOU TRY IT 1

Find the sum of 4.62, 27.9, and 0.62054.

Your solution

EXAMPLE 2

Add: $0.83 + 7.942 + 15$

Solution

$$\begin{array}{r} \overset{1\ 1}{0.83} \\ 7.942 \\ +\ 15. \\ \hline 23.772 \end{array}$$

YOU TRY IT 2

Add: $6.05 + 12 + 0.374$

Your solution

Solutions on p. S9

ESTIMATION: Estimating the Sum of Two or More Decimals

Calculate $23.037 + 16.7892$. Then use estimation to determine whether the sum is reasonable.

Add to find the exact sum.

$23.037 \ \boxed{+} \ 16.7892 \ \boxed{=} \ 39.8262$

To estimate the sum, round each number to the same place value. Here we have rounded to the nearest whole number. Then add. The estimated answer is 40, which is very close to the exact sum, 39.8262.

$$\begin{array}{r} 23.037 \approx\ \ 23 \\ +16.7892 \approx +17 \\ \hline 40 \end{array}$$

OBJECTIVE B   *To solve application problems*

⬤ During a recent month, U.S. Internet users watched an average of 889.1 minutes (14.8 hours) of video on the Internet. The table at the right shows how much video content was watched per viewer on some popular Internet sites during that month. Use this table for Example 3 and You Try It 3.

Online Video Content Viewing	
Internet Site	Minutes Watched per Viewer
Google	275.6
AOL	39.2
Yahoo! sites	42.1
Facebook	19.2
Hulu	215.5
Microsoft	47.2

Source: comScore

EXAMPLE 3

What is the total number of minutes watched per viewer for the three most-watched Internet sites listed in the table?

Strategy

To find the total number of minutes:
• Read the table to determine the three largest numbers.
• Add the numbers.

Solution

The three largest numbers are 275.6, 215.5, and 47.2. The sum of the numbers is

$$275.6 + 215.5 + 47.2 = 538.3$$

The total number of minutes watched per viewer for the three sites is 538.3 minutes.

YOU TRY IT 3

Determine the total number of minutes watched per viewer by Internet users on Facebook.com and Hulu.

Your strategy

Your solution

EXAMPLE 4

Dan Burhoe earned a salary of $210.48 for working 3 days this week as a food server. He also received $82.75, $75.80, and $99.25 in tips during the 3 days. Find his total income for the 3 days of work.

Strategy

To find the total income, add the tips (82.75, 75.80, and 99.25) to the salary (210.48).

Solution

$$210.48 + 82.75 + 75.80 + 99.25 = 468.28$$

Dan's total income for the 3 days of work was $468.28.

YOU TRY IT 4

Anita Khavari earns a monthly salary of $875 as an insurance agent. During the past month, she received commissions of $985.80, $791.46, $829.75, and $635.42. Find her total income for the past month.

Your strategy

Your solution

Solutions on p. S9

3.2 EXERCISES

Concept Check

1. When adding decimals, why is it necessary to write the numbers so that the decimal points line up?

2. Without adding, determine whether the following sums are equal.

   $3.450 + 29.000 + 126.008$ $3.45 + 29 + 126.008$

OBJECTIVE A   *To add decimals*

For Exercises 3 to 14, add.

3. $16.008 + 2.0385 + 132.06$

4. $17.32 + 1.0579 + 16.5$

5. $1.792 + 67 + 27.0526$

6. $8.772 + 1.09 + 26.5027$

7. $3.02 + 62.7 + 3.924$

8. $9.06 + 4.976 + 59.6$

9. $82.006 + 9.95 + 0.927$

10. $0.826 + 8.76 + 79.005$

11. $4.307 + 99.82 + 9.078$

12. $4.9257 + 27.05 + 9.0063$

13. $8.72 + 99.073 + 2.9736$

14. $62.4 + 9.827 + 692.44$

15. Find the sum of $0.0944 + 1.5522$.

16. What is the total of 0.4117 and 5.355?

17. Find 99.552 more than 8.09.

18. Find the sum of 22.877 and 0.001776.

For Exercises 19 to 22, use a calculator to add. Then round the numbers to the nearest whole number and use estimation to determine whether your sum is reasonable.

19.
```
   219.9
   0.872
 + 13.42
```

20.
```
   342.42
   89.625
 + 176.2
```

21.
```
   678.92
   97.6
 +  5.423
```

22.
```
   823.9
   82.65
 + 46.923
```

23. If none of the addends of a decimal addition problem is a whole number, is it possible for the sum to be a whole number?

OBJECTIVE B   *To solve application problems*

24. Mechanics   Find the length of the shaft.

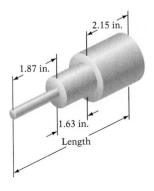

25. Mechanics   Find the length of the shaft.

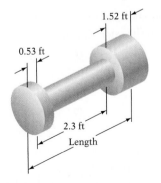

26. **Banking** You have $2143.57 in your checking account. You make deposits of $210.98, $45.32, $1236.34, and $27.99. Find the amount in your checking account after you have made the deposits if no money has been withdrawn.

27. **Geometry** One side of a garden window is in the shape of a trapezoid, as shown outlined in red. The perimeter of the trapezoid is the sum of the lengths of the four sides. Find the perimeter of the trapezoid that has sides measuring 1.36 meters, 0.55 meter, 1.12 meters, and 0.5 meter.

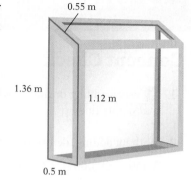

0.55 m

1.36 m   1.12 m

0.5 m

28. ● **Demography** The world's population in 2050 is expected to be 8.9 billion people. It is projected that in that year, Asia's population will be 5.3 billion and Africa's population will be 1.8 billion. What are the expected combined populations of Asia and Africa in 2050? (*Source:* United Nations Population Division, World Population Prospects)

29. ● **TV Viewership** The table at the right shows the average number of viewers per day, in millions, of three network news programs for the week of September 12 to September 16, 2011. Calculate the total average number of viewers per day for these three news programs that week.

Average Number of Viewers per Day (in millions)

15
10 —8.2—   7.2
5   5.7
0

NBC   ABC   CBS
Nightly   World   Evening
News   News   News

Network News Programs September 12–16, 2011

Source: TV by the Numbers

30. ● **The Stock Market** On September 26, 2011, the Dow Jones Industrial Average climbed 272.38 points after starting the day at 10,771.48. Find the value of the Dow Jones Industrial Average at the end of the trading day on September 26, 2011.

31. 🔲 **Measurement** Can a piece of rope 4 feet long be wrapped all the way around the box shown at the right?

1.4 ft

1.4 ft   1.4 ft

Critical Thinking

Consumerism The table at the right gives the prices for selected products in a grocery store. Use this table for Exercises 32 and 33.

32. Does a customer with $10 have enough money to purchase raisin bran, bread, milk, and butter?

33. Name three items that would cost more than $8 but less than $9. (There is more than one answer.)

Product	Cost
Raisin bran	$3.29
Butter	$2.79
Bread	$1.99
Popcorn	$2.19
Potatoes	$3.49
Mayonnaise	$3.99
Lunch meat	$3.39
Milk	$2.59

Projects or Group Activities

Recall that a decimal number can be represented as a fraction. For instance, $0.27 = \frac{27}{100}$. For Exercises 34 to 37, write each decimal as a fraction and then add.

34. $0.29 + 0.7$

35. $0.079 + 0.13$

36. $0.003 + 0.7 + 0.17$

37. $0.053 + 0.09 + 0.1077$

38. 📝 Read the Point of Interest on page 133. Do you agree with Stevin's claim that working with decimals is easier than working with fractions? Explain.

SECTION

3.3 | Subtraction of Decimals

OBJECTIVE A   *To subtract decimals*

To subtract decimals, write the numbers so that the decimal points are on a vertical line. Subtract as for whole numbers, and write the decimal point in the difference directly below the decimal point in the subtrahend.

HOW TO 1   Subtract 21.532 − 9.875 and check.

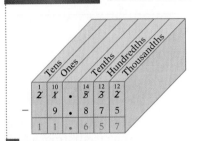

Placing the decimal points on a vertical line ensures that digits of the same place value are subtracted.
21.532 − 9.875 = 11.657

Check:	Subtrahend
	+ Difference
	= Minuend

$$\begin{array}{r} \overset{11\ \ 11}{9.875} \\ + 11.657 \\ \hline 21.532 \end{array}$$

HOW TO 2   Subtract 4.3 − 1.7942 and check.

$$\begin{array}{r} \overset{3\ \ \ \ 12\ 9\ 9\ 10}{4.3000} \\ - 1.7942 \\ \hline 2.5058 \end{array}$$

If necessary, insert zeros in the minuend before subtracting.

$$Check:\ \ \begin{array}{r} \overset{1\ 1\ 1\ 1}{1.7942} \\ + 2.5058 \\ \hline 4.3000 \end{array}$$

EXAMPLE 1

Subtract 39.047 − 7.96 and check.

Solution
$$\begin{array}{r} \overset{8\ \ 9\ 14}{39.047} \\ - 7.96 \\ \hline 31.087 \end{array}$$
$$Check:\ \ \begin{array}{r} \overset{1\ 1}{7.96} \\ + 31.087 \\ \hline 39.047 \end{array}$$

YOU TRY IT 1

Subtract 72.039 − 8.47 and check.

Your solution

EXAMPLE 2

Find 9.23 less than 29 and check.

Solution
$$\begin{array}{r} \overset{1\ 18\ \ 9\ 10}{29.00} \\ - 9.23 \\ \hline 19.77 \end{array}$$
$$Check:\ \ \begin{array}{r} \overset{11\ \ 1}{9.23} \\ + 19.77 \\ \hline 29.00 \end{array}$$

YOU TRY IT 2

Find 9.67 less than 35 and check.

Your solution

EXAMPLE 3

Subtract 27.35 − 9.6793 and check.

Solution
$$\begin{array}{r} \overset{1\ 16\ \ 12\ 14\ 9\ 10}{27.3500} \\ - 9.6793 \\ \hline 17.6707 \end{array}$$
$$Check:\ \ \begin{array}{r} \overset{11\ 111}{9.6793} \\ + 17.6707 \\ \hline 27.3500 \end{array}$$

YOU TRY IT 3

Subtract 3.7 − 1.9715 and check.

Your solution

Solutions on p. S9

ESTIMATION: Estimating the Difference Between Two Decimals

Calculate $820.23 - 475.748$. Then use estimation to determine whether the difference is reasonable.

Subtract to find the exact difference.

$$820.23 \boxed{-} 475.748 \boxed{=} 344.482$$

To estimate the difference, round each number to the same place value. Here we have rounded to the nearest ten. Then subtract. The estimated answer is 340, which is very close to the exact difference, 344.482.

$$
\begin{array}{rcr}
820.23 & \approx & 820 \\
- 475.748 & \approx & - 480 \\
\hline
& & 340
\end{array}
$$

OBJECTIVE B   *To solve application problems*

EXAMPLE 4

You bought a book for $15.87. How much change did you receive from a $20 bill?

Strategy

To find the amount of change, subtract the cost of the book (15.87) from $20.

Solution

$$
\begin{array}{r}
20.00 \\
-15.87 \\
\hline
4.13
\end{array}
$$

You received $4.13 in change.

YOU TRY IT 4

Your breakfast cost $6.85. How much change did you receive from a $10 bill?

Your strategy

Your solution

EXAMPLE 5

You had a balance of $87.93 on your student debit card. You then used the card, deducting $15.99 for a CD, $6.85 for lunch, and $28.50 for a ticket to a football game. What is your new student debit card balance?

Strategy

To find your new debit card balance:
- Add to find the total of the three deductions (15.99 + 6.85 + 28.50).
- Subtract the total of the three deductions from the old balance (87.93).

Solution

$$
\begin{array}{r}
15.99 \\
6.85 \\
+ 28.50 \\
\hline
51.34
\end{array}
\text{ total of deductions}
\qquad
\begin{array}{r}
87.93 \\
- 51.34 \\
\hline
36.59
\end{array}
$$

Your new debit card balance is $36.59.

YOU TRY IT 5

You had a balance of $2472.69 in your checking account. You then wrote checks for $1025.60, $79.85, and $162.47. Find the new balance in your checking account.

Your strategy

Your solution

Solutions on p. S9

3.3 EXERCISES

✔ Concept Check

For Exercises 1 to 4, use the given subtraction statement to help you complete the addition statement.

1. $9.37 - 6.19 = 3.18$
$9.37 = $ _____ $+ 3.18$

2. $81.1 - 73.43 = 7.67$
$7.67 + 73.43 = $ _____

3. $0.03 - 0.0095 = 0.0205$
$0.0205 + $ _____ $= 0.03$

4. $0.005 - 0.00067 = 0.00433$
$0.00067 + $ _____ $= 0.005$

OBJECTIVE A   *To subtract decimals*

For Exercises 5 to 28, subtract and check.

5. $24.037 - 18.41$

6. $26.029 - 19.31$

7. $123.07 - 9.4273$

8. $214 - 7.143$

9. $16.5 - 9.7902$

10. $13.2 - 8.6205$

11. $235.79 - 20.093$

12. $463.27 - 40.095$

13. $63.005 - 9.1274$

14. $23.004 - 7.2175$

15. $92 - 19.2909$

16. $41.2405 - 25.2709$

17. $0.32 - 0.0058$

18. $0.78 - 0.0073$

19. $3.005 - 1.982$

20. $6.007 - 2.734$

21. $352.16 - 90.994$

22. $872 - 80.753$

23. $724.32 - 69$

24. $625.46 - 77.509$

25. $362.394 - 19.4672$

26. $421.385 - 17.5293$

27. $19 - 10.372$

28. $23.4 - 0.921$

29. Find 97.732 less than 282.46.

30. Find 0.6206 less than 2.244.

31. What is the difference between 0.3145 and 0.03852?

32. What is the difference between 621.94 and 9.8482?

For Exercises 33 to 35, use the relationship between addition and subtraction to write the subtraction problem you would use to find the missing addend.

33. _____ + 2.325 = 7.01

34. 5.392 + _____ = 8.07

35. _____ + 8.967 = 19.35

For Exercises 36 to 39, use a calculator to subtract. Then round the numbers to the nearest whole number and use estimation to determine whether the difference you calculated is reasonable.

36.   93.079256
       − 66.09249

37.   3.7529
       − 1.00784

38.   76.53902
       − 45.73005

39.   9.07325
       − 1.924

OBJECTIVE B *To solve application problems*

40. Mechanics Find the missing dimension.

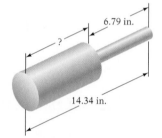

41. Mechanics Find the missing dimension.

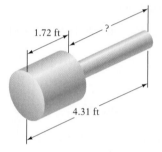

42. Business The manager of the Edgewater Cafe takes a reading of the cash register tape each hour. At 1:00 P.M., the cash register tape read $967.54. At 2:00 P.M., the tape read $1437.15. Find the amount of sales between 1:00 P.M. and 2:00 P.M.

43. ● **Moviegoing** The graph at the right shows the average price of a movie theater ticket for theaters in the United States. By how much did the average price of a ticket increase between 2007 and 2009?

44. ● **Coal** In a recent year, 1.163 billion tons of coal were produced in the United States. In the same year, U.S. consumption of coal was 1.112 billion tons. (*Source:* Department of Energy) How many more million tons of coal were produced than were consumed that year?

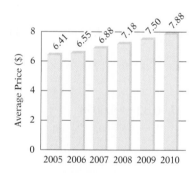

Average Price of a Movie Theater Ticket

Source: National Association of Theatre Owners

45. ● **Super Bowl** Super Bowl XLII was watched on the Fox network by 97.4 million people. On the same network, 63.9 million people watched the Super Bowl post-game show. (*Source:* Nielsen Network Research) How many more people watched Super Bowl XLII than watched the Super Bowl post-game show?

46. You have $30 to spend, and you make purchases that cost $6.74 and $13.68. Which expressions correctly represent the amount of money you have left?
(i) 30 − 6.74 + 13.68
(ii) (6.74 + 13.68) − 30
(iii) 30 − (6.74 + 13.68)
(iv) 30 − 6.74 − 13.68

Critical Thinking

47. Find the largest amount by which the estimate of the sum of two decimals rounded to the given place value could differ from the exact sum.
   a. Tenths   **b.** Hundredths   **c.** Thousandths

Projects or Group Activities

In HOW TO 2, we suggested that you insert zeros in the minuend before subtracting. This ensures that numbers of the same place value will be subtracted. For Exercises 48–51, first write each decimal as a fraction and then subtract the fractions. This may help you see why zeros are inserted in the minuend.

48. $0.9 - 0.51$ **49.** $0.87 - 0.531$ **50.** $0.71 - 0.1633$ **51.** $0.097 - 0.069531$

✔ CHECK YOUR PROGRESS: CHAPTER 3

For Exercises 1 to 4, write the decimal as a fraction.

1. 0.7   **2.** 0.017   **3.** 0.93   **4.** 0.00087

5. Write 23.045 in words.

6. Write three hundred five and fifty-seven ten-thousandths in standard form.

7. Round 357.79645 to the nearest hundredth.

For Exercises 8 to 10, place the correct symbol, $<$ or $>$, between the numbers.

8. 0.357   0.4   **9.** 0.056   0.0107   **10.** 0.00319   0.005

For Exercises 11 to 16, perform the indicated operation.

11. $9.03 + 1.15 + 6$ **12.** $27.47 - 9.5$ **13.** $308.7 - 192.483$

14. $7.306 + 82.9912 + 0.1$ **15.** $96.54 + 749.453 + 154.007$ **16.** $72.107 - 53.9562$

3.4 Multiplication of Decimals

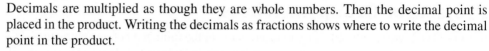

OBJECTIVE A | *To multiply decimals*

 Point of Interest

Benjamin Banneker (1731–1806) was the first African American to earn distinction as a mathematician and scientist. He was on the survey team that determined the boundaries of Washington, D.C. The mathematics of surveying requires extensive use of decimals.

Decimals are multiplied as though they are whole numbers. Then the decimal point is placed in the product. Writing the decimals as fractions shows where to write the decimal point in the product.

$$0.3 \times 5 = \frac{3}{10} \times \frac{5}{1} = \frac{15}{10} = 1.5$$

1 decimal place   1 decimal place

$$0.3 \times 0.5 = \frac{3}{10} \times \frac{5}{10} = \frac{15}{100} = 0.15$$

1 decimal place   1 decimal place   2 decimal places

$$0.3 \times 0.05 = \frac{3}{10} \times \frac{5}{100} = \frac{15}{1000} = 0.015$$

1 decimal place   2 decimal places   3 decimal places

To multiply decimals, multiply as with whole numbers. Write the decimal point in the product so that the number of decimal places in the product is the sum of the numbers of decimal places in the factors.

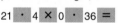 **Integrating Technology**

Scientific calculators have a floating decimal point. This means that the decimal point is automatically placed in the answer. For example, for the product at the right, enter

21 `.` 4 `×` 0 `.` 36 `=`

The display reads 7.704, with the decimal point in the correct position.

HOW TO 1   Multiply: 21.4×0.36

$$\begin{array}{r} 21.4 \\ \times\ 0.36 \\ \hline 1284 \\ 642 \\ \hline 7.704 \end{array}$$

21.4   1 decimal place
× 0.36   2 decimal places

7.704   3 decimal places

HOW TO 2   Multiply: 0.037×0.08

$$\begin{array}{r} 0.037 \\ \times\ \ 0.08 \\ \hline 0.00296 \end{array}$$

0.037   3 decimal places
× 0.08   2 decimal places
0.00296   5 decimal places

• **Two zeros must be inserted between the 2 and the decimal point so that there are 5 decimal places in the product.**

APPLY THE CONCEPT ···

The cost, including tax, of one adult admission to a theme park is $53.46. What is the total cost of 4 adult tickets to this theme park?

To find the total cost, multiply the admission price ($53.46) by the number of tickets (4).

$$\begin{array}{r} 53.46 \\ \times\ \ \ \ \ 4 \\ \hline 213.84 \end{array}$$

The total cost is $213.84.

To multiply a decimal by a power of 10 (10, 100, 1000, . . .), move the decimal point to the right the same number of places as there are zeros in the power of 10.

$3.892 \times 10 = 38.92$
1 zero   1 decimal place

$3.892 \times 100 = 389.2$
2 zeros   2 decimal places

$3.892 \times 1000 = 3892.$
3 zeros   3 decimal places

$3.892 \times 10,000 = 38,920.$
4 zeros   4 decimal places

• Note that a zero must be inserted before the decimal point.

Note that if the power of 10 is written in exponential notation, the exponent indicates how many places to move the decimal point.

$3.892 \times 10^1 = 38.92$
1 decimal place

$3.892 \times 10^2 = 389.2$
2 decimal places

$3.892 \times 10^3 = 3892.$
3 decimal places

$3.892 \times 10^4 = 38,920.$
4 decimal places

EXAMPLE 1

Multiply: 920×3.7

Solution
```
      920
×     3.7     • 1 decimal place
     644 0
    2760
    3404.0    • 1 decimal place
```

YOU TRY IT 1

Multiply: 870×4.6

Your solution

EXAMPLE 2

Find 0.00079 multiplied by 0.025.

Solution
```
   0.00079     • 5 decimal places
×    0.025     • 3 decimal places
     395
   158
 0.00001975    • 8 decimal places
```

YOU TRY IT 2

Find 0.000086 multiplied by 0.057.

Your solution

EXAMPLE 3

Find the product of 3.69 and 2.07.

Solution
```
    3.69      • 2 decimal places
×   2.07      • 2 decimal places
    2583
   7380
   7.6383     • 4 decimal places
```

YOU TRY IT 3

Find the product of 4.68 and 6.03.

Your solution

Solutions on p. S9

EXAMPLE 4

Multiply: $42.07 \times 10,000$

Solution

$42.07 \times 10,000 = 420,700$

YOU TRY IT 4

Multiply: 6.9×1000

Your solution

EXAMPLE 5

Find 3.01 times 10^3.

Solution

$3.01 \times 10^3 = 3010$

YOU TRY IT 5

Find 4.0273 times 10^2.

Your solution

Solutions on p. S9

ESTIMATION: Estimating the Product of Two Decimals

Calculate 28.259×0.029. Then use estimation to determine whether the product is reasonable.

Multiply to find the exact product.

$28.259 \quad \boxed{\times} \quad 0.029 \quad \boxed{=} \quad 0.819511$

To estimate the product, round each number so that it contains one nonzero digit. Then multiply. The estimated answer is 0.90, which is very close to the exact product, 0.819511.

$$\begin{array}{r} 28.259 \approx 30 \\ \times 0.029 \approx \times 0.03 \\ \hline 0.90 \end{array}$$

OBJECTIVE B   *To solve application problems*

The tables that follow list water rates and meter fees for a city. These tables are used for Example 6 and You Try It 6.

Water Charges	
Commercial	$1.39/1000 gal
Comm Restaurant	$1.39/1000 gal
Industrial	$1.39/1000 gal
Institutional	$1.39/1000 gal
Res—No Sewer	
Residential—SF	
>0 <200 gal per day	$1.15/1000 gal
>200 <1500 gal per day	$1.39/1000 gal
>1500 gal per day	$1.54/1000 gal

Meter Charges	
Meter	Meter Fee
5/8" & 3/4"	$13.50
1"	$21.80
1-1/2"	$42.50
2"	$67.20
3"	$133.70
4"	$208.20
6"	$415.10
8"	$663.70

EXAMPLE 6

Use the tables on page 148. Find the total bill for an industrial water user with a 6-inch meter that used 152,000 gallons of water for July and August.

Strategy

To find the total cost of water:

- Find the cost of water by multiplying the cost per 1000 gallons (1.39) by the number of 1000-gallon units used.
- Add the cost of the water to the meter fee (415.10).

Solution

Cost of water $= \dfrac{152,000}{1000} \cdot 1.39 = 211.28$

Total cost $= 211.28 + 415.10 = 626.38$

The total cost is $626.38.

YOU TRY IT 6

Use the tables on page 148. Find the total bill for a commercial user that used 5000 gallons of water per day for July and August. The user has a 3-inch meter.

Your strategy

Your solution

EXAMPLE 7

It costs $.036 an hour to operate an electric motor. How much does it cost to operate the motor for 120 hours?

Strategy

To find the cost of running the motor for 120 hours, multiply the hourly cost (0.036) by the number of hours the motor is run (120).

Solution

Total cost $= 0.036 \times 120 = 4.320$

The cost of running the motor for 120 hours is $4.32.

YOU TRY IT 7

The cost of electricity to run a freezer for 1 hour is $.035. This month the freezer has run for 210 hours. Find the total cost of running the freezer this month.

Your strategy

Your solution

EXAMPLE 8

Jason Ng earns a salary of $440 for a 40-hour workweek. This week he worked 12 hours of overtime at a rate of $16.50 for each hour of overtime worked. Find his total income for the week.

Strategy

To find Jason's total income for the week:

- Find the overtime pay by multiplying the hourly overtime rate (16.50) by the number of hours of overtime worked (12).
- Add the overtime pay to the weekly salary (440).

Solution

Overtime pay $= 16.50 \times 12 = 198.00$

Total income $= 440.00 + 198.00 = 638.00$

Jason's total income for the week is $638.00.

YOU TRY IT 8

You make a down payment of $175 on an electronic drum kit and agree to make payments of $37.18 per month for the next 18 months to repay the remaining balance. Find the total cost of the electronic drum kit.

Your strategy

Your solution

Solutions on pp. S9–S10

3.4 EXERCISES

✔ Concept Check

For Exercises 1 to 3, write the number in exponential notation.

1. 100   **2.** 100,000   **3.** 1,000,000

For Exercises 4 to 6, simplify the exponential expression.

4. 10^3 **5.** 10^7 **6.** 10^4

For Exercises 7 to 10, without actually multiplying the numbers, state the number of decimal places in the product of the numbers.

7. 0.98×0.3 **8.** 12.304×96.0017 **9.** 0.09×3.009 **10.** 28.17×0.59

OBJECTIVE A   *To multiply decimals*

For Exercises 11 to 60, multiply.

11. 0.9
$\times$ 0.4

12. 0.7
$\times$ 0.9

13. 0.5
$\times$ 0.5

14. 0.7
$\times$ 0.7

15. 7.7
$\times$ 0.9

16. 3.4
$\times$ 0.4

17. 9.2
$\times$ 0.2

18. 2.6
$\times$ 0.7

19. 7.4
$\times$ 0.1

20. 3.8
$\times$ 0.1

21. 7.9
$\times$ 5

22. 9.3
$\times$ 7

23. 0.68
$\times$ 4

24. 0.83
$\times$ 9

25. 0.67
$\times$ 0.9

26. 0.84
$\times$ 0.3

27. 2.5
$\times$ 5.4

28. 3.9
$\times$ 1.9

29. 0.83
$\times$ 5.2

30. 0.24
$\times$ 2.7

31. 1.47
$\times$ 0.09

32. 6.37
$\times$ 0.05

33. 8.92
$\times$ 0.004

34. 6.75
$\times$ 0.007

35. 0.49
$\times$ 0.16

36. 0.38
$\times$ 0.21

37. 7.6
$\times$ 0.01

38. 5.1
$\times$ 0.01

39. 8.62
$\times$ 4

40. 5.83
$\times$ 7

41. 64.5
$\times$ 9

42. 37.8
$\times$ 8

43. 2.19
$\times$ 9.2

44. 1.25
$\times$ 5.6

45. 1.85
$\times$ 0.023

46. 37.8
$\times$ 0.052

47. 0.478
$\times$ 0.37

48. 0.526
$\times$ 0.22

49. 48.3
$\times$ 0.0041

50. 67.2
$\times$ 0.0086

51. 4.29×0.1 **52.** 6.78×0.1 **53.** 5.29×0.4 **54.** 6.78×0.5 **55.** 0.68×0.7

56. 0.56×0.9 **57.** 1.4×0.73 **58.** 6.3×0.37 **59.** 3.8×0.61 **60.** 7.2×0.72

61. Sports One meter is approximately 3.2808 feet. What is the height, in feet, of a diving board that is 3 meters above the water?

62. Cooking A pastry chef buys fine chocolate for $23.45 per pound. How much will 2.5 pounds of chocolate cost? Round to the nearest cent.

For Exercises 63 to 78, multiply.

63. 0.32×10

64. 6.93×10

65. 0.065×100

66. 0.039×100

67. 6.2856×1000

68. 3.2954×1000

69. $3.57 \times 10,000$

70. $0.006 \times 10,000$

71. 0.63×10^1

72. 8.52×10^1

73. 0.039×10^2

74. 82.9×10^2

75. 4.9×10^4

76. 6.8×10^3

77. 0.067×10^2

78. 6.83×10^4

79. Find the product of 0.0035 and 3.45.

80. Find the product of 237 and 0.34.

81. Multiply 3.005 by 0.00392.

82. Multiply 20.34 by 1.008.

83. Multiply 1.348 by 0.23.

84. Multiply 0.000358 by 3.56.

85. Find the product of 23.67 and 0.0035.

86. Find the product of 0.00346 and 23.1.

87. Find the product of 5, 0.45, and 2.3.

88. Find the product of 0.03, 23, and 9.45.

For Exercises 89 to 100, use a calculator to multiply. Then use estimation to determine whether the product you calculated is reasonable.

89.   28.5
      $\times$ 3.2

90.   86.3
      $\times$ 4.4

91.   2.38
      $\times$ 0.44

92.   9.82
      $\times$ 0.77

93.   0.866
      $\times$ 4.5

94.   0.239
      $\times$ 8.2

95.   4.34
      $\times$ 2.59

96.   6.87
      $\times$ 9.98

97.   8.434
      $\times$ 0.044

98.   7.037
      $\times$ 0.094

99.   28.44
      $\times$ 1.12

100.   86.57
       $\times$ 7.33

OBJECTIVE B   *To solve application problems*

101. Recycling Four hundred empty soft drink cans weigh 18.75 pounds. A recycling center pays $.75 per pound for the cans. Find the amount received for the 400 cans. Round to the nearest cent.

102. Recycling A recycling center pays $.045 per pound for newspapers.
  a. Estimate the payment for recycling 520 pounds of newspapers.
  b. Find the actual amount received from recycling the newspapers.

103. ● **Electricity** In the United States, the average residential monthly bill for electricity is $103.67. (*Source:* U.S. Energy Information Administration) What is a U.S. homeowner's average annual cost of electricity?

104. **Transportation** A long-haul truck driver earns $.43 for each mile driven. How much will a truck driver earn for driving 1507 miles from Boston to Miami?

● **Taxes** For tax purposes, the Internal Revenue Service (IRS) allows a deduction on tax returns if the taxpayer uses a car for business, charitable work, medical needs, or relocating. The allowable amounts for 2011 are given in the table at the right. Use this table for Exercises 105 to 108.

IRS Mileage Deduction Table	
Business	$.50 per mile
Charitable work	$.14 per mile
Medical needs	$.165 per mile
Relocating	$.165 per mile

Source: Internal Revenue Service

105. During 2011, an accountant drove 1843 miles while doing charitable work for a college scholarship program. What is the accountant's mileage deduction for charitable work in 2011?

106. A welder specializing in electron beam welding relocated from Denver, Colorado, to Boston, Massachusetts, a distance of 1971 miles. What is the welder's mileage deduction for relocating in 2011? Round to the nearest cent.

107. 🐾 Describe what the numerical expression 2374 × 0.50 represents.

108. 🐾 Is the mileage deduction for medical needs less than or greater than the mileage deduction for charitable work?

109. ● **Taxes** The tax per gallon of gasoline in California is $.477. (*Source:* Tax Foundation) If you fill your gasoline tank with 12.5 gallons of gasoline in California, how much will you pay in taxes? Round to the nearest cent.

110. **Geometry** The perimeter of a square is equal to four times the length of a side of the square. Find the perimeter of a square whose side measures 2.8 meters.

2.8 m

111. **Geometry** The area of a rectangle is equal to the product of the length of the rectangle times its width. Find the area of a rectangle that has a length of 6.75 feet and a width of 3.5 feet. The area will be in square feet.

3.5 ft

6.75 ft

112. **Finance** You bought a car for $5000 down and made payments of $499.50 each month for 36 months.
 a. Find the amount of the payments over the 36 months.
 b. Find the total cost of the car.

113. **Compensation** A certified nurse anesthetist (CRNA) earns a salary of $3440 for a 40-hour work week. This week the CRNA worked 15 hours of overtime at a rate of $149.35 for each hour of overtime worked.
 a. Find the CRNA's overtime pay.
 b. Find the CRNA's total income for the week.

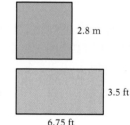

In the NEWS!

No More Paper Checks

With a paper check now costing $0.92 more to issue than an electronic payment, the federal government has eliminated the paper check option for Social Security recipients.

Source: usnews.com

114. **Consumerism** Bay Area Rental Cars charges $25 a day and $.25 per mile for renting a car. You rented a car for 3 days and drove 235 miles. Find the total cost of renting the car.

115. **Social Security** Use the information in the news clipping at the right. If the federal government issued about 136 million checks during its last year of issuing paper checks, how much money would have been saved that year by eliminating the paper check option?

116. **Transportation**   A taxi costs $2.50 and $.20 for each $\frac{1}{8}$ mile driven. Find the cost of hiring a taxi to get from the airport to the hotel, a distance of $5\frac{1}{2}$ miles.

117. **Business**   The table at the right lists three pieces of steel required for a repair project.
   a. Find the total cost of grade 1.
   b. Find the total cost of grade 2.
   c. Find the total cost of grade 3.
   d. Find the total cost of the three pieces of steel.

Grade of Steel	Weight (pounds per foot)	Required Number of Feet	Cost per Pound
1	2.2	8	$3.20
2	3.4	6.5	$3.35
3	6.75	15.4	$3.94

118. **Business**   A confectioner ships holiday packs of candy and nuts anywhere in the United States. At the left below is a price list for nuts and candy, and at the right below is a table of shipping charges to zones in the United States.

Code	Description	Price
112	Almonds 16 oz	$6.75
116	Cashews 8 oz	$5.90
117	Cashews 16 oz	$8.50
130	Macadamias 7 oz	$7.25
131	Macadamias 16 oz	$11.95
149	Pecan halves 8 oz	$8.25
155	Mixed nuts 8 oz	$6.80
160	Cashew brittle 8 oz	$5.95
182	Pecan roll 8 oz	$6.70
199	Chocolate peanuts 8 oz	$5.90

Pounds	Zone 1	Zone 2	Zone 3	Zone 4
1–3	$7.55	$7.85	$8.25	$8.75
4–6	$8.10	$8.40	$8.80	$9.30
7–9	$8.50	$8.80	$9.20	$9.70
10–12	$8.90	$9.20	$9.60	$10.10

Corbis/Jupiter Images

Use the information in the tables above to find the cost of sending each of the following orders to the given mail zone. For any fraction of a pound, use the next higher weight. Sixteen ounces (16 oz) is equal to 1 pound.

a.

Code	Quantity
116	2
130	1
149	3
182	4
Mail to zone 4.	

b.

Code	Quantity
112	1
117	4
131	2
160	3
182	5
Mail to zone 3.	

c.

Code	Quantity
117	3
131	1
155	2
160	4
182	1
199	3
Mail to zone 2.	

Critical Thinking

119. Show how the decimal is placed in the product of 1.3×2.31 by first writing each number as a fraction and then multiplying. Then change the product back to decimal notation.

120. ◥ Explain how the decimal point is placed when a number is multiplied by 10, 100, 1000, 10,000, etc.

121. ◥ Explain how the decimal point is placed in the product of two decimals.

Projects or Group Activities

122. Automotive Repair   Chris works at B & W Garage as an auto mechanic and has just completed an engine overhaul for a customer. To determine the cost of the repair job, Chris keeps a list of times worked and parts used. A parts list and a list of the times worked are shown below.

Parts Used		Time Spent	
Item	Quantity	Day	Hours
Gasket set	1	Monday	7.0
Ring set	1	Tuesday	7.5
Valves	8	Wednesday	6.5
Wrist pins	8	Thursday	8.5
Valve springs	16	Friday	9.0
Rod bearings	8		
Main bearings	5		
Valve seals	16		
Timing chain	1		

Price List		
Item Number	Description	Unit Price
27345	Valve spring	$9.25
41257	Main bearing	$17.49
54678	Valve	$16.99
29753	Ring set	$169.99
45837	Gasket set	$174.90
23751	Timing chain	$50.49
23765	Fuel pump	$229.99
28632	Wrist pin	$23.55
34922	Rod bearing	$13.69
2871	Valve seal	$1.69

a. Organize a table of data showing the parts used, the unit price for each part, and the price of the quantity used. *Hint:* Use the following headings for the table.

Quantity   Item Number   Description   Unit Price   Total

b. Add up the numbers in the "Total" column to find the total cost of the parts.

c. If the charge for labor is $46.75 per hour, compute the cost of labor.

d. What is the total cost for parts and labor?

SECTION

3.5

Division of Decimals

OBJECTIVE A

To divide decimals

To divide decimals, move the decimal point in the divisor to the right to make the divisor a whole number. Move the decimal point in the dividend the same number of places to the right. Place the decimal point in the quotient directly above the decimal point in the dividend, and then divide as with whole numbers.

HOW TO 1   Divide: $3.25\overline{)15.275}$

$$3.\underbrace{25.}\overline{)15.\underbrace{27}.5}$$

- Move the decimal point 2 places to the right in the divisor and then in the dividend. Place the decimal point in the quotient.

$$
\begin{array}{r}
4.7 \\
325.\overline{)\ 1527.5} \\
-1300 \\
\hline
227\ 5 \\
-227\ 5 \\
\hline
0
\end{array}
$$

- Divide as with whole numbers.

Moving the decimal point the same number of decimal places in the divisor and dividend does not change the value of the quotient, because this process is the same as multiplying the numerator and denominator of a fraction by the same number. In HOW TO 1 above,

$$3.25\overline{)15.275} = \frac{15.275}{3.25} = \frac{15.275 \times 100}{3.25 \times 100} = \frac{1527.5}{325} = 325\overline{)1527.5}$$

When dividing decimals, we usually round the quotient off to a specified place value, rather than writing the quotient with a remainder.

HOW TO 2   Divide: $0.3\overline{)0.56}$

Round to the nearest hundredth.

$$
\begin{array}{r}
1.866 \approx 1.87 \\
0.3.\overline{)\ 0.5.600} \\
-\ 3 \\
\hline
2\ 6 \\
-2\ 4 \\
\hline
20 \\
-18 \\
\hline
20 \\
-18
\end{array}
$$

We must carry the division to the thousandths place to round the quotient to the nearest hundredth. Therefore, zeros must be inserted in the dividend so that the quotient has a digit in the thousandths place.

Integrating Technology

A calculator displays the quotient to the limit of the calculator's display. Enter

| 5 | · | 793 | ÷ | 3 | · | 24 | = |

to determine the number of places your calculator displays.

HOW TO 3 Find the quotient of 5.793 and 3.24. Round to the nearest thousandth.

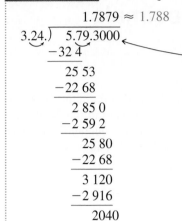

$$1.7879 \approx 1.788$$

$$
\begin{array}{r}
3.24.\overline{)\,5.79.3000} \\
-32\ 4 \\
\hline
25\ 53 \\
-22\ 68 \\
\hline
2\ 85\ 0 \\
-2\ 59\ 2 \\
\hline
25\ 80 \\
-22\ 68 \\
\hline
3\ 120 \\
-2\ 916 \\
\hline
2040 \\
-1944 \\
\end{array}
$$

Zeros must be inserted in the dividend so that the quotient has a digit in the ten-thousandths place.

APPLY THE CONCEPT

Three friends decide to share equally in the cost of lunch. If the total bill for lunch is $38.19, what amount is owed by each person?

To find the amount owed by each person, divide the total bill ($38.19) by the number of friends (3).

$$
\begin{array}{r}
12.73 \\
3\overline{)38.19}
\end{array}
$$

The amount owed by each person is $12.73.

To divide a decimal by a power of 10 (10, 100, 1000, . . .), move the decimal point to the left the same number of places as there are zeros in the power of 10.

$34.65 \div 1\underline{0} = 3.465$
    1 zero   1 decimal place

$34.65 \div 1\underline{00} = 0.3465$
    2 zeros   2 decimal places

$34.65 \div 1\underline{000} = 0.03465$
    3 zeros   3 decimal places

• Note that a zero must be inserted between the 3 and the decimal point.

$34.65 \div 1\underline{0,000} = 0.003465$
    4 zeros   4 decimal places

• Note that two zeros must be inserted between the 3 and the decimal point.

If the power of 10 is written in exponential notation, the exponent indicates how many places to move the decimal point.

$34.65 \div 10^1 = 3.465$ 1 decimal place $34.65 \div 10^3 = 0.03465$ 3 decimal places

$34.65 \div 10^2 = 0.3465$ 2 decimal places $34.65 \div 10^4 = 0.003465$ 4 decimal places

---

EXAMPLE 1

Divide: $0.1344 \div 0.032$

Solution

$$
\begin{array}{r}
4.2 \\
0.032.\overline{)\,0.134.4} \\
-\ 128 \\
\hline
6\ 4 \\
-6\ 4 \\
\hline
0
\end{array}
$$

• Move the decimal point 3 places to the right in the divisor and the dividend.

YOU TRY IT 1

Divide: $0.1404 \div 0.052$

Your solution

Solution on p. S10

EXAMPLE 2

Divide: 58.092 ÷ 82
Round to the nearest thousandth.

Solution

$$
\begin{array}{r}
0.7084 \approx 0.708 \\
82{\overline{\smash{\big)}\,58.0920}} \\
-57\ 4 \\
\hline
69 \\
-\ 0 \\
\hline
692 \\
-656 \\
\hline
360 \\
-328 \\
\hline
\end{array}
$$

EXAMPLE 3

Find the quotient of 420.9 and 7.06.
Round to the nearest tenth.

Solution

$$
\begin{array}{r}
59.61 \approx 59.6 \\
7.06{\overline{\smash{\big)}\,420.90.00}} \\
-353\ 0 \\
\hline
67\ 90 \\
-63\ 54 \\
\hline
4\ 36\ 0 \\
-4\ 23\ 6 \\
\hline
12\ 40 \\
-\ 7\ 06 \\
\hline
\end{array}
$$

EXAMPLE 4

Divide: 402.75 ÷ 1000

Solution   402.75 ÷ 1000 = 0.40275

EXAMPLE 5

What is 0.625 divided by 10^2?

Solution $0.625 \div 10^2 = 0.00625$

YOU TRY IT 2

Divide: 37.042 ÷ 76
Round to the nearest thousandth.

Your solution

YOU TRY IT 3

Find the quotient of 370.2 and 5.09.
Round to the nearest tenth.

Your solution

YOU TRY IT 4

Divide: 309.21 ÷ 10,000

Your solution

YOU TRY IT 5

What is 42.93 divided by 10^4?

Your solution

Solutions on p. S10

ESTIMATION: Estimating the Quotient of Two Decimals

Calculate 282.18 ÷ 0.48. Then use estimation to determine whether the quotient is reasonable.

Divide to find the exact quotient.   282.18 ÷ 0.48 = 587.875

To estimate the quotient, round each number $282.18 \div 0.48 \approx 300 \div 0.5$
so that it contains one nonzero digit. Then $= 600$
divide. The estimated answer is 600, which
is very close to the exact quotient, 587.875.

OBJECTIVE B *To solve application problems*

The graph at the right shows average hourly earnings in the United States for selected years. Use this table for Example 6 and You Try It 6.

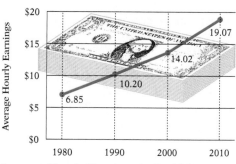

Average Hourly Earnings in the U.S.

Source: Bureau of Labor Statistics

EXAMPLE 6

How many times greater were the average hourly earnings in 2000 than in 1980? Round to the nearest whole number.

Strategy

To find how many times greater the average hourly earnings were, divide the 2000 average hourly earnings (14.02) by the 1980 average hourly earnings (6.85).

Solution

$14.02 \div 6.85 \approx 2$

The average hourly earnings in 2000 were about 2 times greater than in 1980.

YOU TRY IT 6

How many times greater were the average hourly earnings in 2010 than in 1980? Round to the nearest tenth.

Your strategy

Your solution

EXAMPLE 7

You purchased a car for $15,317.28 and made a down payment of $3000. The balance was paid in 48 monthly payments. Find the monthly car payment.

Strategy

To find the monthly car payment:

• Subtract the down payment (3000) from the purchase price (15,317.28). This is the amount financed.
• Divide the amount financed by 48.

Solution

$$\begin{array}{r} 15{,}317.28 \\ -\ 3000.00 \\ \hline 12{,}317.28 \end{array}$$ amount financed

$$\begin{array}{r} 256.61 \\ 48\overline{)12{,}317.28} \end{array}$$

The monthly car payment was $256.61.

YOU TRY IT 7

A Nielsen survey of the average number of people (in millions) who watch television each day of the week is given in the table below.

Mon.	Tues.	Wed.	Thu.	Fri.	Sat.	Sun.
91.9	89.8	90.6	93.9	78.0	77.1	87.7

Find the average number of people who watch television per day.

Your strategy

Your solution

Solutions on p. S10

3.5 EXERCISES

✔ Concept Check

For Exercises 1 and 2, fill in the blanks to complete the sentences.

1. To determine the placement of the decimal point in the quotient of two decimals, move the decimal point in the divisor to the _____ to make the divisor a _____ number. Move the decimal point in the dividend the same number of places to the _____ . Place the decimal point in the quotient directly above the decimal point in the _____ .

2. When dividing by a power of 10, move the decimal point to the _____ the same number of places as the _____ on 10.

OBJECTIVE A   *To divide decimals*

For Exercises 3 to 22, divide.

3. $3\overline{)2.46}$

4. $7\overline{)3.71}$

5. $0.8\overline{)3.84}$

6. $0.9\overline{)6.93}$

7. $0.7\overline{)62.3}$

8. $0.4\overline{)52.8}$

9. $0.4\overline{)24}$

10. $0.5\overline{)65}$

11. $0.7\overline{)59.01}$

12. $0.9\overline{)8.721}$

13. $0.5\overline{)16.15}$

14. $0.8\overline{)77.6}$

15. $0.7\overline{)3.542}$

16. $0.6\overline{)2.436}$

17. $6.3\overline{)8.19}$

18. $3.2\overline{)7.04}$

19. $3.6\overline{)0.396}$

20. $2.7\overline{)0.648}$

21. $6.9\overline{)26.22}$

22. $1.7\overline{)84.66}$

For Exercises 23 to 30, divide. Round to the nearest tenth.

23. $55.62 \div 8.8$

24. $25.43 \div 5.4$

25. $5.427 \div 9.5$

26. $1.837 \div 1.4$

27. $18.4 \div 7.3$

28. $52.9 \div 8.1$

29. $0.183 \div 0.17$

30. $0.381 \div 0.47$

For Exercises 31 to 38, divide. Round to the nearest hundredth.

31. $6.467 \div 8$

32. $4.817 \div 16$

33. $0.0647 \div 0.72$

34. $0.0418 \div 0.53$

35. $38.665 \div 0.95$

36. $7 \div 0.55$

37. $27.738 \div 60.8$

38. $3.171 \div 45.6$

For Exercises 39 to 46, divide. Round to the nearest thousandth.

39. $1.028 \div 54$

40. $6.729 \div 27$

41. $34.31 \div 95.3$

42. $75.469 \div 77.8$

43. $0.4871 \div 4.72$

44. $0.2695 \div 2.67$

45. $0.2307 \div 26.7$

46. $0.1142 \div 17.2$

For Exercises 47 to 54, divide. Round to the nearest whole number.

47. $89.76 \div 90$ **48.** $16.5 \div 4$ **49.** $1.0478 \div 0.413$ **50.** $2.148 \div 0.519$

51. $0.79 \div 0.778$ **52.** $3.092 \div 0.075$ **53.** $392 \div 6.9$ **54.** $8.729 \div 0.075$

55. Geometry A square has four sides of equal length. If the total distance around a square, called its perimeter, is 4.15 meters, what is the length of one side of the square?

56. Fuel Cost The cost of 16.5 gallons of gasoline is $62.37. What is the cost of 1 gallon of gasoline?

For Exercises 57 to 72, divide.

57. $4.07 \div 10$ **58.** $0.039 \div 10$ **59.** $42.67 \div 10$ **60.** $389.7 \div 100$

61. $1.037 \div 100$ **62.** $237.835 \div 100$ **63.** $8.295 \div 1000$ **64.** $82,547 \div 1000$

65. $0.32 \div 10^1$ **66.** $87.65 \div 10^1$ **67.** $23.627 \div 10^2$ **68.** $2.954 \div 10^2$

69. $0.0053 \div 10^2$ **70.** $289.32 \div 10^3$ **71.** $1.8932 \div 10^3$ **72.** $0.139 \div 10^3$

73. Divide 44.208 by 2.4.   **74.** Divide 0.04664 by 0.44.

75. Find the quotient of 723.15 and 45.   **76.** Find the quotient of 3.3463 and 3.07.

77. Divide 13.5 by 10^3.   **78.** Divide 0.045 by 10^5.

79. Find the quotient of 23.678 and 1000.   **80.** Find the quotient of 7.005 and 10,000.

81. What is 0.0056 divided by 0.05?   **82.** What is 123.8 divided by 0.02?

For Exercises 83 to 91, use a calculator to divide. Round to the nearest ten-thousandth. Then use estimation to determine whether the quotient you calculated is reasonable.

83. $42.42 \div 3.8$ **84.** $69.8 \div 7.2$ **85.** $389 \div 0.44$

86. $642 \div 0.83$ **87.** $6.394 \div 3.5$ **88.** $8.429 \div 4.2$

89. $1.235 \div 0.021$ **90.** $7.456 \div 0.072$ **91.** $95.443 \div 1.32$

92.   A four-digit whole number is divided by 1000. Is the quotient less than 1 or greater than 1?

OBJECTIVE B   *To solve application problems*

93. A 12-pack of bottled spring water sells for $3.85. State whether to use *multiplication* or *division* to find the specified amount.
   a. The cost of one bottle of spring water
   b. The cost of four 12-packs of spring water

94. A city school district spends $8754 per student, and the school district in a nearby suburb spends $10,296 per student. Which expression represents how many times greater the amount spent per student by the suburban schools is than the amount spent per student by the city schools?
   (i) 10,296 − 8754   **(ii)** 10,296 ÷ 8754
   (iii) 8754 ÷ 10,296   **(iv)** 10,296 × 8754

95. **Transportation**   A truck driver is paid by the number of miles driven. If a truck driver earns $.46 per mile, how many miles must the trucker drive in 1 hour to earn $16.00 per hour? Round to the nearest mile.

96. **Tourism**   See the news clipping at the right. Find the average amount spent by each visitor to Washington, D.C. Round to the nearest cent.

97. **Sports**   Ramon, a high school football player, gained 162 yards on 26 carries in a high school football game. Find the average number of yards gained per carry. Round to the nearest hundredth.

98. **Consumerism**   A case of diet cola costs $6.79. If there are 24 cans in a case, find the cost per can. Round to the nearest cent.

99. **Carpentry**   Anne is building a bookcase that is 3.4 feet long. How many complete shelves can be cut from a 12-foot board?

100. **Travel**   When the Massachusetts Turnpike opened, the toll for a passenger car that traveled the entire 136 miles of it was $5.60. Calculate the cost per mile. Round to the nearest cent.

101. **Consumerism**   Neil purchased a truck for $14,307.60 and made a down payment of $1500. If the remaining balance was paid over five years in 60 equal monthly payments, find the monthly truck payment.

102. **Consumerism**   Leanne purchased a high-definition 3D 1080p plasma television for $1208.76. She made a down payment of $300 and paid the remaining balance in 12 equal monthly payments. What were her monthly payments?

103. **Fuel Efficiency**   A car with an odometer reading of 17,814.2 is filled with 9.4 gallons of gas. At an odometer reading of 18,130.4, the tank is empty and the car is filled with 12.4 gallons of gas. How many miles does the car travel on 1 gallon of gasoline?

104. **Carbon Footprint**   One ton of coal can produce about 3000 kilowatt-hours of electricity. Suppose a family uses 25 kilowatt-hours of electricity per month. How many tons of coal will the family use in one year?

105. **Carbon Footprint**   One barrel of oil produces approximately 800 kilowatt-hours of electricity. Suppose you use 27 kilowatt-hours of electricity per month. How many barrels of oil will you use in one year?

In the NEWS!

Tourists Boost the Economy

This past summer, 17.28 million visitors came to Washington, D.C., spending $5680 million.
Source: washington.org

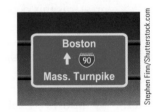

Boston
↑ (90)
Mass. Turnpike

Stephen Finn/Shutterstock.com

106. ● **Carbon Footprint** Use the information in the article at the right. Find the reduction in greenhouse gas emissions per month if 9 million U.S. households substituted chicken, fish, or eggs for red meat and dairy products one day a week.

Critical Thinking

107. ● **Education** According to the National Center for Education Statistics, 10.03 million women and 7.46 million men were enrolled at institutions of higher learning in a recent year. How many more women than men were attending institutions of higher learning that year?

● **The Military** The table at the right shows the advertising budgets of four branches of the U.S. armed services in a recent year. Use this table for Exercises 108 to 110.

Service	Advertising Budget
Army	$85.3 million
Air Force	$41.1 million
Navy	$20.5 million
Marines	$15.9 million

Source: CMR/TNS Media Intelligence

108. Find the difference between the Army's advertising budget and the Marines' advertising budget.

109. How many times greater was the Army's advertising budget than the Navy's advertising budget? Round to the nearest tenth.

110. What was the total of the advertising budgets for the four branches of the service?

111. ● **Population Growth** The U.S. population of people ages 85 and over is expected to grow from 4.2 million in 2000 to 8.9 million in 2030. How many times greater is this population expected to be in 2030 than in 2000? Round to the nearest tenth.

112. ◤ Explain how the decimal point is moved when a number is divided by 10, 100, 1000, 10,000, etc.

113. ◤ **Sports** Explain how baseball batting averages are determined. Then find Detroit Tiger's right fielder Magglio Ordonez's batting average with 216 hits out of 595 at bats. Round to the nearest thousandth.

Projects or Group Activities

For Exercises 114 to 119, insert $+$, $-$, $\times$, or $\div$ into the square so that the statement is true.

114. $3.45 \;\square\; 0.5 = 6.9$

115. $3.46 \;\square\; 0.24 = 0.8304$

116. $6.009 \;\square\; 4.68 = 1.329$

117. $0.064 \;\square\; 1.6 = 0.1024$

118. $9.876 \;\square\; 23.12 = 32.996$

119. $3.0381 \;\square\; 1.23 = 2.47$

For Exercises 120 to 123, fill in the square to make a true statement.

120. $6.47 - \square = 1.253$

121. $6.47 + \square = 9$

122. $0.009 \div \square = 0.36$

123. $\square \times 1.06 = 0.2862$

SECTION

3.6

Comparing and Converting Fractions and Decimals

OBJECTIVE A   *To convert fractions to decimals*

To convert a fraction to a decimal, divide the numerator by the denominator.

HOW TO 1   Convert $\frac{5}{8}$ to a decimal.

Divide the numerator by the denominator.

In this case, the remainder is 0. This fraction can be written as a **terminating decimal,** which is a decimal whose remainder is eventually 0.

$$
\begin{array}{r}
0.625 \\
8\overline{)\,5.000} \\
-\,4\,8 \\
\hline
20 \\
-\,16 \\
\hline
40 \\
-\,40 \\
\hline
0
\end{array}
$$

$$\frac{5}{8} = 0.625$$

HOW TO 2   Convert $\frac{7}{11}$ to a decimal.

Divide the numerator by the denominator.

> **Take Note**
>
> The decimal representation of every fraction either terminates or repeats. However, the repeating cycle may be quite long. For instance, there are 22 digits in the repeating cycle of the decimal representation of $\frac{9}{23}$.

In this case, the remainder is never 0. This fraction can be written as a **repeating decimal,** which is a decimal whose remainder is never 0. When a remainder begins to repeat (as 4 does in this example), the digits in the quotient will begin to repeat.

It is common practice to write a bar over the repeating digits of a decimal.

$$
\begin{array}{r}
0.6363 \\
11\overline{)\,7.0000} \\
-\,6.6 \\
\hline
40 \\
-\,33 \\
\hline
70 \\
-\,66 \\
\hline
40 \\
-\,33 \\
\hline
7
\end{array}
$$

$$\frac{7}{11} = 0.6363... = 0.\overline{63}$$

EXAMPLE 1

Convert $\frac{5}{12}$ to a decimal.

Solution

$$
\begin{array}{r}
0.4166 \\
12\overline{)\,5.0000} \\
-\,4\,8 \\
\hline
20 \\
-\,12 \\
\hline
80 \\
-\,72 \\
\hline
80
\end{array}
$$

• Divide the numerator by the denominator. Continue to divide until the remainder is 0 or the remainder repeats.

$$\frac{5}{12} = 0.41\overline{6}$$

YOU TRY IT 1

Convert $\frac{11}{18}$ to a decimal.

Your solution

Solution on p. S10

EXAMPLE 2

Convert $\frac{5}{16}$ to a decimal.

Solution

$$
\begin{array}{r}
0.3125 \\
16{\overline{\smash{\big)}\,5.0000}} \\
-4\,8 \\
\hline
20 \\
-16 \\
\hline
40 \\
-32 \\
\hline
80 \\
-80 \\
\hline
0
\end{array}
$$

• Divide the numerator by the denominator. Continue to divide until the remainder is 0 or the remainder repeats.

$$\frac{5}{16} = 0.3125$$

YOU TRY IT 2

Convert $\frac{7}{25}$ to a decimal.

Your solution

EXAMPLE 3

Convert $\frac{32}{15}$ to a decimal.

Solution

$$
\begin{array}{r}
2.133 \\
15{\overline{\smash{\big)}\,32.000}} \\
-30 \\
\hline
2\,0 \\
-1\,5 \\
\hline
50 \\
-45 \\
\hline
50
\end{array}
$$

• Divide the numerator by the denominator. Continue to divide until the remainder is 0 or the remainder repeats.

$$\frac{32}{15} = 2.1\overline{3}$$

YOU TRY IT 3

Convert $\frac{13}{6}$ to a decimal.

Your solution

Solutions on p. S11

OBJECTIVE B   *To convert decimals to fractions*

To convert a decimal to a fraction, remove the decimal point and place the decimal part over a denominator equal to the place value of the last digit in the decimal. Then write the fraction in simplest form.

HOW TO 3   Convert 0.275 to a fraction.

$$0.275 = \frac{275}{1000} = \frac{\cancel{5} \cdot \cancel{5} \cdot 11}{2 \cdot 2 \cdot 2 \cdot \cancel{5} \cdot \cancel{5} \cdot 5} = \frac{11}{40}$$

(thousandths)

HOW TO 4   Convert 0.33 to a fraction.

$$0.33 = \frac{33}{100} = \frac{3 \cdot 11}{2 \cdot 2 \cdot 5 \cdot 5} = \frac{33}{100}$$

(hundredths)

EXAMPLE 4

Convert 7.45 to a mixed number.

Solution $7.45 = 7\dfrac{45}{100} = 7\dfrac{9}{20}$

YOU TRY IT 4

Convert 0.0005 to a fraction.

Your solution

Solution on p. S11

OBJECTIVE C *To compare a fraction and a decimal*

One way to determine the order relation between a decimal and a fraction is to write the decimal as a fraction and then compare the fractions.

HOW TO 5 Place the correct symbol, $<$ or $>$, between the two numbers.

$$0.8 \qquad \frac{8}{9}$$

$$0.8 \qquad \frac{8}{9}$$

Write the decimal as a fraction.

$$\frac{8}{10} \qquad \frac{8}{9}$$

Write the fractions with a common denominator.

$$\frac{72}{90} \qquad \frac{80}{90}$$

Compare the fractions.

$$\frac{72}{90} < \frac{80}{90}$$

$$0.8 < \frac{8}{9}$$

EXAMPLE 5

Place the correct symbol, $<$ or $>$, between the two numbers.

$$0.7 \qquad \frac{3}{4}$$

Solution

$$0.7 \qquad \frac{3}{4}$$

$$\frac{7}{10} \qquad \frac{3}{4}$$ • Write the decimal as a fraction.

$$\frac{14}{20} \qquad \frac{15}{20}$$ • Write the fractions with a common denominator.

$$\frac{14}{20} < \frac{15}{20}$$ • Compare the fractions.

$$0.7 < \frac{3}{4}$$

YOU TRY IT 5

Place the correct symbol, $<$ or $>$, between the two numbers.

$$\frac{5}{6} \qquad 0.83$$

Your solution

Solution on p. S11

3.6 EXERCISES

✔ **Concept Check**

For Exercises 1 to 5, give the place value of the digit 3.

1. 0.45367   **2.** 0.40032   **3.** 4.3976   **4.** 7308.4987   **5.** 6.03049

6. ✎ Explain the meaning of a terminating decimal and a repeating decimal.

For Exercises 7 to 10, without actually doing any division, state whether the decimal equivalent of the given fraction is greater than 1 or less than 1.

7. $\dfrac{97}{96}$ **8.** $\dfrac{2012}{2010}$ **9.** $\dfrac{79}{80}$ **10.** $\dfrac{1999}{2000}$

OBJECTIVE A   *To convert fractions to decimals*

For Exercises 11 to 35, convert the fraction to a terminating or a repeating decimal. Place a bar over any repeating digits.

11. $\dfrac{2}{3}$ **12.** $\dfrac{5}{9}$ **13.** $\dfrac{7}{8}$ **14.** $\dfrac{15}{16}$ **15.** $\dfrac{13}{18}$

16. $\dfrac{8}{15}$ **17.** $\dfrac{20}{33}$ **18.** $\dfrac{8}{11}$ **19.** $\dfrac{17}{36}$ **20.** $\dfrac{5}{12}$

21. $\dfrac{27}{37}$ **22.** $\dfrac{71}{111}$ **23.** $\dfrac{25}{27}$ **24.** $\dfrac{17}{22}$ **25.** $\dfrac{35}{74}$

26. $\dfrac{3}{40}$ **27.** $\dfrac{17}{20}$ **28.** $\dfrac{37}{80}$ **29.** $\dfrac{6}{7}$ **30.** $\dfrac{5}{13}$

31. $\dfrac{11}{32}$ **32.** $\dfrac{29}{4}$ **33.** $\dfrac{77}{20}$ **34.** $\dfrac{53}{22}$ **35.** $\dfrac{233}{55}$

OBJECTIVE B   *To convert decimals to fractions*

For Exercises 36 to 55, convert the decimal to a fraction or a mixed number.

36. 0.8   **37.** 0.4   **38.** 0.32   **39.** 0.48

40. 0.125   **41.** 0.485   **42.** 1.25   **43.** 3.75

44. 2.7125   **45.** 3.175   **46.** 9.05   **47.** 11.004

48. 8.437   **49.** 9.279   **50.** 2.25   **51.** 0.224

52. 0.0025   **53.** 0.052   **54.** 0.084   **55.** 0.00015

The repeating cycle of the decimal representation of some fractions may be quite long. For instance, there are 22 digits in the repeating cycle of $\frac{17}{23}$. In such cases, it may be convenient to round the decimal representation to a given place value. For Exercises 56 to 63, round the decimal representation of the fraction to the given place value.

56. $\frac{9}{71}$ Hundredths   **57.** $\frac{21}{67}$ Hundredths

58. $\frac{19}{53}$ Thousandths   **59.** $\frac{7}{43}$ Thousandths

60. $\frac{15}{29}$ Thousandths   **61.** $\frac{5}{56}$ Thousandths

62. $\frac{17}{23}$ Ten-thousandths   **63.** $\frac{12}{17}$ Ten-thousandths

OBJECTIVE C   *To compare a decimal and a fraction*

For Exercises 64 to 75, place the correct symbol, $<$ or $>$, between the two numbers.

64. 0.7 $\frac{3}{4}$ **65.** $\frac{7}{8}$ 0.9   **66.** $\frac{7}{16}$ 0.45   **67.** 0.13 $\frac{5}{40}$

68. $\frac{23}{40}$ 0.57   **69.** $\frac{12}{55}$ 0.22   **70.** 0.07 $\frac{1}{15}$ **71.** 0.55 $\frac{5}{9}$

72. $\frac{5}{12}$ 0.42   **73.** $\frac{17}{18}$ 0.94   **74.** $\frac{16}{9}$ 1.8   **75.** $\frac{22}{7}$ 3.14

Critical Thinking

76. 📱 **Air Pollution** An emissions test for cars requires that of the total engine exhaust, less than 1 part per thousand $\left(\frac{1}{1000} = 0.001\right)$ be hydrocarbon emissions. Using this figure, determine which of the cars in the table below would fail the emissions test.

Car	Total Engine Exhaust	Hydrocarbon Emission
1	367,921	360
2	401,346	420
3	298,773	210
4	330,045	320
5	432,989	450

Projects or Group Activities

As we have stated, the decimal representation of a fraction always terminates or repeats. In this project, we will explore terminating decimal representations.

77. Using a calculator, find the terminating decimal representation of each fraction shown below.

$$\frac{1}{2}, \frac{3}{4}, \frac{5}{8}, \frac{9}{16}, \frac{3}{10}, \frac{7}{20}, \frac{19}{32}, \frac{23}{40}, \frac{7}{25}, \frac{19}{50}$$

78. Find the prime factorization of each denominator in Exercise 77.

79. What are the only prime number factors of the denominators in Exercise 77?

80. Make up some fractions in simplest form, with denominators that contain only the prime factors you listed in Exercise 79. Find the decimal representations of these fractions. Do they all have terminating decimal representations?

81. Make up some fractions in simplest form, with denominators that contain at least one prime factor other than those you listed in Exercise 79. Find the decimal representations of these fractions. Do any of these fractions have terminating decimal representations?

82. Based on your results in Exercises 77 to 81, make a conjecture about the denominator of a fraction with a terminating decimal representation.

CHAPTER

3 | Summary

Key Words

A number written in **decimal notation** has three parts: a **whole-number part**, a **decimal point**, and a **decimal part**. The decimal part of a number represents a number less than 1. A number written in decimal notation is often simply called a **decimal**. [3.1A, p. 130]

Examples

For the decimal 31.25, 31 is the whole-number part and 25 is the decimal part.

Essential Rules and Procedures

To write a decimal in words, write the decimal part as if it were a whole number. Then name the place value of the last digit. The decimal point is read as "and." [3.1A, p. 130]

Examples

The decimal 12.875 is written in words as twelve and eight hundred seventy-five thousandths.

To write a decimal in standard form when it is written in words, write the whole-number part, replace the word *and* with a decimal point, and write the decimal part so that the last digit is in the given place-value position. [3.1A, p. 130]

The decimal forty-nine and sixty-three thousandths is written in standard form as 49.063.

To round a decimal to a given place value, use the same rules used with whole numbers, except drop the digits to the right of the given place value instead of replacing them with zeros. [3.1B, p. 132]

2.7134 rounded to the nearest tenth is 2.7. 0.4687 rounded to the nearest hundredth is 0.47.

To add decimals, write the decimals so that the decimal points are on a vertical line. Add as you would with whole numbers. Then write the decimal point in the sum directly below the decimal points in the addends. [3.2A, p. 137]

$$
\begin{array}{r}
{}^{1}\ {}^{1} \\
1.35 \\
20.8 \\
+\ 0.76 \\
\hline
22.91
\end{array}
$$

To subtract decimals, write the decimals so that the decimal points are on a vertical line. Subtract as you would with whole numbers. Then write the decimal point in the difference directly below the decimal point in the subtrahend. [3.3A, p. 141]

$$
\begin{array}{r}
{}^{2}\ {}^{15}\ {}^{6}\ {}^{10} \\
3\,5\,.\,8\,7\,0 \\
-\ 9\,.\,6\,4\,1 \\
\hline
2\,6\,.\,2\,2\,9
\end{array}
$$

To multiply decimals, multiply the numbers as you would whole numbers. Then write the decimal point in the product so that the number of decimal places in the product is the sum of the numbers of decimal places in the factors. [3.4A, p. 146]

$$
\begin{array}{rl}
26.83 & \text{2 decimal places} \\
\times \quad 0.45 & \text{2 decimal places} \\
\hline
13415 & \\
10732 \quad\; & \\
\hline
12.0735 & \text{4 decimal places}
\end{array}
$$

To multiply a decimal by a power of 10, move the decimal point to the right the same number of places as there are zeros in the power of 10. If the power of 10 is written in exponential notation, the exponent indicates how many places to move the decimal point. [3.4A, p. 147]

$3.97 \cdot 10{,}000 = 39{,}700$
$0.641 \cdot 10^5 = 64{,}100$

To divide decimals, move the decimal point in the divisor to the right so that the divisor is a whole number. Move the decimal point in the dividend the same number of places to the right. Place the decimal point in the quotient directly above the decimal point in the dividend. Then divide as you would with whole numbers. [3.5A, p. 155]

$$
\begin{array}{r}
6.2 \\
0.39\overline{)\,2.41.8} \\
-2\,34 \\
\hline
7\,8 \\
-7\,8 \\
\hline
0
\end{array}
$$

To divide a decimal by a power of 10, move the decimal point to the left the same number of places as there are zeros in the power of 10. If the power of 10 is written in exponential notation, the exponent indicates how many places to move the decimal point. [3.5A, p. 156]

$972.8 \div 1000 = 0.9728$
$61.305 \div 10^4 = 0.0061305$

To convert a fraction to a decimal, divide the numerator of the fraction by the denominator. Continue to divide until the remainder is 0 or the remainder repeats. [3.6A, p. 163]

$\dfrac{7}{8} = 7 \div 8 = 0.875$ • **Terminating decimal**

$\dfrac{5}{6} = 5 \div 6 = 0.8\overline{3}$ • **Repeating decimal**

To convert a decimal to a fraction, remove the decimal point and place the decimal part over a denominator equal to the place value of the last digit in the decimal. [3.6B, p. 164]

0.85 is eighty-five <u>hundredths</u>.

$0.85 = \dfrac{85}{100} = \dfrac{17}{20}$

To find the order relation between a decimal and a fraction, first rewrite the decimal as a fraction. Then compare the two fractions. [3.6C, p. 165]

$0.9 = \dfrac{9}{10} = \dfrac{36}{40}$

$\dfrac{7}{8} = \dfrac{35}{40}$

Because $\dfrac{36}{40} > \dfrac{35}{40}$, $0.9 > \dfrac{7}{8}$.

3 | Review Exercises

1. Find the quotient of 3.6515 and 0.067.

2. Find the sum of 369.41, 88.3, 9.774, and 366.474.

3. Place the correct symbol, $<$ or $>$, between the two numbers.
0.055   0.1

4. Write 22.0092 in words.

5. Round 0.05678235 to the nearest hundred-thousandth.

6. Write $\frac{17}{80}$ as a terminating or repeating decimal. Place a bar over any repeating digits.

7. Convert 0.375 to a fraction.

8. Add: $3.42 + 0.794 + 32.5$

9. Write thirty-four and twenty-five thousandths in standard form.

10. Place the correct symbol, $<$ or $>$, between the two numbers.
$\frac{5}{8}$ 0.62

11. Convert $\frac{7}{22}$ to a terminating or repeating decimal. Place a bar over any repeating digits.

12. Convert 0.66 to a fraction.

13. Subtract: $27.31 - 4.4465$

14. Round 7.93704 to the nearest hundredth.

15. Find the product of 3.08 and 2.9.

16. Write 342.37 in words.

17. Write three and six thousand seven hundred fifty-three hundred-thousandths in standard form.

18. Multiply: $\begin{array}{r} 34.79 \\ \times\ 0.74 \end{array}$

19. Divide: $0.053\overline{)0.349482}$

20. What is 7.796 decreased by 2.9175?

21.  **Fuel Consumption** Read the news clipping at the right. What is the total number of gallons of fuel saved this year by the airline? What is the airline's average cost per gallon of fuel for the year? Round to the nearest cent.

22. Banking You had a balance of $895.68 in your checking account. You then wrote checks for $145.72 and $88.45. Find the new balance in your checking account.

23. **Travel** In a recent year, 30.6 million Americans drove to their destinations over Thanksgiving, and 4.8 million Americans traveled by plane. (*Source:* AAA) How many times greater is the number who drove than the number who flew? Round to the nearest tenth.

24. **Nutrition** According to the American School Food Service Association, 1.9 million gallons of milk are served in school cafeterias every day. How many gallons of milk are served in school cafeterias during a 5-day school week?

> # In the NEWS!
>
> ### Airline Reduces Fuel Costs
>
> One airline estimates that it will save $131 million in fuel costs this year by taking the following steps to reduce fuel consumption:
>
> Remove outdated equipment and replace beverage carts with lighter-weight models: 2.9 million gallons saved
>
> Wash airplane engines: 7.2 million gallons saved
>
> Tow airplanes when they are on the ground: 3.6 million gallons saved
>
> Install winglets to improve aerodynamics: 35.4 million gallons saved
>
> *Source:* news.travel.aol.com

CHAPTER

3　TEST

1. Place the correct symbol, < or >, between the two numbers.
0.0068　0.000963

2. Subtract: $13.027 - 8.94$

3. Write 45.0302 in words.

4. Write two hundred nine and seven thousand eighty-six hundred-thousandths in standard form.

5. Convert 0.825 to a fraction.

6. Place the correct symbol, < or >, between the two numbers.
$\dfrac{13}{8}$　0.72

7. Find the quotient of 0.0569 and 0.037. Round to the nearest thousandth.

8. Find 9.23674 less than 37.003.

9. Subtract: $65.34 - 39.4592$

10. Convert $\frac{13}{40}$ to a terminating or repeating decimal. Place a bar over any repeating digits.

11. Round 7.0954625 to the nearest thousandth.

12. Divide: $1.392 \div 0.06$

13. Add:　270.93
　　　　　　97.
　　　　　　　1.976
　　　　+　88.675

14. Convert $\frac{15}{22}$ to a terminating or repeating decimal. Place a bar over any repeating digits.

15. Find the product of 1.37 and 0.004.

16. Find the sum of 62.3, 4.007, and 189.65.

17. Find 17.1496 times 10^3.

18. What is 15.923 divided by 10^4?

19. Construction   The cost of a $4\frac{1}{2}$-inch carriage bolt is $1.44. What is the cost of 15 of these carriage bolts?

20. Finances   A car was bought for $16,734.40, with a down payment of $2500. The balance was paid in 36 monthly payments. Find the amount of each monthly payment.

21. Compensation   You received a salary of $727.50, a commission of $1909.64, and a bonus of $450. Find your total income.

22. Consumerism   A long-distance telephone call costs $.85 for the first 3 minutes and $.42 for each additional minute. Find the cost of a 12-minute long-distance telephone call.

Cumulative Review Exercises

1. Divide: $89\overline{)20,932}$

2. Simplify: $2^3 \cdot 4^2$

3. Simplify: $2^2 - (7 - 3) \div 2 + 1$

4. Find the LCM of 9, 12, and 24.

5. Write $\frac{22}{5}$ as a mixed number.

6. Write $4\frac{5}{8}$ as an improper fraction.

7. Write an equivalent fraction with the given denominator.
$$\frac{5}{12} = \frac{}{60}$$

8. Add: $\frac{3}{8} + \frac{5}{12} + \frac{9}{16}$

9. What is $5\frac{7}{12}$ increased by $3\frac{7}{18}$?

10. Subtract: $9\frac{5}{9} - 3\frac{11}{12}$

11. Multiply: $\frac{9}{16} \times \frac{4}{27}$

12. Find the product of $2\frac{1}{8}$ and $4\frac{5}{17}$.

13. Divide: $\frac{11}{12} \div \frac{3}{4}$

14. What is $2\frac{3}{8}$ divided by $2\frac{1}{2}$?

15. Simplify: $\left(\frac{2}{3}\right)^2 \cdot \left(\frac{3}{4}\right)^3$

16. Simplify: $\left(\frac{2}{3}\right)^2 - \left(\frac{2}{3} - \frac{1}{2}\right) + 2$

17. Write 65.0309 in words.

18. Add: 379.006
            27.523
             9.8707
         + 88.2994

19. What is 29.005 decreased by 7.9286?

20. Multiply: 9.074
            $\times$ 6.09

21. Divide: $8.09\overline{)17.42963}$
Round to the nearest thousandth.

22. Convert $\frac{11}{15}$ to a terminating or a repeating decimal. Place a bar over any repeating digits.

23. Convert 0.425 to a fraction.

24. Place the correct symbol, $<$ or $>$, between the two numbers.
$$\frac{8}{9} \quad 0.98$$

25. 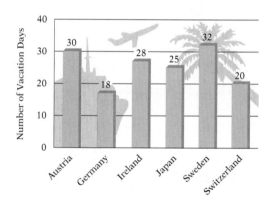 **Vacation**   The graph at the right shows the number of legally-mandated vacation days per year for several countries. How many more vacation days does Sweden mandate than Germany?

26. **Health**   A patient is put on a diet to lose 24 pounds in 3 months. The patient loses $9\frac{1}{2}$ pounds the first month and $6\frac{3}{4}$ pounds the second month. How much weight must the patient lose during the third month to achieve the goal?

27. **Banking**   You have a checking account balance of $814.35. You then write checks for $42.98, $16.43, and $137.56. Find your checking account balance after you write the checks.

28. **Mechanics**   A machine lathe takes 0.017 inch from a brass bushing that is 1.412 inches thick. Find the resulting thickness of the bushing.

29. **Taxes**   The state income tax on your business is $820 plus 0.08 times your profit. You made a profit of $64,860 last year. Find the amount of income tax you paid last year.

30. **Finances**   You bought a camera costing $410.96. The down payment was $40, and the balance is to be paid in 8 equal monthly payments. Find the monthly payment.

Number of Legally Mandated Vacation Days

Sources: Economic Policy Institute; *World Almanac*

Lichtmeister/Shutterstock.com

Ratio and Proportion

OBJECTIVES

SECTION 4.1
A To write the ratio of two quantities in simplest form
B To solve application problems

SECTION 4.2
A To write rates
B To write unit rates
C To solve application problems

SECTION 4.3
A To determine whether a proportion is true
B To solve proportions
C To solve application problems

Focus on Success

Are you making attending class a priority? Remember that to be successful, you must attend class. You need to be in class to hear your instructor's explanations and instructions, as well as to ask questions when something is unclear. Most students who miss a class fall behind and then find it very difficult to catch up. (See Class Time, page AIM-5.)

Monkey Business Images/shutterstock.com

Prep Test

Are you ready to succeed in this chapter? Take the Prep Test below to find out if you are ready to learn the new material.

1. Simplify: $\dfrac{8}{10}$

2. Simplify: $\dfrac{450}{650 + 250}$

3. Write $\dfrac{372}{15}$ as a terminating or repeating decimal.

4. Which is greater, 4×33 or 62×2?

5. Complete: $? \times 5 = 20$

SECTION

4.1   Ratio

OBJECTIVE A   *To write the ratio of two quantities in simplest form*

Quantities such as 3 feet, 12 cents, and 9 cars are number quantities written with units.

3 feet

12 cents   These are some examples of units. Shirts, dollars, trees, miles,

9 cars   and gallons are further examples.

↑
units

A **ratio** is a comparison of two quantities that have the *same* units. This comparison can be written in three different ways:

1. As a fraction
2. As two numbers separated by a colon (:)
3. As two numbers separated by the word *to*

The ratio of the lengths of two boards, one 8 feet long and the other 10 feet long, can be written as

1. $\dfrac{8 \text{ feet}}{10 \text{ feet}} = \dfrac{8}{10} = \dfrac{4}{5}$

2. $8 \text{ feet} : 10 \text{ feet} = 8 : 10 = 4 : 5$

3. $8 \text{ feet to } 10 \text{ feet} = 8 \text{ to } 10 = 4 \text{ to } 5$

Writing the **simplest form of a ratio** means writing it so that the two numbers have no common factor other than 1.

This ratio means that the smaller board is $\frac{4}{5}$ the length of the longer board.

EXAMPLE 1

Write the comparison $6 to $8 as a ratio in simplest form using a fraction, a colon, and the word *to*.

Solution $\dfrac{\$6}{\$8} = \dfrac{6}{8} = \dfrac{3}{4}$

$\$6 : \$8 = 6 : 8 = 3 : 4$

$\$6 \text{ to } \$8 = 6 \text{ to } 8 = 3 \text{ to } 4$

YOU TRY IT 1

Write the comparison 20 pounds to 24 pounds as a ratio in simplest form using a fraction, a colon, and the word *to*.

Your solution

EXAMPLE 2

Write the comparison 18 quarts to 6 quarts as a ratio in simplest form using a fraction, a colon, and the word *to*.

Solution $\dfrac{18 \text{ quarts}}{6 \text{ quarts}} = \dfrac{18}{6} = \dfrac{3}{1}$

$18 \text{ quarts} : 6 \text{ quarts} = 18 : 6 = 3 : 1$

$18 \text{ quarts to } 6 \text{ quarts} = 18 \text{ to } 6$
$= 3 \text{ to } 1$

YOU TRY IT 2

Write the comparison 64 miles to 8 miles as a ratio in simplest form using a fraction, a colon, and the word *to*.

Your solution

Solutions on p. S11

OBJECTIVE B   *To solve application problems*

Christian Delbert/Shutterstock.com

The table below shows the number of board feet in stock at a lumber store for each of four types of wood. Use the table for Example 3 and You Try It 3.

Board Feet of Wood at a Lumber Store			
Pine	Ash	Oak	Cedar
20,000	18,000	10,000	12,000

EXAMPLE 3

Find, as a fraction in simplest form, the ratio of the number of board feet of pine to the number of board feet of oak.

Strategy

To find the ratio, write the ratio of board feet of pine (20,000) to board feet of oak (10,000) in simplest form.

Solution

$$\frac{20,000}{10,000} = \frac{2}{1}$$

The ratio is $\frac{2}{1}$.

YOU TRY IT 3

Find, as a fraction in simplest form, the ratio of the number of board feet of cedar to the number of board feet of ash.

Your strategy

Your solution

EXAMPLE 4

The cost of building a patio cover was $500 for labor and $700 for materials. What, as a fraction in simplest form, is the ratio of the cost of materials to the total cost for labor and materials?

Strategy

To find the ratio, write the ratio of the cost of materials ($700) to the total cost ($500 + $700) in simplest form.

Solution

$$\frac{\$700}{\$500 + \$700} = \frac{700}{1200} = \frac{7}{12}$$

The ratio is $\frac{7}{12}$.

YOU TRY IT 4

A company spends $600,000 a month for television advertising and $450,000 a month for radio advertising. What, as a fraction in simplest form, is the ratio of the cost of radio advertising to the total cost of radio and television advertising?

Your strategy

Your solution

Solutions on p. S11

4.1 EXERCISES

✔ Concept Check

1. How do you read $\frac{3}{8}$ as a ratio?

2. How do you read 8 : 3 as a ratio?

OBJECTIVE A   *To write the ratio of two quantities in simplest form*

For Exercises 3 to 20, write the comparison as a ratio in simplest form using a fraction, a colon (:), and the word *to*.

3. 3 pints to 15 pints

4. 6 pounds to 8 pounds

5. $40 to $20

6. 10 feet to 2 feet

7. 3 miles to 8 miles

8. 2 hours to 3 hours

9. 6 minutes to 6 minutes

10. 8 days to 12 days

11. 35 cents to 50 cents

12. 28 inches to 36 inches

13. 30 minutes to 60 minutes

14. 25 cents to 100 cents

15. 32 ounces to 16 ounces

16. 12 quarts to 4 quarts

17. 30 yards to 12 yards

18. 12 quarts to 18 quarts

19. 20 gallons to 28 gallons

20. 14 days to 7 days

21. 🖎 To write a ratio that compares 3 days to 3 weeks, change 3 weeks into an equivalent number of _____.

22. 🖎 Is the ratio 3 : 4 the same as the ratio 4 : 3?

OBJECTIVE B   *To solve application problems*

Budgets   For Exercises 23 to 26, use the information in the table. Write ratios in simplest form using a fraction.

Family Budget						
Housing	Food	Transportation	Taxes	Utilities	Miscellaneous	Total
$1600	$800	$600	$700	$300	$800	$4800

23. Find the ratio of utilities costs to food costs.

24. Find the ratio of food costs to total expenses.

25. Find the ratio of housing costs to total expenses.

26. 🖎 Write a verbal description of two ratios represented by 1 : 2.

27.  **Facial Hair**   Using the data in the news clipping at the right and the figure 110 million for the number of adult males in the United States, write the ratio of the number of men who participated in Movember to the number of adult males in the U.S. Write the ratio as a fraction in simplest form.

28. **Real Estate**   A house with an original value of $180,000 increased in value to $220,000 in 5 years. What is the ratio of the increase in value to the original value of the house?

29. **Energy Prices**   The price per gallon of gasoline rose from $2.70 to $3.24 in one year. What is the ratio of the increase in price to the original price?

30. **Sports**   National Collegiate Athletic Association (NCAA) statistics show that for every 75,000 high school seniors playing basketball, about 2250 play college basketball as first-year students. Write the ratio of the number of first-year students playing college basketball to the number of high school seniors playing basketball.

31. **Sports**   NCAA statistics show that of about 3750 college seniors playing college basketball, about 45 will play as rookies in the National Basketball Association. Write the ratio of the number of National Basketball Association rookies to the number of college seniors playing basketball.

32. **Consumerism**   In a recent year, women spent $2 million on swimwear and purchased 92,000 swimsuits. During the same year, men spent $500,000 on swimwear and purchased 37,000 swimsuits. (*Source:* NPD Group) **a.** Find the ratio of the amount men spent on swimwear to the amount women spent on swimwear. **b.** Find the ratio of the amount men spent on swimwear to the total amount men and women spent on swimwear. Write the ratios as fractions in simplest form.

In the NEWS!

Grow a Mustache, Save a Life

Movember, a month-long mustache-growing event during November, raises money for the Prostate Cancer Foundation. Last year, 65,000 U.S. men took part in Movember, raising $7.5 million.

Source: The Sacramento Bee

Critical Thinking

33. Is the value of a ratio always less than 1? Explain.

Projects or Group Activities

34. Ratios can be extended to include more than two numbers. For instance, the ratio of the sides of the triangle at the right below can be written $3 : 4 : 5$. The study of the ratios of the sides of a triangle is part of a branch of mathematics called **trigonometry,** which has important applications to science and engineering. The Canadarm2 uses trigonometry in the design of its robotic system on the international space station.

   a. Are the sides of a triangle whose sides measure 18 inches, 24 inches, and 30 inches in the ratio $3 : 4 : 5$?
   b. Are the sides of a triangle whose sides measure 9 inches, 16 inches, and 25 inches in the ratio $3 : 4 : 5$?
   c. For the triangle at the right, find the ratio of Side B to Side A.
   d. For the triangle at the right, find the ratio of Side B to Side C.
   e. For the triangle at the right, find the ratio of Side A to Side C.

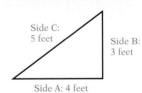

Side C: 5 feet

Side B: 3 feet

Side A: 4 feet

35. Get a large bag of M&Ms and find the ratio of the number of red, blue, green, yellow, and orange candies.

4.2 Rates

OBJECTIVE A · *To write rates*

Point of Interest

Listed below are rates at which various crimes are committed in our nation.

Crime	Every
Larceny	4 seconds
Burglary	14 seconds
Robbery	60 seconds
Rape	6 minutes
Murder	31 minutes

A **rate** is a comparison of two quantities that have *different* units. A rate is written as a fraction.

A distance runner ran 26 miles in 4 hours. The distance-to-time rate is written

$$\frac{26 \text{ miles}}{4 \text{ hours}} = \frac{13 \text{ miles}}{2 \text{ hours}}$$

Notice that the above rate is written in simplest form. Writing the **simplest form of a rate** means writing it so that the two numbers that form the rate have no common factor other than 1.

EXAMPLE 1

Write "6 roof supports for every 9 feet" as a rate in simplest form.

Solution

$$\frac{6 \text{ supports}}{9 \text{ feet}} = \frac{2 \text{ supports}}{3 \text{ feet}}$$

YOU TRY IT 1

Write "15 pounds of fertilizer for 12 trees" as a rate in simplest form.

Your solution

Solution on p. S11

OBJECTIVE B · *To write unit rates*

Point of Interest

According to a Gallup Poll, women see doctors more often than men do. On average, men visit the doctor 3.8 times per year, whereas women go to the doctor 5.8 times per year.

A **unit rate** is a rate in which the number in the denominator is 1.

$$\frac{\$3.25}{1 \text{ pound}}$$ or $3.25/pound is read "$3.25 per pound."

To find a unit rate, divide the number in the numerator of the rate by the number in the denominator of the rate.

APPLY THE CONCEPT ....

A car was driven 344 miles on 16 gallons of gasoline. How many miles did the car travel on 1 gallon of gasoline?

The rate that compares miles to gallons is $\frac{344 \text{ miles}}{16 \text{ gallons}}$.

To find the miles per gallon (the unit rate), divide the numerator (344 miles) by the denominator (16 gallons).

344 miles ÷ 16 gallons = 21.5 miles/gallon

The car traveled 21.5 miles per gallon of gasoline.

EXAMPLE 2

Write "300 feet in 8 seconds" as a unit rate.

Solution

$$\frac{300 \text{ feet}}{8 \text{ seconds}} \qquad 8\overline{)300.0} \; = 37.5$$

37.5 feet/second

YOU TRY IT 2

Write "260 miles in 8 hours" as a unit rate.

Your solution

Solution on p. S11

OBJECTIVE C *To solve application problems*

Denver Airport

Integrating Technology

To calculate the costs per mile using a calculator, perform four divisions:

683 ÷ 2475 =

536 ÷ 1464 =

525 ÷ 1302 =

483 ÷ 1050 =

In each case, round the number in the display to the nearest hundredth.

HOW TO 1 The table at the right shows miles flown and air fares for some routes in the continental United States. Determine the most expensive route and the least expensive route per mile.

Long Routes	Miles	Fare
New York–Los Angeles	2475	$683
San Francisco–Dallas	1464	$536
Denver–Pittsburgh	1302	$525
Minneapolis–Hartford	1050	$483

Strategy

Find the cost per mile for each route by dividing the fare by the miles flown. Compare the costs per mile to determine the most and least expensive routes.

Solution New York–Los Angeles $\qquad \frac{683}{2475} \approx 0.28$

San Francisco–Dallas $\qquad \frac{536}{1464} \approx 0.37$

Denver–Pittsburgh $\qquad \frac{525}{1302} \approx 0.40$

Minneapolis–Hartford $\qquad \frac{483}{1050} = 0.46$

$0.28 < 0.37 < 0.40 < 0.46$

The Minneapolis–Hartford route is the most expensive per mile, and the New York–Los Angeles route is the least expensive per mile.

EXAMPLE 3

A motorcycle racer completed a 6-mile lap in 0.05 hour (3 minutes). Find the racer's speed in miles per hour.

Strategy

To find the speed in miles per hour, divide the length of the lap (6 miles) by the time (0.05 hour).

Solution

$$\frac{6 \text{ miles}}{0.05 \text{ hour}} = 120 \text{ miles/hour}$$

The racer's speed was 120 miles/hour.

YOU TRY IT 3

A landscape technician purchased 40 feet of $\frac{3}{4}$-inch PVC pipe for $22.40. What is the per-foot cost of the pipe?

Your strategy

Your solution

Solution on p. S11

4.2 EXERCISES

✔ Concept Check

1. 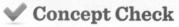 What is the difference between a ratio and a rate?

2. How is a unit rate calculated?

OBJECTIVE A   *To write rates*

For Exercises 3 to 10, write each phrase as a rate in simplest form.

3. 3 pounds of meat for 4 people

4. 30 ounces in 24 glasses

5. $80 for 12 boards

6. 84 cents for 3 candy bars

7. 300 miles on 15 gallons

8. 88 feet in 8 seconds

9. 16 gallons in 2 hours

10. 25 ounces in 5 minutes

11. If the rate at which water flows through a nozzle is given in gallons per minute, how do you find the rate in gallons per second?

OBJECTIVE B   *To write unit rates*

For Exercises 12 to 14, complete the unit rate.

12. 5 miles in ___ hour

13. 15 feet in ___ second

14. 5 grams of fat in ___ serving

For Exercises 15 to 24, write each phrase as a unit rate.

15. 10 feet in 4 seconds

16. 816 miles in 6 days

17. $3900 earned in 4 weeks

18. $51,000 earned in 12 months

19. 1100 trees planted on 10 acres

20. 3750 words on 15 pages

21. $131.88 earned in 7 hours

22. 628.8 miles in 12 hours

23. 409.4 miles on 11.5 gallons of gasoline

24. $11.05 for 3.4 pounds

25. Fuel Efficiency   A hybrid electric vehicle used 15 gallons of gasoline to travel 639 miles. How many miles per gallon did the car get?

26. Audio Technology   An audio-visual technician spent 2 hours preparing a surround sound recommendation for a homeowner. If the technician charged $99 for this service, what is the technician's hourly wage?

OBJECTIVE C   *To solve application problems*

Miles per Dollar   One measure of how expensive it is to drive your car is calculated as miles per dollar, which is the number of miles you drive on 1 dollar's worth of gasoline. Use this information for Exercises 27 and 28.

27. Suppose you get 26 miles per gallon of gasoline and gasoline costs $3.49 per gallon. Calculate your miles per dollar. Round to the nearest tenth.

28. Suppose you get 23 miles per gallon of gasoline and gasoline costs $3.15 per gallon. It costs you $44.10 to fill the tank. Calculate your miles per dollar. Round to the nearest tenth.

29. Bike Sharing   Use the information in the news clipping at the right. Find the average number of rides per day during the Hubway program's first month. Round to the nearest whole number of rides per day.

In the NEWS!

Hubway's First Month a Success

In recent years, bike sharing programs have been rolled out in cities across the United States and around the world. In its first 30 days of operation, Boston's Hubway program saw its bicycles used for 36,612 rides.

Source: boston.com

30. Construction   An architect designed a house that contains 1850 square feet. A home builder estimates that it will cost $172,050 to build the house. What is the estimated cost per square foot to build the house?

31. ● **Advertising**   The advertising fee for a 30-second spot for the 2011 Super Bowl was approximately $3 million. If 106 million viewers watched the Super Bowl, what is the advertiser's cost per viewer for a 30-second ad? Round to the nearest cent. (*Source:* money.cnn.com)

32. Air Flow A tire containing 732 cubic inches of air is punctured and begins a slow leak. After 4 hours, the tire is flat and there are 36 cubic inches of air remaining in the tire. What is the rate, in cubic feet per minute, at which air escaped from the tire?

33. Gas Pump A quality control inspector needs to measure the flow rate of a gasoline pump. The inspector pumps 10 gallons of gas into a container in 50 seconds. What is the rate, in gallons per minute, at which the pump dispenses gas?

● **Exchange Rates** One application of rates is in the area of international trade. Suppose a company in Canada purchases a shipment of sneakers from an American company. The Canadian company must exchange Canadian dollars for U.S. dollars in order to pay for the order. The number of Canadian dollars that are equivalent to 1 U.S. dollar is called the **exchange rate.** The table at the right below shows the exchange rates per U.S. dollar for three foreign countries and for the euro at the time of this writing. Use this table for Exercises 34 to 36.

34. How many euros would be paid for an order of American computer hardware costing $120,000?

Exchange Rates per U.S. Dollar	
Russian Ruble	30.4006
Brazilian Real	1.9831
Japanese Yen	79.8700
Euro	0.7788

35. Calculate the cost, in Japanese yen, of an American car costing $34,000.

36. 🖎 What does the quantity 1.9831 × 2500 represent?

37. ● **Demography** The table below shows the population and area of three countries. The population density of a country is the number of people per square mile.

Country	Population	Area (in square miles)
Australia	21,767,000	2,968,000
India	1,189,173,000	1,269,000
United States	311,051,000	3,619,000

a. Which country has the least population density?
b. How many more people per square mile are there in India than in the United States? Round to the nearest whole number.

Critical Thinking

38. Compensation You have a choice of receiving a wage of $34,000 per year, $2840 per month, $650 per week, or $18 per hour. Which pay choice would you take? Assume a 40-hour work week with 52 weeks of work per year.

39. ◼ The price–earnings ratio of a company's stock is one measure used by stock market analysts to assess the financial well-being of the company. Explain the meaning of the price–earnings ratio.

Projects or Group Activities

Other Bases for Rates   Some unit rates are so small that they are difficult to read, so a base other than 1 is used. Some common bases are 1000, 100,000, 1,000,000, and 1,000,000,000. For instance, a smog test on a car may be reported as 650 parts per million, abbreviated 650 ppm. This means that there are 650 smog molecules (such as nitrogen dioxide or carbon monoxide) per million molecules of exhaust. This rate is easier to understand than a unit rate of $\frac{650}{1,000,000} = 0.00065$ smog molecule per 1 molecule of exhaust.

40. ● Infant mortality rates are reported in deaths per 1000 live births. Work through the following steps to find the infant mortality rate in the United States for a recent year, given that there were 4,316,000 live births and 29,000 deaths.
    a. Divide the number of deaths by the number of live births.
    b. Multiply the answer by 1000. Round to the nearest tenth. This is the infant mortality rate per thousand.

41. The Environmental Projection Agency (EPA) has started using a new statistic on EPA fuel economy stickers—gallons of gas used per 100 miles driven. To find the number of gallons used per 100 miles, divide 100 by the car's miles-per-gallon (mpg) rating. What is the number of gallons per 100 miles for a car that has a rating of 28 mpg? Round to the nearest tenth.

42. The maximum amount of arsenic that is allowed in safe drinking water is 0.010 ppm. What is this amount in parts per billion (ppb)?

43. A safe level of beryllium in drinking water is set at 4 ppb. What is this amount in parts per million (ppm)?

✔ CHECK YOUR PROGRESS: CHAPTER 4

For Exercises 1 to 3, write the ratio in simplest form using a fraction and a colon.

1. 12 minutes to 48 minutes
2. 24 pounds to 36 pounds
3. 25 miles to 60 miles

For Exercises 4 to 6, write the rate as a unit rate. Round to the nearest tenth.

4. $96 in 4 hours
5. 100 yards in 9.6 seconds
6. 525 miles on 18 gallons of gasoline

7. **Lawn Care**   A fertilizer manufacturer recommends using 10 gallons of liquid fertilizer for every 400 square feet of lawn. What is the recommended amount of fertilizer per square foot of lawn?

8. **Nutrition**   There are 150 calories in an 8-ounce glass of whole milk. What is the number of calories per ounce in whole milk?

9. **Consumerism**   One dozen long-stemmed roses cost $51. What is the cost per rose?

10. **Consumerism**   A certain cyan print cartridge will print 2000 pages before it needs to be replaced. If the cost of the cartridge is $85, what is the cost per page for this cartridge?

SECTION

4.3 | Proportions

OBJECTIVE A   *To determine whether a proportion is true*

 Point of Interest

Proportions were studied by the earliest mathematicians. Clay tablets uncovered by archaeologists show evidence of proportions in Egyptian and Babylonian cultures dating from 1800 B.C.

A **proportion** is an expression of the equality of two ratios or rates.

$$\frac{50 \text{ miles}}{4 \text{ gallons}} = \frac{25 \text{ miles}}{2 \text{ gallons}}$$ Note that the units of the numerators are the same and the units of the denominators are the same.

$$\frac{3}{6} = \frac{1}{2}$$ This is the equality of two ratios.

A proportion is **true** if the fractions are equal when written in simplest form.
In any true proportion, the **cross products** are equal.

HOW TO 1   Is $\frac{2}{3} = \frac{8}{12}$ a true proportion?

$$\frac{2}{3} \diagup\hspace{-0.5em}\diagdown \frac{8}{12}$$ $3 \times 8 = 24$ The cross products *are* equal.
    $2 \times 12 = 24$ $\frac{2}{3} = \frac{8}{12}$ is a true proportion.

A proportion is **not true** if the fractions are not equal when reduced to simplest form.

If the cross products are not equal, then the proportion is not true.

HOW TO 2   Is $\frac{4}{5} = \frac{8}{9}$ a true proportion?

$$\frac{4}{5} \diagup\hspace{-0.5em}\diagdown \frac{8}{9}$$ $5 \times 8 = 40$ The cross products *are not* equal.
    $4 \times 9 = 36$ $\frac{4}{5} = \frac{8}{9}$ is not a true proportion.

EXAMPLE 1

Is $\frac{5}{8} = \frac{10}{16}$ a true proportion?

Solution

$$\frac{5}{8} \diagup\hspace{-0.5em}\diagdown \frac{10}{16}$$ $8 \times 10 = 80$
    $5 \times 16 = 80$

The cross products are equal.
The proportion is true.

YOU TRY IT 1

Is $\frac{6}{10} = \frac{9}{15}$ a true proportion?

Your solution

EXAMPLE 2

Is $\frac{62 \text{ miles}}{4 \text{ gallons}} = \frac{33 \text{ miles}}{2 \text{ gallons}}$ a true proportion?

Solution

$$\frac{62}{4} \diagup\hspace{-0.5em}\diagdown \frac{33}{2}$$ $4 \times 33 = 132$
    $62 \times 2 = 124$

The cross products are not equal.
The proportion is not true.

YOU TRY IT 2

Is $\frac{\$32}{6 \text{ hours}} = \frac{\$90}{8 \text{ hours}}$ a true proportion?

Your solution

Solutions on p. S11

OBJECTIVE B   *To solve proportions*

Tips for Success
An important element of success is practice. We cannot do anything well if we do not practice it repeatedly. Practice is crucial to success in mathematics. In this objective you are learning a new skill: how to solve a proportion. You will need to practice this skill over and over again in order to be successful at it.

Sometimes one of the numbers in a proportion is unknown. In this case, it is necessary to *solve* the proportion.

To **solve a proportion,** find a number to replace the unknown so that the proportion is true.

HOW TO 3   Solve: $\dfrac{9}{6} = \dfrac{3}{n}$

$$\dfrac{9}{6} = \dfrac{3}{n}$$

$9 \times n = 6 \times 3$ • Find the cross products.

$9 \times n = 18$

$n = 18 \div 9$ • Think of $9 \times n = 18$ as $9)\overline{18}$.

$n = 2$

Check:

$\dfrac{9}{6} \quad \rightarrow 3 \rightarrow 6 \times 3 = 18$

$\qquad\quad 2 \rightarrow 9 \times 2 = 18$

EXAMPLE 3

Solve $\dfrac{n}{12} = \dfrac{25}{60}$ and check.

Solution

$n \times 60 = 12 \times 25$ • Find the cross

$n \times 60 = 300$ products. Then

$\quad n = 300 \div 60$ solve for n.

$\quad n = 5$

Check:

$\dfrac{5}{12} \quad \rightarrow 25 \rightarrow 12 \times 25 = 300$

$\qquad\quad 60 \rightarrow 5 \times 60 = 300$

YOU TRY IT 3

Solve $\dfrac{n}{14} = \dfrac{3}{7}$ and check.

Your solution

EXAMPLE 4

Solve $\dfrac{4}{9} = \dfrac{n}{16}$. Round to the nearest tenth.

Solution

$4 \times 16 = 9 \times n$ • Find the cross

$\quad 64 = 9 \times n$ products. Then

$64 \div 9 = n$ solve for n.

$\quad 7.1 \approx n$

Note: A rounded answer is an approximation.
Therefore, the answer to a check will not be exact.

YOU TRY IT 4

Solve $\dfrac{5}{7} = \dfrac{n}{20}$. Round to the nearest tenth.

Your solution

Solutions on pp. S11–S12

EXAMPLE 5

Solve $\frac{28}{52} = \frac{7}{n}$ and check.

Solution

$28 \times n = 52 \times 7$ • Find the cross
$28 \times n = 364$ products. Then
       $n = 364 \div 28$ solve for n.
       $n = 13$

Check:

$$\frac{28}{52} \quad\diagdown\!\!\!\!\diagup\quad \frac{7}{13} \quad \begin{array}{l} 52 \times 7 = 364 \\ 28 \times 13 = 364 \end{array}$$

YOU TRY IT 5

Solve $\frac{15}{20} = \frac{12}{n}$ and check.

Your solution

EXAMPLE 6

Solve $\frac{15}{n} = \frac{8}{3}$. Round to the nearest hundredth.

Solution

$15 \times 3 = n \times 8$
$\quad\quad 45 = n \times 8$
$45 \div 8 = n$
$\quad 5.63 \approx n$

YOU TRY IT 6

Solve $\frac{12}{n} = \frac{7}{4}$. Round to the nearest hundredth.

Your solution

EXAMPLE 7

Solve $\frac{n}{9} = \frac{3}{1}$ and check.

Solution

$n \times 1 = 9 \times 3$
$n \times 1 = 27$
$\quad\quad n = 27 \div 1$
$\quad\quad n = 27$

Check:

$$\frac{27}{9} \quad\diagdown\!\!\!\!\diagup\quad \frac{3}{1} \quad \begin{array}{l} 9 \times 3 = 27 \\ 27 \times 1 = 27 \end{array}$$

YOU TRY IT 7

Solve $\frac{n}{12} = \frac{4}{1}$ and check.

Your solution

Solutions on p. S12

OBJECTIVE C   *To solve application problems*

The application problems in this objective require you to write and solve a proportion. When setting up a proportion, remember to keep the same units in the numerators and the same units in the denominators.

EXAMPLE 8

The dosage of a certain medication is 2 ounces for every 50 pounds of body weight. How many ounces of this medication are required for a person who weighs 175 pounds?

Strategy

To find the number of ounces of medication for a person weighing 175 pounds, write and solve a proportion using n to represent the number of ounces of medication for a 175-pound person.

Solution

$$\frac{2 \text{ ounces}}{50 \text{ pounds}} = \frac{n \text{ ounces}}{175 \text{ pounds}}$$

• The unit "ounces" is in the numerator. The unit "pounds" is in the denominator.

$$2 \times 175 = 50 \times n$$
$$350 = 50 \times n$$
$$350 \div 50 = n$$
$$7 = n$$

A 175-pound person requires 7 ounces of medication.

YOU TRY IT 8

Three tablespoons of a liquid plant fertilizer are to be added to every 4 gallons of water. How many tablespoons of fertilizer are required for 10 gallons of water?

Your strategy

Your solution

EXAMPLE 9

A mason determines that 9 cement blocks are required for a retaining wall that is 2 feet long. At this rate, how many cement blocks are required for a retaining wall that is 24 feet long?

Strategy

To find the number of cement blocks required for a retaining wall that is 24 feet long, write and solve a proportion using n to represent the number of blocks required.

Solution

$$\frac{9 \text{ cement blocks}}{2 \text{ feet}} = \frac{n \text{ cement blocks}}{24 \text{ feet}}$$

$$9 \times 24 = 2 \times n$$
$$216 = 2 \times n$$
$$216 \div 2 = n$$
$$108 = n$$

A 24-foot retaining wall requires 108 cement blocks.

YOU TRY IT 9

Twenty-four jars can be packed in 6 identical boxes. At this rate, how many jars can be packed in 15 boxes?

Your strategy

Your solution

Solutions on p. S12

4.3 EXERCISES

✔ Concept Check

Solving a proportion requires rewriting a multiplication problem as a division problem. For instance, the multiplication problem $7 \times 9 = 63$ has the related division problems $63 \div 9 = 7$ and $63 \div 7 = 9$. For Exercises 1 to 4, rewrite the given multiplication problem as a division problem whose quotient is n.

1. $n \times 15 = 45$ **2.** $12 \times n = 60$ **3.** $72 = n \times 9$ **4.** $54 = 6 \times n$

OBJECTIVE A   *To determine whether a proportion is true*

For Exercises 5 to 22, determine whether the proportion is true or not true.

5. $\dfrac{4}{8} = \dfrac{10}{20}$ **6.** $\dfrac{39}{48} = \dfrac{13}{16}$ **7.** $\dfrac{7}{8} = \dfrac{11}{12}$ **8.** $\dfrac{15}{7} = \dfrac{17}{8}$

9. $\dfrac{27}{8} = \dfrac{9}{4}$ **10.** $\dfrac{3}{18} = \dfrac{4}{19}$ **11.** $\dfrac{45}{135} = \dfrac{3}{9}$ **12.** $\dfrac{3}{4} = \dfrac{54}{72}$

13. $\dfrac{50 \text{ miles}}{2 \text{ gallons}} = \dfrac{25 \text{ miles}}{1 \text{ gallon}}$ **14.** $\dfrac{16 \text{ feet}}{10 \text{ seconds}} = \dfrac{24 \text{ feet}}{15 \text{ seconds}}$

15. $\dfrac{6 \text{ minutes}}{5 \text{ cents}} = \dfrac{30 \text{ minutes}}{25 \text{ cents}}$ **16.** $\dfrac{16 \text{ pounds}}{12 \text{ days}} = \dfrac{20 \text{ pounds}}{14 \text{ days}}$

17. $\dfrac{\$15}{4 \text{ pounds}} = \dfrac{\$45}{12 \text{ pounds}}$ **18.** $\dfrac{270 \text{ trees}}{6 \text{ acres}} = \dfrac{90 \text{ trees}}{2 \text{ acres}}$

19. $\dfrac{300 \text{ feet}}{4 \text{ rolls}} = \dfrac{450 \text{ feet}}{7 \text{ rolls}}$ **20.** $\dfrac{1 \text{ gallon}}{4 \text{ quarts}} = \dfrac{7 \text{ gallons}}{28 \text{ quarts}}$

21. $\dfrac{\$65}{5 \text{ days}} = \dfrac{\$26}{2 \text{ days}}$ **22.** $\dfrac{80 \text{ miles}}{2 \text{ hours}} = \dfrac{110 \text{ miles}}{3 \text{ hours}}$

23. 🔧 Suppose in a true proportion you switch the numerator of the first fraction with the denominator of the second fraction. Must the result be another true proportion?

24. 🔧 Write a true proportion in which the cross products are equal to 36.

OBJECTIVE B   *To solve proportions*

25. 🔖 Consider the proportion $\frac{n}{7} = \frac{9}{21}$ in Exercise 27. The simplest form of the ratio $\frac{9}{21}$ is $\frac{3}{7}$. Will solving the proportion $\frac{n}{7} = \frac{3}{7}$ give the same result for n as found in Exercise 27?

For Exercises 26 to 45, solve. Round to the nearest hundredth, if necessary.

26. $\frac{n}{4} = \frac{6}{8}$

27. $\frac{n}{7} = \frac{9}{21}$

28. $\frac{12}{18} = \frac{n}{9}$

29. $\frac{7}{21} = \frac{35}{n}$

30. $\frac{6}{n} = \frac{24}{36}$

31. $\frac{3}{n} = \frac{15}{10}$

32. $\frac{n}{6} = \frac{2}{3}$

33. $\frac{5}{12} = \frac{n}{144}$

34. $\frac{n}{5} = \frac{7}{8}$

35. $\frac{4}{n} = \frac{9}{5}$

36. $\frac{5}{12} = \frac{n}{8}$

37. $\frac{36}{20} = \frac{12}{n}$

38. $\frac{n}{15} = \frac{21}{12}$

39. $\frac{40}{n} = \frac{15}{8}$

40. $\frac{28}{8} = \frac{12}{n}$

41. $\frac{n}{30} = \frac{65}{120}$

42. $\frac{0.3}{5.6} = \frac{n}{25}$

43. $\frac{1.3}{16} = \frac{n}{30}$

44. $\frac{0.7}{9.8} = \frac{3.6}{n}$

45. $\frac{1.9}{7} = \frac{13}{n}$

OBJECTIVE C   *To solve application problems*

46. 🔖 Jesse walked 3 miles in 40 minutes. Let n be the number of miles Jesse can walk in 60 minutes at the same rate. To determine how many miles Jesse can walk in 60 minutes, a student used the proportion $\frac{40}{3} = \frac{60}{n}$. Is this a valid proportion to use in solving this problem?

47. Nutrition A 6-ounce package of Puffed Wheat contains 600 calories. How many calories are contained in a 0.5-ounce serving of the cereal?

48. ⬤ **Health** Using the information in the news clipping at the right and a figure of 309 million for the number of Americans, determine the number of **a.** overweight Americans and **b.** obese Americans.

49. Fuel Efficiency A car travels 70.5 miles on 3 gallons of gas. Find the distance the car can travel on 14 gallons of gas.

In the NEWS!

Small Gains in Obesity Battle

A recent study shows a small but encouraging increase in the number of Americans of normal weight. Still, obesity remains a major health problem in the United States, with approximately 1 in 3 Americans falling in the overweight category, and 1 in 4 in the obese category.

Source: msnbc.com

50. Landscaping Ron Stokes uses 2 pounds of fertilizer for every 100 square feet of lawn for landscape maintenance. At this rate, how many pounds of fertilizer did he use on a lawn that measures 3500 square feet?

51. Gardening A nursery prepares a liquid plant food by adding 1 gallon of water for each 2 ounces of plant food. At this rate, how many gallons of water are required for 25 ounces of plant food?

52. Masonry A brick wall 20 feet in length contains 1040 bricks. At the same rate, how many bricks would it take to build a wall 48 feet in length?

53. Cartography The scale on the map at the right is "1.25 inches equals 10 miles." Find the distance between Carlsbad and Del Mar, which are 2 inches apart on the map.

54. Architecture The scale on the plans for a new house is "1 inch equals 3 feet." Find the width and the length of a room that measures 5 inches by 8 inches on the drawing.

55. Medicine The dosage for a medication is $\frac{1}{3}$ ounce for every 40 pounds of body weight. At this rate, how many ounces of medication should a physician prescribe for a patient who weighs 150 pounds? Write the answer as a decimal.

56. Banking A bank requires a monthly payment of $33.45 on a $2500 loan. At the same rate, find the monthly payment on a $10,000 loan.

57. Elections A pre-election survey showed that 2 out of every 3 eligible voters would cast ballots in the county election. At this rate, how many people in a county of 240,000 eligible voters would vote in the election?

58. Interior Design A paint manufacturer suggests using 1 gallon of paint for every 400 square feet of wall. At this rate, how many gallons of paint would be required for a room that has 1400 square feet of wall?

59. Insurance A 60-year-old male can obtain $10,000 of life insurance for $35.35 per month. At this rate, what is the monthly cost for $50,000 of life insurance?

60. ⬤ Food Waste At the rate given in the news clipping, find the cost of food wasted yearly by **a.** the average family of three and **b.** the average family of five.

61. Manufacturing Suppose a computer chip manufacturer knows that in an average production run of 2000 circuit boards, 60 will be defective. How many defective circuit boards are expected in a run of 25,000 circuit boards?

62. Investments You own 240 shares of stock in a computer company. The company declares a stock split of 5 shares for every 3 owned. How many shares of stock will you own after the stock split?

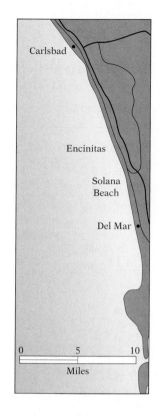

Carlsbad

Encinitas

Solana
Beach

Del Mar

0   5   10
Miles

© tom carter/Alamy

In the NEWS!

How Much Food Do You Waste?

In the United States, the estimated cost of food wasted each year by the average family of four is $590.
Source: University of Arizona

63. ● **Physics** The ratio of weight on the moon to weight on Earth is 1:6. If a bowling ball weighs 16 pounds on Earth, what would it weigh on the moon? Round to the nearest hundredth of a pound.

Michael Dunning/Getty Images

64. **Automobiles** When engineers designed a new car, they first built a model of the car. The ratio of the size of a part on the model to the actual size of the part is 2:5. If a door is 1.3 feet long on the model, what is the length of the door on the car?

65. **Investments** Carlos Capasso owns 50 shares of Texas Utilities that pay dividends of $153. At this rate, what dividend would Carlos receive after buying 300 additional shares of Texas Utilities?

Critical Thinking

66. ◪ ● **Gaming** Use the information in the news clipping at the right. Explain how a proportion can be used to determine the number of Nintendo DS systems sold given the number of Nintendo 3DS systems sold.

> ## In the NEWS!
>
> ### Old DS Outsells New 3D System
> Figures released for the month of June show that the Nintendo DS handheld game system outsold the newer Nintendo 3DS by 2.7 systems to 1.
> *Source:* msnbc.com

67. ◪ ● **Social Security** According to the Social Security Administration, the numbers of workers per retiree in the future are expected to be as given in the table below.
Why is the shrinking number of workers per retiree of importance to the Social Security Administration?

Year	2020	2030	2040
Number of workers per retiree	2.5	2.1	2.0

68. ◪ **Elections** A survey of voters in a city claimed that 2 people of every 5 who voted cast a ballot in favor of city amendment A and that 3 people of every 4 who voted cast a ballot against amendment A. Is this possible? Explain your answer.

Projects or Group Activities

69. **Anatomy** The average circumference (the distance around an object) of a baby's head at birth is approximately 13.7 inches. The average length of a baby at birth is approximately 20 inches. Measure the circumference of your head and your height in inches. Is the ratio of a baby's head circumference at birth to your head circumference equal to the ratio of a baby's length at birth to your height? Based on your findings, does the circumference of a person's head grow more slowly or more quickly than the person's height?

70. **Biology** One way biologists measure a wildlife population is by capturing a certain species of animal, tagging it, and then releasing it back into the wild. Suppose a biologist captures 100 trout from a lake, tags them, and releases them back into the water. One month later, the biologist captures 50 trout from the same lake and finds that 3 trout have tags. Based on this information, approximate the number of trout in the lake.

CHAPTER

4 Summary

Key Words

A **ratio** is the comparison of two quantities with the same units. A ratio can be written in three ways: as a fraction, as two numbers separated by a colon (:), or as two numbers separated by the word *to*. A ratio is in **simplest form** when the two numbers do not have a common factor other than 1. [4.1A, p. 178]

A **rate** is the comparison of two quantities with different units. A rate is written as a fraction. A rate is in **simplest form** when the numbers that form the rate do not have a common factor other than 1. [4.2A, p. 182]

A **unit rate** is a rate in which the number in the denominator is 1. [4.2B, p. 182]

A **proportion** is an expression of the equality of two ratios or rates. A proportion is true if the fractions are equal when written in simplest form; in any true proportion, the **cross products** are equal. A proportion is not true if the fractions are not equal when written in simplest form; if the cross products are not equal, the proportion is not true. [4.3A, p. 188]

Examples

The comparison 16 to 24 ounces can be written as a ratio in simplest form as $\frac{2}{3}$, 2 : 3, or 2 to 3.

You earned \$63 for working 6 hours. The rate is written in simplest form as $\frac{\$21}{2 \text{ hours}}$.

You traveled 144 miles in 3 hours. The unit rate is 48 miles per hour.

The proportion $\frac{3}{5} = \frac{12}{20}$ is true because the cross products are equal:
$3 \times 20 = 5 \times 12$.
The proportion $\frac{3}{4} = \frac{12}{20}$ is not true because the cross products are not equal:
$3 \times 20 \neq 4 \times 12$.

Essential Rules and Procedures

To find a unit rate, divide the number in the numerator of the rate by the number in the denominator of the rate. [4.2B, p. 182]

To solve a proportion, find a number to replace the unknown so that the proportion is true. [4.3B, p. 189]

To set up a proportion, keep the same units in the numerators and the same units in the denominators. [4.3C, p. 190]

Examples

You earned \$41 for working 4 hours.
$$\frac{41}{4} = 41 \div 4 = 10.25$$
The unit rate is \$10.25/hour.

$$\frac{6}{24} = \frac{9}{n}$$
$6 \times n = 24 \times 9$ • **Find the cross products.**

$6 \times n = 216$
$n = 216 \div 6$
$n = 36$

Three machines fill 5 cereal boxes per minute. How many boxes can 8 machines fill per minute?
$$\frac{3 \text{ machines}}{5 \text{ cereal boxes}} = \frac{8 \text{ machines}}{n \text{ cereal boxes}}$$

CHAPTER

4 | Review Exercises

1. Is $\frac{2}{9} = \frac{10}{45}$ a true proportion?

2. Write the comparison 32 dollars to 80 dollars as a ratio in simplest form using a fraction, a colon (:), and the word *to*.

3. Write "250 miles in 4 hours" as a unit rate.

4. Is $\frac{8}{15} = \frac{32}{60}$ a true proportion?

5. Solve the proportion.

$$\frac{16}{n} = \frac{4}{17}$$

6. Write "$500 earned in 40 hours" as a unit rate.

7. Write "$8.75 for 5 pounds" as a unit rate.

8. Write the comparison 8 feet to 28 feet as a ratio in simplest form using a fraction, a colon (:), and the word *to*.

9. Solve the proportion.

$$\frac{n}{8} = \frac{9}{2}$$

10. Solve the proportion. Round to the nearest hundredth.

$$\frac{18}{35} = \frac{10}{n}$$

11. Write the comparison 6 inches to 15 inches as a ratio in simplest form using a fraction, a colon (:), and the word *to*.

12. Is $\frac{3}{8} = \frac{10}{24}$ a true proportion?

13. Write "$35 in 4 hours" as a rate in simplest form.

14. Write "326.4 miles on 12 gallons" as a unit rate.

15. Write the comparison 12 days to 12 days as a ratio in simplest form using a fraction, a colon (:), and the word *to*.

16. Is $\frac{5}{7} = \frac{25}{35}$ a true proportion?

17. Solve the proportion. Round to the nearest hundredth.

$$\frac{24}{11} = \frac{n}{30}$$

18. Write "100 miles in 3 hours" as a rate in simplest form.

19. Business   In 5 years, the price of a calculator went from $80 to $48. What is the ratio, as a fraction in simplest form, of the decrease in price to the original price?

20. Taxes   The property tax on a $245,000 home is $4900. At the same rate, what is the property tax on a home valued at $320,000?

21. Consumerism   Rita Sterling bought a computer system for $2400. Five years later, she sold the computer for $900. Find the ratio of the amount she received for the computer to the cost of the computer.

22. Manufacturing   The total cost of manufacturing 1000 camera phones was $36,600. Of the phones made, 24 did not pass inspection. What is the cost per phone of the phones that *did* pass inspection?

23. Masonry   A brick wall 40 feet in length contains 448 concrete blocks. At the same rate, how many blocks would it take to build a wall that is 120 feet in length?

24. Advertising   A retail computer store spends $30,000 a year on radio advertising and $12,000 on newspaper advertising. Find the ratio, as a fraction in simplest form, of radio advertising to newspaper advertising.

25. Consumerism   A 15-pound turkey costs $13.95. What is the cost per pound?

26. Travel   Mahesh drove 198.8 miles in 3.5 hours. Find the average number of miles he drove per hour.

27. Insurance   An insurance policy costs $9.87 for every $1000 of insurance. At this rate, what is the cost of $50,000 of insurance?

28. Investments   Pascal Hollis purchased 80 shares of stock for $3580. What was the cost per share?

29. Landscaping   Monique uses 1.5 pounds of fertilizer for every 200 square feet of lawn. How many pounds of fertilizer will she have to use on a lawn that measures 3000 square feet?

30. Real Estate   A house had an original value of $160,000, but its value increased to $240,000 in 2 years. Find the ratio, as a fraction in simplest form, of the increase to the original value.

CHAPTER

4   TEST

1. Write "$46,036.80 earned in 12 months" as a unit rate.

2. Write the comparison 40 miles to 240 miles as a ratio in simplest form using a fraction, a colon (:), and the word *to*.

3. Write "18 supports for every 8 feet" as a rate in simplest form.

4. Is $\frac{40}{125} = \frac{5}{25}$ a true proportion?

5. Write the comparison 12 days to 4 days as a ratio in simplest form using a fraction, a colon (:), and the word *to*.

6. Solve the proportion.
$$\frac{5}{12} = \frac{60}{n}$$

7. Write "256.2 miles on 8.4 gallons of gas" as a unit rate.

8. Write the comparison 27 dollars to 81 dollars as a ratio in simplest form using a fraction, a colon (:), and the word *to*.

9. Is $\frac{5}{14} = \frac{25}{70}$ a true proportion?

10. Solve the proportion.
$$\frac{n}{18} = \frac{9}{4}$$

11. Write "9 feet for 6 boards" as a rate in simplest form.

12. Write the comparison 18 feet to 30 feet as a ratio in simplest form using a fraction, a colon (:), and the word *to*.

13. **Investments** Fifty shares of a utility stock pay a dividend of $62.50. At the same rate, what is the dividend paid on 500 shares of the utility stock?

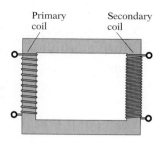

Primary coil   Secondary coil

14. **Electricity** A transformer has 40 turns in the primary coil and 480 turns in the secondary coil. State the ratio of the number of turns in the primary coil to the number of turns in the secondary coil.

15. **Travel** A plane travels 2421 miles in 4.5 hours. Find the plane's speed in miles per hour.

16. **Physiology** A research scientist estimates that the human body contains 88 pounds of water for every 100 pounds of body weight. At this rate, estimate the number of pounds of water in a college student who weighs 150 pounds.

17. **Business** If 40 feet of lumber costs $69.20, what is the per-foot cost of the lumber?

18. **Medicine** The dosage of a certain medication is $\frac{1}{4}$ ounce for every 50 pounds of body weight. How many ounces of this medication are required for a person who weighs 175 pounds? Write the answer as a decimal.

19. **Sports** A basketball team won 20 games and lost 5 games during the season. Write, as a fraction in simplest form, the ratio of the number of games won to the total number of games played.

20. **Manufacturing** A computer manufacturer discovers through experience that an average of 3 defective hard drives are found in every 100 hard drives manufactured. How many defective hard drives are expected to be found in the production of 1200 hard drives?

Cumulative Review Exercises

1. Subtract: $\begin{array}{r} 20{,}095 \\ -\ 10{,}937 \\ \hline \end{array}$

2. Write $2 \cdot 2 \cdot 2 \cdot 2 \cdot 3 \cdot 3 \cdot 3$ in exponential notation.

3. Simplify: $4 - (5 - 2)^2 \div 3 + 2$

4. Find the prime factorization of 160.

5. Find the LCM of 9, 12, and 18.

6. Find the GCF of 28 and 42.

7. Write $\frac{40}{64}$ in simplest form.

8. Find $4\frac{7}{15}$ more than $3\frac{5}{6}$.

9. What is $4\frac{5}{9}$ less than $10\frac{1}{6}$?

10. Multiply: $\frac{11}{12} \times 3\frac{1}{11}$

11. Find the quotient of $3\frac{1}{3}$ and $\frac{5}{7}$.

12. Simplify: $\left(\frac{2}{5} + \frac{3}{4}\right) \div \frac{3}{2}$

13. Write 4.0709 in words.

14. Round 2.09762 to the nearest hundredth.

15. Divide: $8.09\overline{)16.0976}$
    Round to the nearest thousandth.

16. Convert 0.06 to a fraction.

17. Write the comparison 25 miles to 200 miles as a ratio in simplest form using a fraction.

18. Write "87 cents for 6 pencils" as a rate in simplest form.

19. Write "250.5 miles on 7.5 gallons of gas" as a unit rate.

20. Solve $\frac{40}{n} = \frac{160}{17}$.

21. Travel   A car traveled 457.6 miles in 8 hours. Find the car's speed in miles per hour.

22. Solve the proportion.
$$\frac{12}{5} = \frac{n}{15}$$

23. Banking   You had $1024 in your checking account. You then wrote checks for $192 and $88. What is your new checking account balance?

24. Finance   Malek Khatri buys a tractor for $32,360. A down payment of $5000 is required. The balance remaining is paid in 48 equal monthly installments. What is the monthly payment?

25. Homework Assignments   Yuko is assigned to read a book containing 175 pages. She reads $\frac{2}{5}$ of the book during Thanksgiving vacation. How many pages of the assignment remain to be read?

26. Real Estate   A building contractor bought $2\frac{1}{3}$ acres of land for $84,000. What was the cost of each acre?

27. Consumerism   Benjamin Eli bought a shirt for $45.58 and a tie for $19.18. He used a $100 bill to pay for the purchases. Find the amount of change.

28. Compensation   If you earn an annual salary of $41,619, what is your monthly salary?

29. Erosion   A soil conservationist estimates that a river bank is eroding at the rate of 3 inches every 6 months. At this rate, how many inches will be eroded in 50 months?

Iain Frazer/Shutterstock.com

30. Medicine   The dosage of a certain medication is $\frac{1}{2}$ ounce for every 50 pounds of body weight. How many ounces of this medication are required for a person who weighs 160 pounds? Write the answer as a decimal.

Percents

5

Focus on Success

Did you read Ask the Authors at the front of this text? If you did, then you know that the authors' advice is that you practice, practice, practice—and then practice some more. The more time you spend doing math outside of class, the more successful you will be in this course. (See Ask the Authors, page i, and Make the Commitment to Succeed, page AIM-3.)

© iStockphoto.com/Pete Saloutos

Prep Test

Are you ready to succeed in this chapter? Take the Prep Test below to find out if you are ready to learn the new material.

For Exercises 1 to 6, multiply or divide.

1. $19 \times \dfrac{1}{100}$

2. 23×0.01

3. 0.47×100

4. $0.06 \times 47{,}500$

5. $60 \div 0.015$

6. $8 \div \dfrac{1}{4}$

7. Multiply $\dfrac{5}{8} \times 100$. Write the answer as a decimal.

8. Write $\dfrac{200}{3}$ as a mixed number.

9. Divide $28 \div 16$. Write the answer as a decimal.

5.1 | Introduction to Percents

OBJECTIVE A | *To write a percent as a decimal or a fraction*

Percent means "parts of 100." In the figure at the right, there are 100 parts. Because 13 of the 100 parts are shaded, 13% of the figure is shaded. The symbol % is the **percent sign.**

In most applied problems involving percents, it is necessary either to rewrite a percent as a decimal or a fraction or to rewrite a fraction or a decimal as a percent.

To write a percent as a decimal, remove the percent sign and multiply by 0.01.

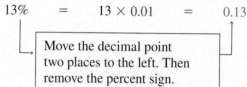

$$13\% \quad = \quad 13 \times 0.01 \quad = \quad 0.13$$

Move the decimal point two places to the left. Then remove the percent sign.

📋 **Take Note**

Recall that division is defined as multiplication by the reciprocal. Therefore, multiplying by $\frac{1}{100}$ is equivalent to dividing by 100.

To write a percent as a fraction, remove the percent sign and multiply by $\frac{1}{100}$.

$$13\% = 13 \times \frac{1}{100} = \frac{13}{100}$$

EXAMPLE 1

Write each percent as a decimal and as a fraction.
a. 120% **b.** 4.3% **c.** 0.45%

Solution

a. $120\% = 120 \times 0.01 = 1.2$

$$120\% = 120 \times \frac{1}{100} = \frac{120}{100} = 1\frac{1}{5}$$

b. $4.3\% = 4.3 \times 0.01 = 0.043$

$$4.3\% = 4.3 \times \frac{1}{100}$$
$$= 4\frac{3}{10} \times \frac{1}{100} \qquad \bullet \ 4.3 = 4\frac{3}{10}$$
$$= \frac{43}{10} \times \frac{1}{100} = \frac{43}{1000} \qquad \begin{array}{l}\bullet \ \textbf{Multiply the} \\ \textbf{fractions.}\end{array}$$

c. $0.45\% = 0.45 \times 0.01 = 0.0045$

$$0.45\% = 0.45 \times \frac{1}{100}$$
$$= \frac{9}{20} \times \frac{1}{100} \qquad \bullet \ 0.45 = \frac{45}{100} = \frac{9}{20}$$
$$= \frac{9}{2000} \qquad \begin{array}{l}\bullet \ \textbf{Multiply the} \\ \textbf{fractions.}\end{array}$$

YOU TRY IT 1

Write each percent as a decimal and as a fraction.
a. 125% **b.** 8.5% **c.** 0.25%

Your solution

Solution on p. S12

EXAMPLE 2

Write $16\frac{2}{3}\%$ as a fraction.

Solution

$$16\frac{2}{3}\% = 16\frac{2}{3} \times \frac{1}{100}$$

$$= \frac{50}{3} \times \frac{1}{100} = \frac{50}{300} = \frac{1}{6}$$

YOU TRY IT 2

Write $33\frac{1}{3}\%$ as a fraction.

Your solution

Solution on p. S12

OBJECTIVE B   *To write a decimal or a fraction as a percent*

A decimal or a fraction can be written as a percent by multiplying by 100%.

HOW TO 1   Write 0.37 as a percent.

$$0.37 \quad = \quad 0.37 \times 100\% \quad = \quad 37\%$$

Move the decimal point two places to the right. Then write the percent sign.

When changing a fraction to a percent, if the fraction can be written as a terminating decimal, the percent is written in decimal form. If the decimal representation of the fraction is a repeating decimal, the answer is written with a fraction.

Take Note

The decimal form of $\frac{3}{8}$ terminates.

```
      0.375
8) 3.000
     -2 4
        60
       -56
        40
       -40
         0
```

HOW TO 2   Write $\frac{3}{8}$ as a percent.

$$\frac{3}{8} = \frac{3}{8} \times \frac{100\%}{1}$$

$$= \frac{300\%}{8}$$

$$= 37.5\%$$

• $\frac{3}{8} = 0.375$ is a terminating decimal.

• The answer is written in decimal form.

Take Note

The decimal form of $\frac{1}{6}$ repeats.

```
      0.166‾
6) 1.000
     -6
      40
     -36
      40
     -36
       4
```

HOW TO 3   Write $\frac{1}{6}$ as a percent.

$$\frac{1}{6} = \frac{1}{6} \times \frac{100\%}{1}$$

$$= \frac{100\%}{6}$$

$$= 16\frac{2}{3}\%$$

• $\frac{1}{6} = 0.1\overline{6}$ is a repeating decimal.

• The answer is written with a fraction.

EXAMPLE 3

Write 0.015 and 2.3 as percents.

Solution

$0.015 = 0.015 \times 100\%$
$= 1.5\%$

$2.3 = 2.3 \times 100\%$
$= 230\%$

YOU TRY IT 3

Write 0.048 and 3.6 as percents.

Your solution

EXAMPLE 4

Write $\frac{19}{80}$ as a percent.

Solution

$\frac{19}{80} \times \frac{100\%}{1} = \frac{1900\%}{80}$
$= 23.75\%$ • Write the answer in decimal form.

YOU TRY IT 4

Write $\frac{5}{16}$ as a percent.

Your solution

EXAMPLE 5

Write $\frac{2}{3}$ as a percent.

Solution

$\frac{2}{3} = \frac{2}{3} \times \frac{100\%}{1}$
$= \frac{200\%}{3}$
$= 66\frac{2}{3}\%$ • Write the answer with a fraction.

YOU TRY IT 5

Write $\frac{5}{6}$ as a percent.

Your solution

5.1 EXERCISES

✔ Concept Check

1. Percent means "parts of ____."

2. If you answered correctly 85% of the questions on a 100-question exam, how many questions did you answer correctly?

3. To change a percent to a decimal, remove the percent sign and move the decimal point two places to the _____.

4. To change a fraction to a percent, multiply the fraction by _____.

OBJECTIVE A   *To write a percent as a decimal or a fraction*

For Exercises 5 to 26, write the percent as a decimal and as a fraction.

5. 72%

6. 65%

7. 23%

8. 79%

9. 36%

10. 69%

11. 59%

12. 24%

13. 41%

14. 25%

15. 25.4%

16. 34%

17. 57.9%

18. 73.6%

19. 6.2%

20. 6.9%

21. 6.4%

22. 7.5%

23. 0.25%

24. 0.875%

25. 0.55%

26. 0.74%

For Exercises 27 to 38, write as a fraction.

27. $66\frac{2}{3}\%$

28. $12\frac{1}{2}\%$

29. $83\frac{1}{3}\%$

30. $3\frac{1}{8}\%$

31. $11\frac{1}{9}\%$

32. $\frac{3}{8}\%$

33. $45\frac{5}{11}\%$

34. $15\frac{3}{8}\%$

35. $4\frac{2}{7}\%$

36. $5\frac{3}{4}\%$

37. $6\frac{2}{3}\%$

38. $8\frac{2}{3}\%$

39. 🖊 When a certain percent is written as a fraction, the result is an improper fraction. Is the percent less than, equal to, or greater than 100%?

OBJECTIVE B   *To write a decimal or a fraction as a percent*

For Exercises 40 to 51, write as a percent.

40. 0.16

41. 0.73

42. 0.05

43. 0.01

44. 1.07

45. 2.94

46. 0.004

47. 0.006

48. 1.012

49. 3.106

50. 0.8

51. 0.7

For Exercises 52 to 71, write as a percent.

52. $\dfrac{27}{50}$　　　**53.** $\dfrac{17}{20}$　　　**54.** $\dfrac{9}{16}$　　　**55.** $\dfrac{2}{5}$　　　**56.** $\dfrac{5}{8}$　　　**57.** $\dfrac{1}{8}$

58. $\dfrac{3}{40}$　　　**59.** $1\dfrac{1}{2}$　　　**60.** $\dfrac{7}{40}$　　　**61.** $\dfrac{9}{4}$　　　**62.** $\dfrac{16}{5}$　　　**63.** $\dfrac{7}{8}$

64. $\dfrac{15}{50}$　　　**65.** $\dfrac{12}{25}$　　　**66.** $\dfrac{7}{30}$　　　**67.** $\dfrac{4}{9}$

68. $\dfrac{7}{12}$　　　**69.** $1\dfrac{2}{3}$　　　**70.** $2\dfrac{1}{6}$　　　**71.** $\dfrac{7}{18}$

72. Does a mixed number represent a percent greater than 100% or less than 100%?

73. A decimal number less than 0 has zeros in the tenths and hundredths places. Does the decimal represent a percent greater than 1% or less than 1%?

74. Write the part of the square that is shaded as a fraction, as a decimal, and as a percent. Write the part of the square that is not shaded as a fraction, as a decimal, and as a percent.

Critical Thinking

75. ● **The Food Industry**   In a survey conducted by Opinion Research Corp. for Lloyd's Barbeque Co., people were asked to name their favorite barbeque side dishes. 38% named corn on the cob, 35% named cole slaw, 11% named corn bread, and 10% named fries. What percent of those surveyed named something other than corn on the cob, cole slaw, corn bread, or fries?

76. Elections   If $\frac{2}{5}$ of the population voted in an election, what percent of the population did not vote?

© iStockphoto.com/Jim Jurica

Projects or Group Activities

There is a quantity similar to percent ("per hundred") called *per mil*, which means *per thousand*. The symbol for per mil is ‰. Using this symbol, $7‰ = \dfrac{7}{1000} = 0.007$. For Exercises 77 to 80, write each per mil as a fraction in simplest form and as a decimal.

77. 53‰　　　**78.** 25‰　　　**79.** 150‰　　　**80.** 600‰

For Exercises 81 to 84, write each per mil as a percent.

81. 5‰　　　**82.** 45‰　　　**83.** 625‰　　　**84.** 1000‰

SECTION

5.2 | Percent Equations: Part I

OBJECTIVE A | *To find the amount when the percent and the base are given*

Problems involving percents frequently are solved using the basic percent equation.

The Basic Percent Equation
Percent $\times$ base $=$ amount

APPLY THE CONCEPT

A real estate broker receives a commission that is 4% of a $285,000 house sale. Find the amount the broker receives.

To find the amount the broker receives, we must answer the question, "4% of $285,000 is what?" This sentence can be written using mathematical symbols and then solved for the unknown number.

4%	of	$285,000	is	what?
$\downarrow$	$\downarrow$	$\downarrow$	$\downarrow$	$\downarrow$

Percent 4%	$\times$	base 285,000	$=$	amount n

of is written as $\times$ (times)
is is written as $=$ (equals)
what is written as n (the unknown number)

$$0.04 \times 285,000 = n$$
$$11,400 = n$$

Note that the percent is written as a decimal.

The broker receives a commission of $11,400.

When solving the basic percent equation, the percent is usually written as a decimal, as in the problem above. However, some percents are more easily written as a fraction than as a decimal. For example,

$$33\frac{1}{3}\% = \frac{1}{3} \qquad 66\frac{2}{3}\% = \frac{2}{3} \qquad 16\frac{2}{3}\% = \frac{1}{6} \qquad 83\frac{1}{3}\% = \frac{5}{6}$$

EXAMPLE 1

Find 5.7% of 160.

Solution

Percent $\times$ base $=$ amount
$0.057 \times 160 = n$
$9.12 = n$

• The word *Find* is used instead of the words *what is*.

YOU TRY IT 1

Find 6.3% of 150.

Your solution

EXAMPLE 2

What is $33\frac{1}{3}\%$ of 90?

Solution

Percent $\times$ base $=$ amount
$\frac{1}{3} \times 90 = n$
$30 = n$

• $33\frac{1}{3}\% = \frac{1}{3}$

YOU TRY IT 2

What is $16\frac{2}{3}\%$ of 66?

Your solution

Solutions on pp. S12–S13

OBJECTIVE B   *To solve application problems*

Solving percent problems requires identifying the three elements of the basic percent equation. Recall that these three parts are the *percent,* the *base,* and the *amount.* Usually the base follows the phrase "percent of."

During a recent year, Americans gave $291 billion to charities. The circle graph at the right shows where that money came from. Use these data for Example 3 and You Try It 3.

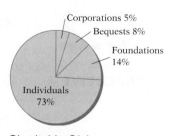

Corporations 5%
Bequests 8%
Foundations 14%
Individuals 73%

Charitable Giving
Sources: American Association of Fundraising Counsel; www.nps.gov

---

EXAMPLE 3

How much of the amount given to charities came from individuals?

Strategy

To determine the amount that came from individuals, write and solve the basic percent equation using n to represent the amount. The percent is 73%. The base is $291 billion.

Solution

Percent $\times$ base $=$ amount
$73\% \times 291 = n$
$0.73 \times 291 = n$
$212.43 = n$

Individuals gave $212.43 billion to charities.

YOU TRY IT 3

How much of the amount given to charities was given by corporations?

Your strategy

Your solution

EXAMPLE 4

A quality control inspector found that 1.2% of 2500 camera phones inspected were defective. How many camera phones inspected were not defective?

Strategy

To find the number of nondefective phones:
• Find the number of defective phones. Write and solve the basic percent equation, using n to represent the number of defective phones (amount). The percent is 1.2% and the base is 2500.
• Subtract the number of defective phones from the number of phones inspected (2500).

Solution

$1.2\% \times 2500 = n$
$0.012 \times 2500 = n$
$\quad\quad\quad 30 = n$ defective phones

$2500 - 30 = 2470$

2470 camera phones were not defective.

YOU TRY IT 4

An electrician's hourly wage was $33.50 before an 8% raise. What is the new hourly wage?

Your strategy

Your solution

Solutions on p. S13

5.2 EXERCISES

✔ Concept Check

1. What is the basic percent equation?

For Exercises 2 to 4, without working the problem, determine whether the base is less than or greater than the amount.

2. What is 37% of 12?

3. 125.5% of 17 is what?

4. Find 0.5% of 33.

OBJECTIVE A   *To find the amount when the percent and the base are given*

For Exercises 5 to 22, solve.

5. 8% of 100 is what?

6. 16% of 50 is what?

7. 27% of 40 is what?

8. 52% of 95 is what?

9. 0.05% of 150 is what?

10. 0.075% of 625 is what?

11. 125% of 64 is what?

12. 210% of 12 is what?

13. Find 10.7% of 485.

14. Find 12.8% of 625.

15. What is 0.25% of 3000?

16. What is 0.06% of 250?

17. 80% of 16.25 is what?

18. 26% of 19.5 is what?

19. What is $1\frac{1}{2}$% of 250?

20. What is $5\frac{3}{4}$% of 65?

21. $16\frac{2}{3}$% of 120 is what?

22. What is $66\frac{2}{3}$% of 891?

23. Which is larger: 5% of 95, or 75% of 6?

24. Which is larger: 112% of 5, or 0.45% of 800?

25. Which is smaller: 79% of 16, or 20% of 65?

26. Which is smaller: 15% of 80, or 95% of 15?

27. Is 15% of a number greater than or less than the number?

28. Is 150% of a number greater than or less than the number?

OBJECTIVE B   *To solve application problems*

29. 🗨 Read Exercise 30. Without doing any calculations, determine whether the number of people in the United States aged 18 to 24 who do not have health insurance is *less than, equal to,* or *greater than* 50 million.

30. ● **Health Insurance**   Approximately 16.2% of the 50 million people in the United States who do not have health insurance are between the ages of 18 and 24. (*Source:* U.S. Census Bureau) About how many people in the United States aged 18 to 24 do not have health insurance?

31. ● **Aviation**   Based on data from the Bureau of Transportation Statistics, there were 629.5 million domestic airline passengers in 2010. If it is forecasted that this number will increase by 22% by the year 2020, how many more domestic airline passengers will there be in 2020?

32. **Jewelry**   An 18-carat, yellow-gold necklace contains 75% gold, 16% silver, and 9% copper. If the necklace weighs 25 grams, how many grams of copper are in the necklace?

33. **Jewelry**   Fourteen-carat yellow gold contains 58.5% gold, 17.5% silver, and 24% copper. If a jeweler has a 50-gram piece of 14-carat yellow gold, how many grams each of gold, silver, and copper are in the piece?

34. **Car Lease Sales Tax**   The base monthly payment for a car lease is $324.76 per month. If a sales tax of 7.25% is added to the base monthly payment, what is the total monthly lease payment? Round to the nearest cent.

35. ● **e-Filed Tax Returns**   Use the information in the news clipping at the right. How many tax returns were filed electronically? Round to the nearest million.

36. ● **Email Spam**   Based on data from Symantec Corporation, Rustock was one of the largest spam-sending botnets. During one year, Rustock was responsible for 47.5 percent of the approximately 93 million spam emails sent each day. How many spam emails did Rustock send each day that year?

37. **Car Payment**   A state sales tax of 6.75% is added to the purchase of a car. If the purchase price of a car is $28,995, what is the total cost of the car, including sales tax? If that amount is repaid in 48 equal monthly payments, what is the monthly payment? Round to the nearest cent.

Critical Thinking

38. **Jewelry**   Eighteen-carat white gold contains 75% gold, 15% silver, and 10% platinum. A jeweler wants to make a 2-ounce, 18-carat, white-gold ring. If gold costs $900 per ounce, silver costs $17.20 per ounce, and platinum costs $1900 per ounce, what is the cost of the metal used to make the ring?

In the NEWS!

E-Filing Still Rising

The Internal Revenue Service reports that of 141.5 million federal tax returns filed in 2010, about 69.8% were filed electronically.

Source: www.efile.com

Projects or Group Activities

The table at the right shows how to determine weekly federal withholding tax for a single person in 2011. Use this table for Exercises 39 to 43.

Income is between	Withholding amount
$0 and $40	$0
$40 and $204	$0 + 10% of amount over $40
$204 and $704	$16.40 + 15% of amount over $204
$704 and $1648	$91.40 + 25% of amount over $704
$1648 and $3394	$327.40 + 28% of amount over $1648
$3394 and $7332	$816.28 + 33% of amount over $3394
More than $7332	$2115.82 + 35% of amount over $7332

Source: Internal Revenue Service

39. What is the withholding tax for a person who earns $38 in one week?

40. What is the withholding tax for a person who earns $157 in one week?

41. What is the withholding tax for a person who earns $2542 in one week?

42. What is the withholding tax for a person who earns $8000 in one week?

43. Suppose a person earns $1648 in one week. Would the amount of withholding tax be different if the person used the $704 to $1648 bracket instead of the $1648 to $3394 bracket?

✔ CHECK YOUR PROGRESS: CHAPTER 5

For Exercises 1 to 4, write each percent as a decimal and as a fraction.

1. 85%   **2.** 4%   **3.** 0.25%   **4.** 180%

For Exercises 5 to 8, write the decimal as a percent.

5. 0.15   **6.** 0.027   **7.** 1.45   **8.** 0.00125

For Exercises 9 to 12, write the fraction as a percent.

9. $\dfrac{3}{5}$ **10.** $\dfrac{17}{40}$ **11.** $\dfrac{25}{60}$ **12.** $\dfrac{85}{50}$

13. 35% of 84 is what?

14. Find 5.5% of 250.

15. What is 33% of 120?

16. Find 0.2% of 78.

17. Salary Increase   A police officer earned $1445 per week before receiving a 5% increase in pay. What was the increase in the officer's weekly pay?

5.3 Percent Equations: Part II

OBJECTIVE A *To find the percent when the base and the amount are given*

The basic percent equation can be used to find an unknown percent.

APPLY THE CONCEPT

A student answered 68 questions correctly on an 80-question test. What percent of the questions did the student answer correctly?

To find the percent of questions that were answered correctly, we must answer the question, "What percent of 80 is 68?" This sentence can be written using mathematical symbols and then solved for the unknown percent.

Integrating Technology

The percent key % on a scientific calculator moves the decimal point two places to the right when pressed after a multiplication or division computation. For the example at the right, enter

68 ÷ 80 % =

The display reads 85.

What percent of	80	is	68?
↓	↓	↓	↓

Percent n	×	base 80	=	amount 68

$$n \times 80 = 68$$
$$n = 68 \div 80$$
$$n = 0.85$$
$$n = 85\%$$

• The solution must be written as a percent in order to answer the question.

The student answered 85% of the questions correctly.

EXAMPLE 1

What percent of 40 is 27?

Solution

Percent × base = amount
$$n \times 40 = 27$$
$$n = 27 \div 40$$
$$n = 0.675$$
$$n = 67.5\%$$

YOU TRY IT 1

What percent of 32 is 16?

Your solution

EXAMPLE 2

What percent of 12 is 27?

Solution

Percent × base = amount
$$n \times 12 = 27$$
$$n = 27 \div 12$$
$$n = 2.25$$
$$n = 225\%$$

YOU TRY IT 2

What percent of 15 is 48?

Your solution

EXAMPLE 3

25 is what percent of 75?

Solution

Percent × base = amount
$$n \times 75 = 25$$
$$n = 25 \div 75$$
$$n = \frac{1}{3} = 33\frac{1}{3}\%$$

YOU TRY IT 3

30 is what percent of 45?

Your solution

Solutions on p. S13

OBJECTIVE B   *To solve application problems*

To solve percent problems, remember that it is necessary to identify the percent, base, and amount. Usually the base follows the phrase "percent of."

EXAMPLE 4

The monthly house payment for the Kaminski family is $787.50. What percent of the Kaminskis' monthly income of $3750 is the house payment?

Strategy

To find what percent of the income the house payment is, write and solve the basic percent equation using n to represent the percent. The base is $3750 and the amount is $787.50.

Solution

$$n \times 3750 = 787.50$$
$$n = 787.50 \div 3750$$
$$n = 0.21 = 21\%$$

The house payment is 21% of the monthly income.

YOU TRY IT 4

Tomo Nagata had an income of $33,500 and paid $5025 in income tax. What percent of the income is the income tax?

Your strategy

Your solution

EXAMPLE 5

Scientists recently released one of the most comprehensive estimates of the number of species on Earth. Earth supports an estimated 8.7 million species, of which 2.2 million live in the ocean. What percent of the species live on land? Round to the nearest tenth of a percent.

Strategy

To find the percent of the species living on land:
- Subtract the number of species living in the ocean from the total number of species (8.7 million − 2.2 million). This gives the number of species living on land.
- Write and solve the basic percent equation, using n to represent the percent of species living on land. The base is 8.7 million, and the amount is the number of species living on land.

Solution

8.7 million − 2.2 million = 5.5 million

There are 5.5 million species living on land.

$$n \times 8.7 = 5.5$$
$$n = 5.5 \div 8.7$$
$$n \approx 0.632$$

Approximately 63.2% of the species live on land.

YOU TRY IT 5

In a recent year, there were approximately 302.9 million wireless subscriber connections in the United States. Of these, approximately 112.1 million were subscribers using a smartphone. What percent of wireless subscribers were not using a smartphone? Round to the nearest tenth of a percent.

Your strategy

Your solution

Solutions on p. S13

5.3 EXERCISES

✔ Concept Check

For Exercises 1 to 4, without working the problem, determine whether the answer is *less than* or *greater than* 100%.

1. What percent of 6 is 12?

2. 8 is what percent of 40?

3. 16 is what percent of 8?

4. What percent of 15 is 3?

OBJECTIVE A   *To find the percent when the base and amount are given*

For Exercises 5 to 25, solve.

5. What percent of 75 is 24?

6. What percent of 80 is 20?

7. 15 is what percent of 90?

8. 24 is what percent of 60?

9. What percent of 12 is 24?

10. What percent of 6 is 9?

11. What percent of 16 is 6?

12. What percent of 24 is 18?

13. 18 is what percent of 100?

14. 54 is what percent of 100?

15. 5 is what percent of 2000?

16. 8 is what percent of 2500?

17. What percent of 6 is 1.2?

18. What percent of 2.4 is 0.6?

19. 16.4 is what percent of 4.1?

20. 5.3 is what percent of 50?

21. 1 is what percent of 40?

22. 0.3 is what percent of 20?

23. What percent of 48 is 18?

24. What percent of 400 is 12?

25. What percent of 2800 is 7?

OBJECTIVE B   *To solve application problems*

26. Read Exercise 28. Without doing any calculations, determine whether the percent of those surveyed who were irked by tailgaters is *less than* or *greater than* 25%.

27. **Sociology**   Seven in ten couples disagree about financial issues. (*Source:* Yankelovich Partners for Lutheran Brotherhood) What percent of couples disagree about financial matters?

28. **Sociology**   In a survey, 1236 adults nationwide were asked, "What irks you most about the actions of other motorists?" The response "tailgaters" was given by 293 people. (*Source:* Reuters/Zogby) What percent of those surveyed were most irked by tailgaters? Round to the nearest tenth of a percent.

29. **Agriculture**   According to data from the U.S. Department of Agriculture, of the 63 billion pounds of vegetables produced in the United States in one year, 16 billion pounds were wasted. What percent of the vegetables produced were wasted? Round to the nearest tenth of a percent.

30. ● **Wind Energy**   In a recent year, wind machines in the United States generated 95 billion kilowatt-hours of electricity, enough to serve over 8.7 million households. The nation's total electricity production that year was 28,600 billion kilowatt-hours. (*Source:* Energy Information Administration) What percent of the total energy production was generated by wind machines? Round to the nearest tenth.

31. ● **Diabetes**   Approximately 8.3% of the American population has diabetes. Within this group, 18.8 million are diagnosed, while 7.0 million are undiagnosed. (*Source:* Centers for Disease Control) What percent of Americans with diabetes have not been diagnosed? Round to the nearest tenth of a percent.

32. ● **Internal Revenue Service**   See the news clipping at the right. What percent of Americans reporting an income of over $1 million were audited by the IRS? Round to the nearest hundredth of a percent.

33. **Construction**   In a test of the breaking strength of concrete slabs for freeway construction, 3 of the 200 slabs tested did not meet safety requirements. What percent of the slabs did meet safety requirements?

> **In the NEWS!**
>
> **$1 Million Audits**
>
> Of the 388,684 American taxpayers reporting an annual income of more than $1 million, 32,494 were audited by the Internal Revenue Service.
>
> *Source:* Internal Revenue Service; Bloomberg Businessweek

Critical Thinking

● **Pets**   The graph at the right shows several categories of average lifetime costs of dog ownership. Use this graph for Exercises 34 to 36. Round answers to the nearest tenth of a percent.

34. What percent of the total amount is spent on food?

35. What percent of the total is spent on veterinary care?

36. What percent of the total is spent on all categories except training?

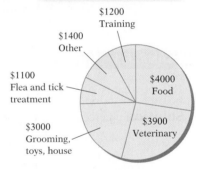

Cost of Owning a Dog
Source: Based on data from the American Kennel Club, *USA Today* research

37. ◣ **Sports**   The Fun in the Sun organization claims to have taken a survey of 350 people, asking them to give their favorite outdoor temperature for hiking. The results are given in the table at the right. Explain why these results are not possible.

Favorite Temperature	Percent
Greater than 90	5%
80–89	28%
70–79	35%
60–69	32%
Below 60	13%

Projects or Group Activities

38. Suppose the annual rainfall for a city in 2012 was 10 inches. In 2013, the annual rainfall increases by 10% from 2012. In 2014, the annual rainfall decreases by 10% from 2013. Is the annual rainfall in 2014 *less than, equal to,* or *greater than* the annual rainfall in 2012?

39. A stock decreased in value from $25 per share to $20 per share.
    a. What was the amount of the decrease?
    b. What percent of the original value of a share is the decrease?
    c. By what percent would the stock need to increase to return to its original value?
    d. Are the answers to parts (b) and (c) the same?

5.4   Percent Equations: Part III

OBJECTIVE A   *To find the base when the percent and the amount are given*

Point of Interest
One gigawatt-hour of energy can supply approximately 165 homes with power for a period of one year.

APPLY THE CONCEPT

In one year, a utility company produced approximately 14,500 gigawatt-hours of energy using renewable energy resources. This was 19% of the total amount of energy produced by the company that year. To find the total amount of energy produced that year by the company, we must answer the question, "19% of what number is 14,500?"

19%	of	what	is	14,500?
↓		↓	↓	↓

$$\begin{array}{c|c}\boxed{\begin{array}{c}\text{Percent}\\19\%\end{array}} \times \boxed{\begin{array}{c}\text{base}\\n\end{array}} = \boxed{\begin{array}{c}\text{amount}\\14{,}500\end{array}}\end{array}$$

$$0.19 \times n = 14{,}500$$
$$n = 14{,}500 \div 0.19$$
$$n \approx 76{,}316$$

The company produced approximately 76,316 gigawatt-hours of energy.

EXAMPLE 1

18% of what is 900?

Solution   Percent × base = amount
$$0.18 \times n = 900$$
$$n = 900 \div 0.18$$
$$n = 5000$$

YOU TRY IT 1

86% of what is 215?

Your solution

EXAMPLE 2

30 is 1.5% of what?

Solution   Percent × base = amount
$$0.015 \times n = 30$$
$$n = 30 \div 0.015$$
$$n = 2000$$

YOU TRY IT 2

15 is 2.5% of what?

Your solution

EXAMPLE 3

$33\frac{1}{3}$% of what is 7?

Solution   Percent × base = amount
$$\frac{1}{3} \times n = 7$$
• Note that the percent is written as a fraction.
$$n = 7 \div \frac{1}{3}$$
$$n = 21$$

YOU TRY IT 3

$16\frac{2}{3}$% of what is 5?

Your solution

Solutions on p. S13

OBJECTIVE B *To solve application problems*

To solve percent problems, it is necessary to identify the percent, the base, and the amount. Usually the base follows the phrase "percent of."

EXAMPLE 4

A business office bought a used copy machine for $900, which was 75% of the original cost. What was the original cost of the copier?

Strategy

To find the original cost of the copier, write and solve the basic percent equation, using n to represent the original cost (base). The percent is 75% and the amount is $900.

Solution

$75\% \times n = 900$
$0.75 \times n = 900$
$\quad\quad n = 900 \div 0.75$
$\quad\quad n = 1200$

The original cost of the copier was $1200.

YOU TRY IT 4

A used car has a value of $10,458, which is 42% of the car's original value. What was the car's original value?

Your strategy

Your solution

EXAMPLE 5

A carpenter's wage this year is $26.40 per hour, which is 110% of last year's wage. What was the increase in the hourly wage over last year?

Strategy

To find the increase in the hourly wage over last year:

• Find last year's wage. Write and solve the basic percent equation, using n to represent last year's wage (base). The percent is 110% and the amount is $26.40.
• Subtract last year's wage from this year's wage (26.40).

Solution

$110\% \times n = 26.40$
$1.10 \times n = 26.40$
$\quad\quad n = 26.40 \div 1.10$
$\quad\quad n = 24.00$ • Last year's wage

$26.40 - 24.00 = 2.40$

The increase in the hourly wage was $2.40.

YOU TRY IT 5

Chang's Sporting Goods has a tennis racket on sale for $89.60, which is 80% of the original price. What is the difference between the original price and the sale price?

Your strategy

Your solution

Solutions on pp. S13–S14

5.4 EXERCISES

✔ Concept Check

For Exercises 1 to 4, without working the problem, determine whether the base is *less than* or *greater than* the amount.

1. 15% of what is 12?

2. 30 is 0.5% of what?

3. 20 is 125% of what?

4. 110% of what is 200?

OBJECTIVE A *To find the base when the percent and amount are given*

For Exercises 5 to 25, solve.

5. 12% of what is 9?

6. 38% of what is 171?

7. 8 is 16% of what?

8. 54 is 90% of what?

9. 10 is 10% of what?

10. 37 is 37% of what?

11. 30% of what is 25.5?

12. 25% of what is 21.5?

13. 2.5% of what is 30?

14. 10.4% of what is 52?

15. 125% of what is 24?

16. 180% of what is 21.6?

17. 18 is 240% of what?

18. 24 is 320% of what?

19. 4.8 is 15% of what?

20. 87.5 is 50% of what?

21. 25.6 is 12.8% of what?

22. 45.014 is 63.4% of what?

23. 30% of what is 2.7?

24. 120 is $33\frac{1}{3}$% of what?

25. 84 is $16\frac{2}{3}$% of what?

OBJECTIVE B *To solve application problems*

26. Read Exercise 27. Without doing any calculations, determine whether the number of travelers who allowed their children to miss school to go on a trip is *less than, equal to,* or *greater than* 1.738 million.

27. ● **Travel** Of the travelers who, during a recent year, allowed their children to miss school to go on a trip, approximately 1.738 million allowed their children to miss school for more than a week. This represented 11% of the travelers who allowed their children to miss school. (*Source:* Travel Industry Association) About how many travelers allowed their children to miss school to go on a trip?

28. ● **Tablet Shipments** Use the information in the news clipping at the right. Find the total number of media tablets shipped in 2010. Round to the nearest million.

In the NEWS!

Tablet Sales Surge
In their first year on the market, media tablets saw a surge in sales at the end of the year. The 10.1 million media tablets shipped worldwide in the fourth quarter represented 56.4% of all tablets shipped in 2010.
Source: International Data Corporation

29. ● **Marathons** In 2011, approximately 98.2% of the runners who started the Boston Marathon, or 23,913 people, crossed the finish line. (*Source:* Boston Athletic Association) How many runners started the Boston Marathon in 2011? Round to the nearest ten.

30. ● **Education** In the United States today, 29.6% of women and 30.3% of men have earned a bachelor's or graduate degree. (*Source:* Census Bureau) What additional information would you need in order to determine how many women in the United States have earned a bachelor's or graduate degree?

31. ● **Fuel Consumption** Use the information in the news clipping at the right. Sailing at full speed, how many tons of fuel per day does a large ship use?

32. ● **Taxes** A TurboTax online survey asked people how they planned to use their tax refunds. Seven hundred forty people, or 22% of the respondents, said they would save the money. How many people responded to the survey?

In the NEWS!

Reducing Cargo Ship Emissions

By using giant kites to power the ships and sailing at slower speeds, shipping companies are reducing the amount of fuel used by cargo ships, thus reducing the ships' CO_2 emissions. By reducing its speed by 20%, a large ship can lower its fuel use by 40%, saving 120 tons of fuel per day.

Source: www.guardian.uk.com

33. **Manufacturing** During a quality control test, Micronics found 24 defective computer boards. This amount was 0.8% of the computer boards tested.
   a. How many computer boards were tested?
   b. How many of the computer boards tested were not defective?

Critical Thinking

34. **Nutrition** The table at the right contains nutrition information about a breakfast cereal. The amount of thiamin in one serving of this cereal with skim milk is 0.45 milligram. Find the recommended daily allowance of thiamin for an adult.

NUTRITION INFORMATION

SERVING SIZE: 1.4 OZ WHEAT FLAKES WITH 0.4 OZ. RAISINS: 39.4 g. ABOUT 1/2 CUP

SERVINGS PER PACKAGE: 14

	CEREAL & RAISINS	WITH 1/2 CUP VITAMINS A & D SKIM MILK

PERCENTAGE OF U.S. RECOMMENDED DAILY ALLOWANCES (U.S. RDA)

PROTEIN	4	15
VITAMIN A	15	20
VITAMIN C	**	2
THIAMIN	25	30
RIBOFLAVIN	25	35
NIACIN	25	35
CALCIUM	**	15
IRON	100	100
VITAMIN D	10	25
VITAMIN B_6	25	25
FOLIC ACID..............	25	25
VITAMIN B_{12}	25	30
PHOSPHOROUS.........	10	15
MAGNESIUM	10	20
ZINC	25	30
COPPER.................	2	4

* 2% MILK SUPPLIES AN ADDITIONAL 20 CALORIES. 2 g FAT, AND 10 mg CHOLESTEROL.

** CONTAINS LESS THAN 2% OF THE U.S. RDA OF THIS NUTRIENT

Projects or Group Activities

35. **a.** Suppose you correctly answer 48 out of 60 questions on a test. What percent of the questions did you answer correctly?
   b. Suppose you correctly answer 56 out of 80 questions on a second test. What percent of the questions did you answer correctly?
   c. What is the average of the two percents in parts (a) and (b)?
   d. Consider the total number of questions on the two tests and the total number you answered correctly. What percent of the questions did you answer correctly? Is this the same number you calculated in part (c)?
   e. Your answers to parts (c) and (d) show that averaging the percent scores for two tests does not necessarily give the correct percent score for the combined tests. Under what conditions would the average of the percent scores give the true percent score for the combined tests? *Hint:* Consider the base of the basic percent equation.

SECTION

5.5   Percent Problems: Proportion Method

OBJECTIVE A   *To solve percent problems using proportions*

Problems that can be solved using the basic percent equation can also be solved using proportions.

The proportion method is based on writing two ratios. One ratio is the percent ratio, written as $\frac{percent}{100}$. The second ratio is the amount-to-base ratio, written as $\frac{amount}{base}$. These two ratios form the proportion

$$\frac{\textbf{percent}}{\textbf{100}} = \frac{\textbf{amount}}{\textbf{base}}$$

To use the proportion method, first identify the percent, the amount, and the base (the base usually follows the phrase "percent of").

Integrating Technology

To use a calculator to solve the proportions at the right for n, enter

23 ✕ 45 ÷ 100 =
100 ✕ 4 ÷ 25 =
100 ✕ 12 ÷ 60 =

What is 23% of 45?

$$\frac{23}{100} = \frac{n}{45}$$

$23 \times 45 = 100 \times n$
$1035 = 100 \times n$
$1035 \div 100 = n$
$10.35 = n$

What percent of 25 is 4?

$$\frac{n}{100} = \frac{4}{25}$$

$n \times 25 = 100 \times 4$
$n \times 25 = 400$
$n = 400 \div 25$
$n = 16$

12 is 60% of what number?

$$\frac{60}{100} = \frac{12}{n}$$

$60 \times n = 100 \times 12$
$60 \times n = 1200$
$n = 1200 \div 60$
$n = 20$

EXAMPLE 1

15% of what is 7? Round to the nearest hundredth.

Solution
$$\frac{15}{100} = \frac{7}{n}$$
$15 \times n = 100 \times 7$
$15 \times n = 700$
$n = 700 \div 15$
$n \approx 46.67$

YOU TRY IT 1

26% of what is 22? Round to the nearest hundredth.

Your solution

EXAMPLE 2

30% of 63 is what?

Solution
$$\frac{30}{100} = \frac{n}{63}$$
$30 \times 63 = 100 \times n$
$1890 = 100 \times n$
$1890 \div 100 = n$
$18.90 = n$

YOU TRY IT 2

16% of 132 is what?

Your solution

Solutions on p. S14

OBJECTIVE B *To solve application problems*

EXAMPLE 3

An antiques dealer found that 86% of the 250 items that were sold during one month sold for under $1000. How many items sold for under $1000?

Strategy

To find the number of items that sold for under $1000, write and solve a proportion, using n to represent the number of items sold for less than $1000 (amount). The percent is 86%, and the base is 250.

Solution

$$\frac{86}{100} = \frac{n}{250}$$
$$86 \times 250 = 100 \times n$$
$$21{,}500 = 100 \times n$$
$$21{,}500 \div 100 = n$$
$$215 = n$$

215 items sold for under $1000.

YOU TRY IT 3

Last year it snowed 64% of the 150 days of the ski season at a resort. How many days did it snow?

Your strategy

Your solution

EXAMPLE 4

In a test of the strength of nylon rope, 5 of the 25 pieces tested did not meet the test standards. What percent of the nylon ropes tested did meet the test standards?

Strategy

To find the percent of ropes tested that met the test standards:

• Find the number of ropes that met the test standards (25 − 5).
• Write and solve a proportion, using n to represent the percent of ropes that met the test standards. The base is 25, and the amount is the number of ropes that met the standards.

Solution

$25 - 5 = 20$ ropes met test standards.
$$\frac{n}{100} = \frac{20}{25}$$
$$n \times 25 = 100 \times 20$$
$$n \times 25 = 2000$$
$$n = 2000 \div 25$$
$$n = 80$$

80% of the ropes tested did meet the test standards.

YOU TRY IT 4

The Rincon Fire Department received 24 false alarms out of a total of 200 alarms received. What percent of the alarms received were not false alarms?

Your strategy

Your solution

Solutions on p. S14

5.5 EXERCISES

✔ Concept Check

1. Write a proportion that can be used to solve problems involving percent.

For Exercises 2 to 4, state whether the unknown n represents *percent, base,* or *amount.*

2. $\dfrac{45}{100} = \dfrac{28}{n}$

3. $\dfrac{n}{100} = \dfrac{30}{50}$

4. $\dfrac{n}{50} = \dfrac{30}{100}$

OBJECTIVE A   *To solve percent problems using proportions*

5. 26% of 250 is what?

6. What is 18% of 150?

7. 37 is what percent of 148?

8. What percent of 150 is 33?

9. 68% of what is 51?

10. 126 is 84% of what?

11. What percent of 344 is 43?

12. 750 is what percent of 50?

13. 82 is 20.5% of what?

14. 2.4% of what is 21?

15. What is 6.5% of 300?

16. 96% of 75 is what?

17. 7.4 is what percent of 50?

18. What percent of 1500 is 693?

19. 50.5% of 124 is what?

20. What is 87.4% of 255?

21. 33 is 220% of what?

22. 160% of what is 40?

23. Which equation(s) below can be used to answer the question, **a.** "What is 12% of 75?" and **b.** to answer the question, "75 is 12% of what?"

(i) $\dfrac{12}{100} = \dfrac{75}{n}$ (ii) $0.12 \times 75 = n$ (iii) $\dfrac{12}{100} = \dfrac{n}{75}$ (iv) $0.12 \times n = 75$

OBJECTIVE B   *To solve application problems*

24. Read Exercise 25. Without doing any calculations, determine whether the length of time the drug will be effective is *less than* or *greater than* 6 hours.

25. **Medicine** A manufacturer of an anti-inflammatory drug claims that the drug will be effective for 6 hours. An independent testing service determined that the drug was effective for only 80% of the length of time claimed by the manufacturer. Find the length of time the drug will be effective as determined by the testing service.

26. ● **Geography** The land area of North America is approximately 9,400,000 square miles. This represents approximately 16% of the total land area of the world. What is the approximate total land area of the world?

27. ● **Girl Scout Cookies** Using the information in the news clipping at the right, calculate the cash generated annually **a.** from sales of Thin Mints and **b.** from sales of Trefoil shortbread cookies.

In the NEWS!

Thin Mints Biggest Seller

Every year, sales from the Girl Scout cookies sold by about 2.7 million girls total $700 million. The most popular cookie, Thin Mints, earn 25% of total sales, while sales of Trefoil shortbread cookies represent only 9% of total sales.

Source: msnbc.com

Jeff Greenberg/age fotostock

28. ● **Charities**   In a recent year, the American Red Cross spent $132,105,934 on administrative expenses. This amount was 3.68% of its total revenue. Find the American Red Cross's total revenue for that year. Round to the nearest ten million.

29. ● **Education**   See the news clipping at the right. What percent of the baby boomers living in the United States have attended college? Round to the nearest tenth of a percent.

30. ● **Mining**   During one year, approximately 2,240,000 ounces of gold went into the manufacturing of electronic equipment in the United States. This was 16% of all the gold mined in the United States that year. How many ounces of gold were mined in the United States that year?

31. ● **Poultry**   In a recent year, North Carolina produced 963,000,000 pounds of turkey. This was 13.5% of the U.S. total in that year. Calculate the U.S. total turkey production for that year. Round to the nearest billion.

32. ● **Police Officers**   The graph at the right shows causes of death for police officers killed in the line of duty during a recent year. What percent of the deaths were due to traffic accidents? Round to the nearest tenth of a percent.

Critical Thinking

33. ● **The Federal Government**   In the 110th Senate, there were 49 Republicans, 49 Democrats, and 2 Independents. In the 110th House of Representatives, there were 202 Republicans, 233 Democrats, and 0 Independents. Which had the larger percentage of Republicans, the 110th Senate or the 110th House of Representatives?

Projects or Group Activities

Gold jewelry comes in various colors. Three typical colors are yellow gold, rose gold, and white gold. The table at the right shows the percent breakdown of the elements used to make three colors of 18-carat gold. Use this table for Exercises 34 to 36.

34. How many grams of each element are needed for a yellow-gold ring that weighs 8 grams?

35. How many grams of each element are needed for a rose-gold ring that weighs 6 grams?

36. How many grams of each element are needed for a white-gold ring that weighs 8 grams?

In the NEWS!

Over Half of Baby Boomers Have College Experience

Of the 78 million baby boomers living in the United States, 45 million have attended college. Twenty-three million baby boomers are high school graduates with no college experience.
Source: USA Today

Numbers of Deaths for Police Officers Killed in the Line of Duty
Source: International Union of Police Associations

Color	Composition
Yellow	Gold, 75% Copper, 25%
Rose	Gold, 75% Copper, 20% Silver, 5%
White	Gold, 75% Palladium, 10% Nickel, 10% Zinc, 5%

5   Summary

Key Words

Examples

Percent means "parts of 100."   [5.1A, p. 204]

23% means 23 of 100 equal parts.

Essential Rules and Procedures

Examples

To write a percent as a decimal, drop the percent sign and multiply by 0.01.   [5.1A, p. 204]

$87\% = 87(0.01) = 0.87$

To write a percent as a fraction, drop the percent sign and multiply by $\frac{1}{100}$.   [5.1A, p. 204]

$56\% = 56\left(\frac{1}{100}\right) = \frac{56}{100} = \frac{14}{25}$

To write a decimal as a percent, multiply by 100%. [5.1B, p. 205]

$0.325 = 0.325(100\%) = 32.5\%$

To write a fraction as a percent, multiply by 100%. [5.1B, p. 205]

$\frac{7}{20} = \frac{7}{20} \times \frac{100\%}{1} = \frac{700\%}{20} = 35\%$

The Basic Percent Equation   [5.2A, p. 209]
The basic percent equation is

$$\text{Percent} \times \text{base} = \text{amount}$$

Solving percent problems requires identifying the three elements of this equation. Usually the base follows the phrase "percent of."

8% of 250 is what number?
Percent × base = amount
$0.08 \times 250 = n$
$20 = n$

Proportion Method of Solving a Percent Problem
[5.5A, p. 222]
The following proportion can be used to solve percent problems.

$$\frac{\text{percent}}{100} = \frac{\text{amount}}{\text{base}}$$

To use the proportion method, first identify the percent, the amount, and the base. The base usually follows the phrase "percent of."

8% of 250 is what number?
$$\frac{\text{percent}}{100} = \frac{\text{amount}}{\text{base}}$$
$$\frac{8}{100} = \frac{n}{250}$$
$8 \times 250 = 100 \times n$
$2000 = 100 \times n$
$2000 \div 100 = n$
$20 = n$

CHAPTER

5 | Review Exercises

1. What is 30% of 200?

2. 16 is what percent of 80?

3. Write $1\frac{3}{4}$ as a percent.

4. 20% of what is 15?

5. Write 12% as a fraction.

6. Find 22% of 88.

7. What percent of 20 is 30?

8. $16\frac{2}{3}\%$ of what is 84?

9. Write 42% as a decimal.

10. What is 7.5% of 72?

11. $66\frac{2}{3}\%$ of what is 105?

12. Write 7.6% as a decimal.

13. Find 125% of 62.

14. Write $16\frac{2}{3}\%$ as a fraction.

15. What percent of 25 is 40? Use the proportion method.

16. 20% of what number is 15? Use the proportion method.

17. Write 0.38 as a percent.

18. 78% of what is 8.5? Round to the nearest tenth.

19. What percent of 30 is 2.2? Round to the nearest tenth of a percent.

20. What percent of 15 is 92? Round to the nearest tenth of a percent.

21. Education   Trent missed 9 out of 60 questions on a history exam. What percent of the questions did he answer correctly? Use the proportion method.

22. Advertising   A company used 7.5% of its $60,000 advertising budget for newspaper advertising. How much of the advertising budget was spent on newspaper advertising?

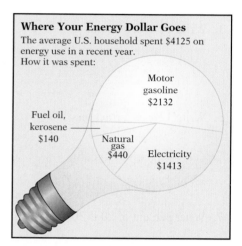

Where Your Energy Dollar Goes

The average U.S. household spent $4125 on energy use in a recent year. How it was spent:

Motor gasoline $2132

Fuel oil, kerosene $140

Natural gas $440

Electricity $1413

23. ◐ Energy   The graph at the right shows the amounts spent by the average U.S. household for energy use. What percent of energy costs is spent on electricity? Round to the nearest tenth of a percent.

24. Consumerism   Joshua purchased a camcorder for $980 and paid a sales tax of 6.25% of the cost. What was the total cost of the camcorder?

Source: Bureau of Labor Statistics

25. Health   In a survey of 350 women and 420 men, 275 of the women and 300 of the men reported that they wore sunscreen often. To the nearest tenth of a percent, what percent of the women wore sunscreen often?

26. ◐ Demography   It is estimated that by the year 2050 the world's population will be 9,400,000,000. This is 155% of the population in 2000. (*Source:* U.S. Census Bureau) What was the world's population in 2000? Round to the nearest hundred million.

27. Computers   A computer system can be purchased for $1800. This is 60% of the cost 4 years ago. What was the cost of the computer system 4 years ago? Use the proportion method.

28. ◐ Agriculture   In a recent year, Wisconsin growers produced 281.72 million pounds of cranberries. This represented 49.25% of the total cranberry crop in the United States that year. Find the total cranberry crop in the United States that year. Round to the nearest million.

5 | TEST

1. Write 97.3% as a decimal.

2. Write $83\frac{1}{3}\%$ as a fraction.

3. Write 0.3 as a percent.

4. Write 1.63 as a percent.

5. Write $\frac{3}{2}$ as a percent.

6. Write $\frac{37}{40}$ as a percent.

7. What is 77% of 65?

8. 47.2% of 130 is what?

9. Write $\frac{11}{18}$ as a percent.

10. Write 0.75% as a fraction.

11. 12 is 15% of what?

12. 42.5 is 150% of what? Round to the nearest tenth.

13. 123 is 86% of what number? Use the proportion method. Round to the nearest tenth.

14. What percent of 12 is 120? Use the proportion method.

15. Advertising　A travel agency uses 6% of its $750,000 budget for advertising. What amount of the budget is spent on advertising?

16. Agriculture　During the packaging process for vegetables, spoiled vegetables are discarded by an inspector. In one day, an inspector found that 6.4% of the 1250 pounds of vegetables were spoiled. How many pounds of vegetables were not spoiled?

Nutrition　The table at the right contains nutrition information about a breakfast cereal. Solve Exercises 17 and 18 with information taken from this table.

17. The recommended amount of potassium per day for an adult is 3000 milligrams (mg). What percent, to the nearest tenth of a percent, of the daily recommended amount of potassium is provided by one serving of this cereal with skim milk?

18. The daily recommended number of calories for a 190-pound man is 2200 calories. What percent, to the nearest tenth of a percent, of the daily recommended number of calories is provided by one serving of this cereal with 2% milk?

NUTRITION INFORMATION		
SERVING SIZE: 1.4 OZ WHEAT FLAKES WITH 0.4 OZ. RAISINS: 39.4 g. ABOUT 1/2 CUP SERVINGS PER PACKAGE: 14		
	CEREAL & RAISINS	WITH 1/2 CUP VITAMINS A & D SKIM MILK
CALORIES	120	180
PROTEIN, g	3	7
CARBOHYDRATE, g	28	34
FAT, TOTAL, g	1	1*
UNSATURATED, g 1		
SATURATED, g 0		
CHOLESTEROL, mg	0	0*
SODIUM, mg	125	190
POTASSIUM, mg	240	440

* 2% MILK SUPPLIES AN ADDITIONAL 20 CALORIES. 2 g FAT, AND 10 mg CHOLESTEROL.
** CONTAINS LESS THAN 2% OF THE U.S. RDA OF THIS NUTRIENT

19. Employment　The Urban Center Department Store has 125 permanent employees and must hire an additional 20 temporary employees for the holiday season. What percent of the number of permanent employees is the number hired as temporary employees for the holiday season?

20. Education　Conchita missed 7 out of 80 questions on a math exam. What percent of the questions did she answer correctly? Round to the nearest tenth of a percent.

21. Manufacturing　A manufacturer of digital cameras found 384 defective digital cameras during a quality control study. This amount was 1.2% of the digital cameras tested. Find the number of digital cameras tested.

22. Real Estate　A new house was bought for $285,000. Five years later, the house sold for $456,000. What percent of the original price was the increase?

23. Wages　An administrative assistant receives a wage of $16.24 per hour. This amount is 112% of last year's wage. What is the dollar increase in the hourly wage over last year? Use the proportion method.

24. Demography　A city has a population of 71,500. Ten years ago the population was 32,500. What percent of the population 10 years ago is the population now? Use the proportion method.

25. Fees　The annual license fee on a car is 1.4% of the value of the car. If the annual license fee is $350, what is the value of the car? Use the proportion method.

Cumulative Review Exercises

1. Simplify: $18 \div (7 - 4)^2 + 2$

2. Find the LCM of 16, 24, and 30.

3. Find the sum of $2\frac{1}{3}$, $3\frac{1}{2}$, and $4\frac{5}{8}$.

4. Subtract: $27\frac{5}{12} - 14\frac{9}{16}$

5. Multiply: $7\frac{1}{3} \times 1\frac{5}{7}$

6. What is $\frac{14}{27}$ divided by $1\frac{7}{9}$?

7. Simplify: $\left(\frac{3}{4}\right)^3 \cdot \left(\frac{8}{9}\right)^2 + \frac{1}{9}$

8. Simplify: $\left(\frac{2}{3}\right)^2 - \left(\frac{3}{8} - \frac{1}{3}\right) \div \frac{1}{2}$

9. Round 3.07973 to the nearest hundredth.

10. Subtract: 3.0902
                    $-\ 1.9706$

11. Divide: $0.032\overline{)1.097}$
     Round to the nearest ten-thousandth.

12. Convert $3\frac{5}{8}$ to a terminating or repeating decimal.

13. Convert 1.75 to a fraction.

14. Place the correct symbol, $<$ or $>$, between the two numbers.
     $\frac{3}{8}$ 0.87

15. Solve the proportion $\frac{3}{8} = \frac{20}{n}$.
     Round to the nearest tenth.

16. Write "$153.60 earned in 8 hours" as a unit rate.

17. Write $18\frac{1}{3}\%$ as a fraction.

18. Write $\frac{13}{18}$ as a percent.

19. 16.3% of 120 is what?

20. 24 is what percent of 18?

21. 12.4 is 125% of what?

22. What percent of 35 is 120? Round to the nearest tenth.

23. Taxes   Sergio has an income of $740 per week. One-fifth of his income is deducted for income tax payments. Find his take-home pay.

24. Finance   Eunice bought a used car for $12,530, with a down payment of $2000. The balance was paid in 36 equal monthly payments. Find the monthly payment.

25. Taxes   The gasoline tax is $.41 per gallon. Find the number of gallons of gasoline used during a month in which $172.20 was paid in gasoline taxes.

26. Taxes   The real estate tax on a $344,000 home is $6880. At the same rate, find the real estate tax on a home valued at $500,000.

27. 🌑 Lodging   The graph at the right shows the breakdown of the locations of the 51,015 hotels throughout the United States. How many of these hotels are located along interstate highways? Round to the nearest whole number.

28. Elections   A survey of 300 people showed that 165 people favored a certain candidate for mayor. What percent of the people surveyed did not favor this candidate?

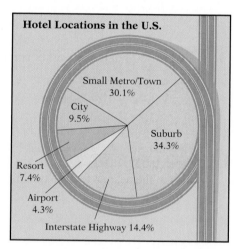

Hotel Locations in the U.S.

Small Metro/Town 30.1%
City 9.5%
Suburb 34.3%
Resort 7.4%
Airport 4.3%
Interstate Highway 14.4%

Source: American Hotel and Lodging Association

29. 🌑 Television   According to the Cabletelevision Advertising Bureau, cable households watch television 36.5% of the time. On average, how many hours per week do cable households spend watching TV? Round to the nearest tenth.

30. 🌑 Health   The Environmental Protection Agency found that 990 out of 5500 children tested had levels of lead in their blood that exceeded federal guidelines. What percent of the children tested had levels of lead that exceeded federal standards?

Cumulative Review Exercises

1. Simplify: $12 - (10 - 8)^2 \div 2 + 3$

2. Add: $3\frac{1}{3} + 4\frac{1}{8} + 1\frac{1}{12}$

3. Find the difference between $12\frac{3}{16}$ and $9\frac{5}{12}$.

4. Find the product of $5\frac{5}{8}$ and $1\frac{9}{15}$.

5. Divide: $3\frac{1}{2} \div 1\frac{3}{4}$

6. Simplify: $\left(\frac{3}{4}\right)^2 \div \left(\frac{3}{8} - \frac{1}{4}\right) + \frac{1}{2}$

7. Divide: $0.059\overline{)3.0792}$
   Round to the nearest tenth.

8. Convert $\frac{17}{12}$ to a terminating or a repeating decimal. Place a bar over any repeating digits.

9. Write "$410 in 8 hours" as a unit rate.

10. Solve the proportion $\frac{5}{n} = \frac{16}{35}$.
    Round to the nearest hundredth.

11. Write $\frac{5}{8}$ as a percent.

12. Find 6.5% of 420.

13. Write 18.2% as a decimal.

14. What percent of 20 is 8.4?

15. 30 is 12% of what?

16. 65 is 42% of what? Round to the nearest hundredth.

17. **Meteorology** A series of late-summer storms produced rainfall amounts of $3\frac{3}{4}$, $8\frac{1}{2}$, and $1\frac{2}{3}$ inches during a 3-week period. Find the total rainfall during the 3 weeks.

18. **Taxes** The Homer family pays $\frac{1}{5}$ of their total monthly income for taxes. The family has a total monthly income of $4850. Find the amount of the monthly income that is paid for taxes.

19. **Consumerism** In 5 years, the cost of a scientific calculator went from $75 to $30. What is the ratio of the decrease in price to the original price?

20. **Fuel Efficiency** A compact car was driven 417.5 miles on 12.5 gallons of gasoline. Find the number of miles driven per gallon of gasoline.

21. **Consumerism** A 14-pound turkey costs $15.40. Find the unit cost. Round to the nearest cent.

22. **Investments** Eighty shares of a stock paid a dividend of $112. At the same rate, find the dividend on 200 shares of the stock.

23. **Discount** A laptop computer that regularly sells for $900 is on sale for 20% off the regular price. What is the sale price?

24. **Markup** A pro skate shop bought a grinding rail for $85 and used a markup rate of 40%. Find the selling price of the grinding rail.

25. **Compensation** Sook Kim, an elementary school teacher, received an increase in salary from $2800 per month to $3024 per month. Find the percent increase in her salary.

26. **Simple Interest** A contractor borrowed $120,000 for 6 months at an annual interest rate of 4.5%. How much simple interest is due on the loan?

27. **Car Expenses** A red Ford Mustang was purchased for $26,900, and a down payment of $2000 was made. The balance was financed for 3 years at an annual interest rate of 9%. Find the monthly payment. Use the Monthly Payment Table in the Appendix. Round to the nearest cent.

DDCoral/Shutterstock.com

28. **Banking** A family had a checking account balance of $1846.78. A check for $568.30 was deposited into the account, and checks for $123.98 and $47.33 were written. Find the new checking account balance.

29. **Car Expenses** During one year, Anna Gonzalez spent $1840 on gasoline and oil, $820 on insurance, $185 on tires, and $432 on repairs for her car. Find the cost per mile to drive the car 10,000 miles during the year. Round to the nearest cent.

30. **Real Estate** A house has a mortgage of $172,000 for 20 years at an annual interest rate of 6%. Find the monthly mortgage payment. Use the Monthly Payment Table in the Appendix. Round to the nearest cent.

Appendix

Table of Properties

Properties of Real Numbers

Commutative Property of Addition
If a and b are real numbers, then $a + b = b + a$.

Commutative Property of Multiplication
If a and b are real numbers, then $a \cdot b = b \cdot a$.

Associative Property of Addition
If a, b, and c are real numbers, then
$(a + b) + c = a + (b + c)$.

Associative Property of Multiplication
If a, b, and c are real numbers, then
$(a \cdot b) \cdot c = a \cdot (b \cdot c)$.

Addition Property of Zero
If a is a real number, then $a + 0 = 0 + a = a$.

Multiplication Property of Zero
If a is a real number, then $a \cdot 0 = 0 \cdot a = 0$.

Multiplication Property of One
If a is a real number, then $a \cdot 1 = 1 \cdot a = a$.

Inverse Property of Addition
If a is a real number, then $a + (-a) = (-a) + a = 0$.

Inverse Property of Multiplication
If a is a real number and $a \neq 0$, then
$a \cdot \dfrac{1}{a} = \dfrac{1}{a} \cdot a = 1$.

Distributive Property
If a, b, and c are real numbers, then

$$a(b + c) = ab + ac.$$

Properties of Zero and One in Division

Any number divided by 1 is the number.
Division by zero is not allowed.

Any number other than zero divided by itself is 1.
Zero divided by a number other than zero is zero.

Compound Interest Table

Compounded Annually

	4%	4.25%	4.50%	4.75%	5.00%	5.25%	5.50%	5.75%
1 year	1.04000	1.04250	1.04500	1.04750	1.05000	1.05250	1.05500	1.05750
5 years	1.21665	1.23135	1.24618	1.26116	1.27628	1.29155	1.30696	1.32252
10 years	1.48024	1.51621	1.55297	1.59052	1.62889	1.66810	1.70814	1.74906
15 years	1.80094	1.86699	1.93528	2.00591	2.07893	2.15443	2.23248	2.31316
20 years	2.19112	2.29891	2.41171	2.52977	2.65330	2.78254	2.91776	3.05920

	6%	6.25%	6.50%	6.75%	7.00%	7.25%	7.50%	7.75%
1 year	1.06000	1.06250	1.06500	1.06750	1.07000	1.07250	1.07500	1.07750
5 years	1.33823	1.35408	1.37009	1.38624	1.40255	1.41901	1.43563	1.45240
10 years	1.79085	1.83354	1.87714	1.92167	1.96715	2.01360	2.06103	2.10947
15 years	2.39656	2.48276	2.57184	2.66390	2.75903	2.85732	2.95888	3.06379
20 years	3.20714	3.36185	3.52365	3.69282	3.86968	4.05458	4.24785	4.44985

	8%	8.25%	8.50%	8.75%	9.00%	9.25%	9.50%	9.75%
1 year	1.08000	1.08250	1.08500	1.08750	1.09000	1.09250	1.09500	1.09750
5 years	1.46933	1.48641	1.50366	1.52106	1.53862	1.55635	1.57424	1.59229
10 years	2.15892	2.20942	2.26098	2.31362	2.36736	2.42222	2.47823	2.53539
15 years	3.17217	3.28412	3.39974	3.51916	3.64248	3.76983	3.90132	4.03709
20 years	4.66096	4.88155	5.11205	5.35285	5.60441	5.86717	6.14161	6.42822

	10%	10.25%	10.50%	10.75%	11.00%	11.25%	11.50%	11.75%
1 year	1.10000	1.10250	1.10500	1.10750	1.11000	1.11250	1.11500	1.11750
5 years	1.61051	1.62889	1.64745	1.66617	1.68506	1.70412	1.72335	1.74276
10 years	2.59374	2.65330	2.71408	2.77611	2.83942	2.90402	2.96995	3.03721
15 years	4.17725	4.32194	4.47130	4.62547	4.78459	4.94880	5.11827	5.29314
20 years	6.72750	7.03999	7.36623	7.70681	8.06231	8.43336	8.82058	9.22467

To use this table:
1. Locate the section that gives the desired compounding period.
2. Locate the interest rate in the top row of that section.
3. Locate the number of years in the left-hand column of that section.
4. Locate the number where the interest-rate column and the number-of-years row meet. This is the compound interest factor.

Example An investment yields an annual interest rate of 10% compounded annually for 5 years. The compounding period is "compounded annually." The interest rate is 10%.

Compound Interest Table (continued)

Compounded Semiannually

	4%	4.25%	4.50%	4.75%	5.00%	5.25%	5.50%	5.75%
1 year	1.04040	1.04295	1.04551	1.04806	1.05063	1.05319	1.05576	1.05833
5 years	1.21899	1.23402	1.24920	1.26456	1.28008	1.29578	1.31165	1.32770
10 years	1.48595	1.52279	1.56051	1.59911	1.63862	1.67905	1.72043	1.76278
15 years	1.81136	1.87915	1.94939	2.02217	2.09757	2.17568	2.25660	2.34043
20 years	2.20804	2.31890	2.43519	2.55715	2.68506	2.81921	2.95987	3.10738

	6%	6.25%	6.50%	6.75%	7.00%	7.25%	7.50%	7.75%
1 year	1.06090	1.06348	1.06606	1.06864	1.07123	1.07381	1.07641	1.07900
5 years	1.34392	1.36032	1.37689	1.39365	1.41060	1.42773	1.44504	1.46255
10 years	1.80611	1.85046	1.89584	1.94227	1.98979	2.03841	2.08815	2.13905
15 years	2.42726	2.51721	2.61037	2.70686	2.80679	2.91029	3.01747	3.12846
20 years	3.26204	3.42419	3.59420	3.77243	3.95926	4.15510	4.36038	4.57553

	8%	8.25%	8.50%	8.75%	9.00%	9.25%	9.50%	9.75%
1 year	1.08160	1.08420	1.08681	1.08941	1.09203	1.09464	1.09726	1.09988
5 years	1.48024	1.49813	1.51621	1.53449	1.55297	1.57165	1.59052	1.60961
10 years	2.19112	2.24440	2.29891	2.35467	2.41171	2.47007	2.52977	2.59083
15 years	3.24340	3.36241	3.48564	3.61322	3.74532	3.88208	4.02366	4.17022
20 years	4.80102	5.03733	5.28497	5.54446	5.81636	6.10125	6.39972	6.71242

	10%	10.25%	10.50%	10.75%	11.00%	11.25%	11.50%	11.75%
1 year	1.10250	1.10513	1.10776	1.11039	1.11303	1.11566	1.11831	1.12095
5 years	1.62889	1.64839	1.66810	1.68801	1.70814	1.72849	1.74906	1.76984
10 years	2.65330	2.71719	2.78254	2.84939	2.91776	2.98768	3.05920	3.13234
15 years	4.32194	4.47899	4.64155	4.80981	4.98395	5.16418	5.35071	5.54374
20 years	7.03999	7.38313	7.74255	8.11902	8.51331	8.92625	9.35869	9.81153

Compound Interest Table (continued)

Compounded Quarterly

	4%	4.25%	4.50%	4.75%	5.00%	5.25%	5.50%	5.75%
1 year	1.04060	1.04318	1.04577	1.04835	1.05095	1.05354	1.05614	1.05875
5 years	1.22019	1.23538	1.25075	1.26630	1.28204	1.29796	1.31407	1.33036
10 years	1.48886	1.52617	1.56438	1.60352	1.64362	1.68470	1.72677	1.76987
15 years	1.81670	1.88539	1.95665	2.03054	2.10718	2.18666	2.26909	2.35457
20 years	2.21672	2.32918	2.44727	2.57128	2.70148	2.83820	2.98174	3.13244

	6%	6.25%	6.50%	6.75%	7.00%	7.25%	7.50%	7.75%
1 year	1.06136	1.06398	1.06660	1.06923	1.07186	1.07450	1.07714	1.07978
5 years	1.34686	1.36354	1.38042	1.39750	1.41478	1.43226	1.44995	1.46784
10 years	1.81402	1.85924	1.90556	1.95300	2.00160	2.05137	2.10235	2.15456
15 years	2.44322	2.53515	2.63047	2.72932	2.83182	2.93810	3.04830	3.16256
20 years	3.29066	3.45677	3.63115	3.81422	4.00639	4.20812	4.41987	4.64214

	8%	8.25%	8.50%	8.75%	9.00%	9.25%	9.50%	9.75%
1 year	1.08243	1.08509	1.08775	1.09041	1.09308	1.09576	1.09844	1.10112
5 years	1.48595	1.50426	1.52279	1.54154	1.56051	1.57970	1.59911	1.61875
10 years	2.20804	2.26281	2.31890	2.37635	2.43519	2.49544	2.55715	2.62035
15 years	3.28103	3.40386	3.53122	3.66325	3.80013	3.94205	4.08917	4.24168
20 years	4.87544	5.12031	5.37732	5.64705	5.93015	6.22724	6.53903	6.86622

	10%	10.25%	10.50%	10.75%	11.00%	11.25%	11.50%	11.75%
1 year	1.10381	1.10651	1.10921	1.11191	1.11462	1.11734	1.12006	1.12278
5 years	1.63862	1.65872	1.67905	1.69962	1.72043	1.74148	1.76278	1.78432
10 years	2.68506	2.75134	2.81921	2.88871	2.95987	3.03275	3.10738	3.18379
15 years	4.39979	4.56369	4.73359	4.90970	5.09225	5.28147	5.47761	5.68090
20 years	7.20957	7.56986	7.94792	8.34462	8.76085	9.19758	9.65579	10.13650

Compound Interest Table (continued)

Compounded Monthly

	4%	4.25%	4.50%	4.75%	5.00%	5.25%	5.50%	5.75%
1 year	1.04074	1.04334	1.04594	1.04855	1.05116	1.05378	1.05641	1.05904
5 years	1.22100	1.23630	1.25180	1.26748	1.28336	1.29943	1.31570	1.33218
10 years	1.49083	1.52844	1.56699	1.60651	1.64701	1.68852	1.73108	1.77469
15 years	1.82030	1.88962	1.96156	2.03622	2.11370	2.19412	2.27758	2.36420
20 years	2.22258	2.33614	2.45547	2.58087	2.71264	2.85111	2.99663	3.14953

	6%	6.25%	6.50%	6.75%	7.00%	7.25%	7.50%	7.75%
1 year	1.06168	1.06432	1.06697	1.06963	1.07229	1.07496	1.07763	1.08031
5 years	1.34885	1.36573	1.38282	1.40011	1.41763	1.43535	1.45329	1.47146
10 years	1.81940	1.86522	1.91218	1.96032	2.00966	2.06023	2.11206	2.16519
15 years	2.45409	2.54738	2.64420	2.74468	2.84895	2.95716	3.06945	3.18599
20 years	3.31020	3.47904	3.65645	3.84286	4.03874	4.24456	4.46082	4.68805

	8%	8.25%	8.50%	8.75%	9.00%	9.25%	9.50%	9.75%
1 year	1.08300	1.08569	1.08839	1.09110	1.09381	1.09652	1.09925	1.10198
5 years	1.48985	1.50846	1.52730	1.54637	1.56568	1.58523	1.60501	1.62504
10 years	2.21964	2.27545	2.33265	2.39127	2.45136	2.51294	2.57606	2.64074
15 years	3.30692	3.43242	3.56265	3.69780	3.83804	3.98358	4.13459	4.29130
20 years	4.92680	5.17766	5.44124	5.71818	6.00915	6.31486	6.63606	6.97352

	10%	10.25%	10.50%	10.75%	11.00%	11.25%	11.50%	11.75%
1 year	1.10471	1.10746	1.11020	1.11296	1.11572	1.11849	1.12126	1.12404
5 years	1.64531	1.66583	1.68660	1.70763	1.72892	1.75046	1.77227	1.79435
10 years	2.70704	2.77499	2.84463	2.91600	2.98915	3.06412	3.14095	3.21969
15 years	4.45392	4.62266	4.79776	4.97945	5.16799	5.36362	5.56661	5.77725
20 years	7.32807	7.70057	8.09192	8.50307	8.93502	9.38881	9.86555	10.36640

Compound Interest Table (continued)

Compounded Daily

	4%	4.25%	4.50%	4.75%	5.00%	5.25%	5.50%	5.75%
1 year	1.04081	1.04341	1.04602	1.04864	1.05127	1.05390	1.05654	1.05918
5 years	1.22139	1.23675	1.25231	1.26806	1.28400	1.30015	1.31650	1.33306
10 years	1.49179	1.52955	1.56827	1.60796	1.64866	1.69040	1.73318	1.77705
15 years	1.82206	1.89168	1.96395	2.03899	2.11689	2.19777	2.28174	2.36892
20 years	2.22544	2.33953	2.45947	2.58555	2.71810	2.85744	3.00392	3.15791

	6%	6.25%	6.50%	6.75%	7.00%	7.25%	7.50%	7.75%
1 year	1.06183	1.06449	1.06715	1.06982	1.07250	1.07519	1.07788	1.08057
5 years	1.34983	1.36680	1.38399	1.40140	1.41902	1.43687	1.45494	1.47323
10 years	1.82203	1.86815	1.91543	1.96391	2.01362	2.06458	2.11684	2.17041
15 years	2.45942	2.55338	2.65094	2.75222	2.85736	2.96653	3.07986	3.19752
20 years	3.31979	3.48997	3.66887	3.85694	4.05466	4.26250	4.48100	4.71070

	8%	8.25%	8.50%	8.75%	9.00%	9.25%	9.50%	9.75%
1 year	1.08328	1.08599	1.08871	1.09143	1.09416	1.09690	1.09965	1.10240
5 years	1.49176	1.51052	1.52951	1.54875	1.56823	1.58795	1.60791	1.62813
10 years	2.22535	2.28167	2.33942	2.39862	2.45933	2.52157	2.58539	2.65082
15 years	3.31968	3.44650	3.57817	3.71487	3.85678	4.00412	4.15709	4.31589
20 years	4.95216	5.20601	5.47286	5.75340	6.04831	6.35833	6.68424	7.02686

	10%	10.25%	10.50%	10.75%	11.00%	11.25%	11.50%	11.75%
1 year	1.10516	1.10792	1.11069	1.11347	1.11626	1.11905	1.12185	1.12466
5 years	1.64861	1.66934	1.69033	1.71159	1.73311	1.75490	1.77697	1.79931
10 years	2.71791	2.78669	2.85722	2.92953	3.00367	3.07968	3.15762	3.23753
15 years	4.48077	4.65194	4.82965	5.01414	5.20569	5.40454	5.61100	5.82533
20 years	7.38703	7.76567	8.16370	8.58214	9.02202	9.48445	9.97057	10.48160

Monthly Payment Table

	4%	4.25%	4.50%	4.75%	5.00%	5.25%	5.50%	5.75%
1 year	0.0851499	0.0852642	0.0853785	0.0854930	0.0856075	0.0857221	0.0858368	0.0859516
2 years	0.0434249	0.0435363	0.0436478	0.0437595	0.0438714	0.0439834	0.0440957	0.0442080
3 years	0.0295240	0.0296353	0.0297469	0.0298588	0.0299709	0.0300833	0.0301959	0.0303088
4 years	0.0225791	0.0226911	0.0228035	0.0229162	0.0230293	0.0231427	0.0232565	0.0233706
5 years	0.0184165	0.0185296	0.0186430	0.0187569	0.0188712	0.0189860	0.0191012	0.0192168
15 years	0.0073969	0.0075228	0.0076499	0.0077783	0.0079079	0.0080388	0.0081708	0.0083041
20 years	0.0060598	0.0061923	0.0063265	0.0064622	0.0065996	0.0067384	0.0068789	0.0070208
25 years	0.0052784	0.0054174	0.0055583	0.0057012	0.0058459	0.0059925	0.0061409	0.0062911
30 years	0.0047742	0.0049194	0.0050669	0.0052165	0.0053682	0.0055220	0.0056779	0.0058357
	6%	6.25%	6.50%	6.75%	7.00%	7.25%	7.50%	7.75%
1 year	0.0860664	0.0861814	0.0862964	0.0864115	0.0865267	0.0866420	0.0867574	0.0868729
2 years	0.0443206	0.0444333	0.0445463	0.0446593	0.0447726	0.0448860	0.0449996	0.0451134
3 years	0.0304219	0.0305353	0.0306490	0.0307629	0.0308771	0.0309915	0.0311062	0.0312212
4 years	0.0234850	0.0235998	0.0237150	0.0238304	0.0239462	0.0240624	0.0241789	0.0242957
5 years	0.0193328	0.0194493	0.0195661	0.0196835	0.0198012	0.0199194	0.0200379	0.0201570
15 years	0.0084386	0.0085742	0.0087111	0.0088491	0.0089883	0.0091286	0.0092701	0.0094128
20 years	0.0071643	0.0073093	0.0074557	0.0076036	0.0077530	0.0079038	0.0080559	0.0082095
25 years	0.0064430	0.0065967	0.0067521	0.0069091	0.0070678	0.0072281	0.0073899	0.0075533
30 years	0.0059955	0.0061572	0.0063207	0.0064860	0.0066530	0.0068218	0.0069921	0.0071641
	8%	8.25%	8.50%	8.75%	9.00%	9.25%	9.50%	9.75%
1 year	0.0869884	0.0871041	0.0872198	0.0873356	0.0874515	0.0875675	0.0876835	0.0877997
2 years	0.0452273	0.0453414	0.0454557	0.0455701	0.0456847	0.0457995	0.0459145	0.0460296
3 years	0.0313364	0.0314518	0.0315675	0.0316835	0.0317997	0.0319162	0.0320329	0.0321499
4 years	0.0244129	0.0245304	0.0246483	0.0247665	0.0248850	0.0250039	0.0251231	0.0252427
5 years	0.0202764	0.0203963	0.0205165	0.0206372	0.0207584	0.0208799	0.0210019	0.0211242
15 years	0.0095565	0.0097014	0.0098474	0.0099945	0.0101427	0.0102919	0.0104422	0.0105936
20 years	0.0083644	0.0085207	0.0086782	0.0088371	0.0089973	0.0091587	0.0093213	0.0094852
25 years	0.0077182	0.0078845	0.0080523	0.0082214	0.0083920	0.0085638	0.0087370	0.0089114
30 years	0.0073376	0.0075127	0.0076891	0.0078670	0.0080462	0.0082268	0.0084085	0.0085915
	10%	10.25%	10.50%	10.75%	11.00%	11.25%	11.50%	11.75%
1 year	0.0879159	0.0880322	0.0881486	0.0882651	0.0883817	0.0884983	0.0886151	0.0887319
2 years	0.0461449	0.0462604	0.0463760	0.0464919	0.0466078	0.0467240	0.0468403	0.0469568
3 years	0.0322672	0.0323847	0.0325024	0.0326205	0.0327387	0.0328572	0.0329760	0.0330950
4 years	0.0253626	0.0254828	0.0256034	0.0257243	0.0258455	0.0259671	0.0260890	0.0262113
5 years	0.0212470	0.0213703	0.0214939	0.0216180	0.0217424	0.0218673	0.0219926	0.0221183
15 years	0.0107461	0.0108995	0.0110540	0.0112095	0.0113660	0.0115234	0.0116819	0.0118413
20 years	0.0096502	0.0098164	0.0099838	0.0101523	0.0103219	0.0104926	0.0106643	0.0108371
25 years	0.0090870	0.0092638	0.0094418	0.0096209	0.0098011	0.0099824	0.0101647	0.0103480
30 years	0.0087757	0.0089610	0.0091474	0.0093348	0.0095232	0.0097126	0.0099029	0.0100941

To use this table:
1. Locate the desired interest rate in the top row.
2. Locate the number of years in the left-hand column.
3. Locate the number where the interest-rate column and the number-of-years row meet. This is the monthly payment factor.

Example A home has a 30-year mortgage at an annual interest rate of 6%.
The interest rate is 6%.
The number of years is 30.
The number where the row and column meet is 0.0059955. This is the monthly payment factor.

Solutions to "You Try It"

Solutions to Chapter 1 "You Try It"

SECTION 1.1

Try It 1

$$\begin{array}{ccccccccccccccc} \vdash & + & + & + & + & + & \blacklozenge & + & + & + & + & + & + & + & \rightarrow \\ 0 & 1 & 2 & 3 & 4 & 5 & 6 & 7 & 8 & 9 & 10 & 11 & 12 & 13 & 14 \end{array}$$

Try It 2   **a.** $45 > 29$ **b.** $27 > 0$

Try It 3   Thirty-six million four hundred sixty-two thousand seventy-five

Try It 4   452,007

Try It 5 $60,000 + 8000 + 200 + 80 + 1$

Try It 6 $100,000 + 9000 + 200 + 7$

Try It 7
$$\begin{array}{l} \quad\quad\rule[1ex]{0.6em}{0.4pt}\!\!\rule[0ex]{0.4pt}{1.2em}\text{ Given place value} \\ 368{,}492 \\ \quad\quad\rule[0ex]{0.4pt}{1.2em}\!\!\rule[0ex]{0.6em}{0.4pt}\, 8 > 5 \end{array}$$
368,492 rounded to the nearest ten-thousand is 370,000.

Try It 8
$$\begin{array}{l} \quad\rule[1ex]{0.6em}{0.4pt}\!\!\rule[0ex]{0.4pt}{1.2em}\text{ Given place value} \\ 3962 \\ \quad\rule[0ex]{0.4pt}{1.2em}\!\!\rule[0ex]{0.6em}{0.4pt}\, 6 > 5 \end{array}$$
3962 rounded to the nearest hundred is 4000.

SECTION 1.2

Try It 1

$$\begin{array}{r} \overset{1\,1}{347} \\ +12{,}453 \\ \hline 12{,}800 \end{array}$$

• $7 + 3 = 10$
Write the 0 in the ones column. Carry the 1 to the tens column.
$1 + 4 + 5 = 10$
Write the 0 in the tens column. Carry the 1 to the hundreds column.
$1 + 3 + 4 = 8$

347 increased by 12,453 is 12,800.

Try It 2

$$\begin{array}{r} \overset{2}{95} \\ 88 \\ + \; 67 \\ \hline 250 \end{array}$$

• $5 + 8 + 7 = 20$
Write the 0 in the ones column.
Carry the 2 to the tens column.

You Try It 3

$$\begin{array}{r} \overset{1\;1\;\;2\,1}{392} \\ 4{,}079 \\ 89{,}035 \\ + \; 4{,}992 \\ \hline 98{,}498 \end{array}$$

You Try It 4

Strategy   To find the total square footage of Walmart stores in the United States, read the table to find the square footage of discount stores, Supercenters, Sam's Clubs, and neighborhood markets. Then add the four numbers.

Solution
$$\begin{array}{r} 68 \\ 560 \\ 81 \\ + \quad 7 \\ \hline 716 \end{array}$$
The total square footage of Walmart stores in the United States is 716 million square feet.

SECTION 1.3

You Try It 1
$$\begin{array}{r} 8925 \\ - \; 6413 \\ \hline 2512 \end{array} \qquad \begin{array}{l} \textit{Check:} \end{array} \qquad \begin{array}{r} 6413 \\ + \; 2512 \\ \hline 8925 \end{array}$$

You Try It 2
$$\begin{array}{r} 17{,}504 \\ - \; 9{,}302 \\ \hline 8{,}202 \end{array} \qquad \begin{array}{l} \textit{Check:} \end{array} \qquad \begin{array}{r} 9{,}302 \\ + \; 8{,}202 \\ \hline 17{,}504 \end{array}$$

You Try It 3
$$\begin{array}{r} \overset{2\;\;14\;\;7\;\;11}{\cancel{3}\;\cancel{4}\;\cancel{8}\;\cancel{1}} \\ - \quad 8\;6\;5 \\ \hline 2\;6\;1\;6 \end{array} \qquad \begin{array}{l} \textit{Check:} \end{array} \qquad \begin{array}{r} 865 \\ + \; 2616 \\ \hline 3481 \end{array}$$

You Try It 4
$$\begin{array}{r} \overset{\quad\quad\;\;15}{\overset{4\;\;5\;\;12}{5\;4{,}\cancel{5}\;\cancel{6}\;2}} \\ - \; 1\;4{,}4\;8\;5 \\ \hline 4\;0{,}0\;7\;7 \end{array} \qquad \begin{array}{l} \textit{Check:} \end{array} \qquad \begin{array}{r} 14{,}485 \\ + \; 40{,}077 \\ \hline 54{,}562 \end{array}$$

You Try It 5

$$
\begin{array}{r}
^{3}^{10}\\
6\ 4\ ,\ \cancel{0}\ 0\ 3\\
-\ 5\ 4\ ,\ 9\ 3\ 6\\
\end{array}
$$

• There are two zeros in the minuend. Borrow 1 thousand from the thousands column and write 10 in the hundreds column.

$$
\begin{array}{r}
^{9}\\
^{3}^{10}^{10}\\
6\ 4\ ,\ \cancel{0}\ \cancel{0}\ 3\\
-\ 5\ 4\ ,\ 9\ 3\ 6\\
\end{array}
$$

• Borrow 1 hundred from the hundreds column and write 10 in the tens column.

$$
\begin{array}{r}
^{13}\ ^{9}\ ^{9}\\
^{5}\ ^{3}\ ^{10}\ ^{10}\ ^{13}\\
\cancel{6}\ \cancel{4}\ ,\ \cancel{0}\ \cancel{0}\ \cancel{3}\\
-\ 5\ 4\ ,\ 9\ 3\ 6\\
\hline
9\ ,\ 0\ 6\ 7\\
\end{array}
$$

• Borrow 1 ten from the tens column and add 10 to the 3 in the ones column.

$$
\begin{array}{r}
Check:\quad 54{,}936\\
+\ 9{,}067\\
\hline
64{,}003\\
\end{array}
$$

You Try It 6

Strategy   To find the difference, subtract the population of the Northeast (55,317,240) from the population of the Midwest (66,927,001).

Solution

$$
\begin{array}{r}
66{,}927{,}001\\
-55{,}317{,}240\\
\hline
11{,}609{,}761\\
\end{array}
$$

There are 11,609,761 more people living in the Midwest than in the Northeast.

You Try It 7

Strategy   To find your take-home pay:
- ▶ Add to find the total of the deductions (127 + 18 + 35).
- ▶ Subtract the total of the deductions from your total salary (638).

Solution

$$
\begin{array}{r}
127\\
18\\
+\ 35\\
\hline
180\\
\end{array}
\qquad
\begin{array}{r}
638\\
-\ 180\\
\hline
458\\
\end{array}
$$

180 in deductions

Your take-home pay is $458.

SECTION 1.4

You Try It 1

$$
\begin{array}{r}
^{3}\,^{5}\\
648\\
\times\quad 7\\
\hline
4536\\
\end{array}
$$

• $7 \times 8 = 56$
Write the 6 in the ones column. Carry the 5 to the tens column.
$7 \times 4 = 28, 28 + 5 = 33$
$7 \times 6 = 42, 42 + 3 = 45$

You Try It 2

$$
\begin{array}{r}
756\\
\times\quad 305\\
\hline
3780\\
22680\\
\hline
230{,}580\\
\end{array}
$$

• $5 \times 756 = 3780$
Write a zero in the tens column for 0×756.
$3 \times 756 = 2268$

You Try It 3

Strategy   To find the amount of food eaten in one ye multiply the amount eaten each day (150) the number of days in one year (365).

Solution

$$
\begin{array}{r}
150\\
\times\quad 365\\
\hline
750\\
900\\
450\\
\hline
54{,}750\\
\end{array}
$$

The elephant will eat 54,750 pounds of foc in one year.

You Try It 4

Strategy   To find the total cost of the order:
- ▶ Find the cost of the sports jackets by mu tiplying the number of jackets (25) by th cost for each jacket (62).
- ▶ Add the product to the cost for the 80 su (7600).

Solution

$$
\begin{array}{r}
62\\
\times\quad 25\\
\hline
310\\
124\\
\hline
1550\\
\end{array}
\qquad
\begin{array}{r}
7600\\
+\ 1550\\
\hline
9150\\
\end{array}
$$

• Cost for jackets

The total cost of the order is $9150.

SECTION 1.5

You Try It 1

$$
\begin{array}{r}
7\\
9\overline{)63}\\
\end{array}
$$

Check: $7 \times 9 = 63$

You Try It 2

$$
\begin{array}{r}
453\\
9\overline{)4077}\\
-36\\
\hline
47\\
-45\\
\hline
27\\
-27\\
\hline
0\\
\end{array}
$$

Check: $453 \times 9 = 4077$

Try It 3

```
        705
    9) 6345
     −63
       04     • Think 9)4. Place 0 in quotient.
      − 0     • Multiply 0 × 9. Subtract.
        45    • Bring down the 5.
      −45
         0
```

Check: 705 × 9 = 6345

Try It 4

```
        870 r5
    6) 5225
     −48
       42
      −42
        05    • Think 6)5. Place 0 in quotient.
       − 0    • Multiply 0 × 6. Subtract.
         5
```

Check: (870 × 6) + 5 =
            5220 + 5 = 5225

Try It 5

```
        3,058 r3
    7) 21,409
     −21
       04     • Think 7)4. Place 0 in quotient.
      − 0     • Multiply 0 × 7. Subtract.
        40
       −35
         59
        −56
          3
```

Check: (3058 × 7) + 3 =
            21,406 + 3 = 21,409

Try It 6

```
        109
    42) 4578
     −42
       37     • Think 42)37. Place 0 in quotient.
      − 0     • Multiply 0 × 42. Subtract.
        378
       −378
          0
```

Check: (109 × 42) = 4578

You Try It 7

```
        470 r29
    39) 18,359
     −15 6
        2 75
       −2 73
          29
         − 0
          29
```

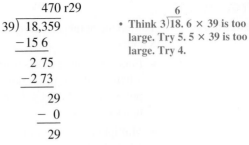

• Think 3)18. 6 × 39 is too large. Try 5. 5 × 39 is too large. Try 4.

Check: (470 × 39) + 29 =
            18,330 + 29 = 18,359

You Try It 8

```
         62 r111
    534) 33,219
      −32 04
        1 179
       −1 068
          111
```

Check: (62 × 534) + 111 =
            33,108 + 111 = 33,219

You Try It 9

```
         421 r33
    515) 216,848
      −206 0
        10 84
       −10 30
          548
         −515
           33
```

Check: (421 × 515) + 33 =
            216,815 + 33 = 216,848

You Try It 10

Strategy   To find the number of tires that can
be stored on each shelf, divide the number of
tires (270) by the number of shelves (15).

Solution

```
        18
    15) 270
     −15
       120
      −120
         0
```

Each shelf can store 18 tires.

You Try It 11

Strategy   To find the number of cases produced in 8 hours:

▶ Find the number of cases produced in 1 hour by dividing the number of cans produced (12,600) by the number of cans to a case (24).

▶ Multiply the number of cases produced in 1 hour by 8.

Solution

$$\begin{array}{r} 525 \\ 24\overline{)\,12,600} \\ -12\,0 \\ \hline 60 \\ -48 \\ \hline 120 \\ -120 \\ \hline 0 \end{array}$$

$$\begin{array}{r} 525 \\ \times \quad 8 \\ \hline 4200 \end{array}$$

In 8 hours, 4200 cases are produced.

SECTION 1.6

You Try It 1 $2 \cdot 2 \cdot 2 \cdot 2 \cdot 3 \cdot 3 \cdot 3 = 2^4 \cdot 3^3$

You Try It 2 $10 \cdot 10 \cdot 10 \cdot 10 \cdot 10 \cdot 10 \cdot 10 = 10^7$

You Try It 3 $2^3 \cdot 5^2 = (2 \cdot 2 \cdot 2) \cdot (5 \cdot 5) = 8 \cdot 25$
$ = 200$

You Try It 4 $5 \cdot (8 - 4)^2 \div 4 - 2$

$= 5 \cdot 4^2 \div 4 - 2$ • Parentheses
$= 5 \cdot 16 \div 4 - 2$ • Exponents
$= 80 \div 4 - 2$ • Multiplication and division
$= 20 - 2$
$= 18$ • Subtraction

SECTION 1.7

You Try It 1

$40 \div 1 = 40$
$40 \div 2 = 20$
$40 \div 3$ • Will not divide evenly
$40 \div 4 = 10$
$40 \div 5 = 8$
$40 \div 6$ • Will not divide evenly
$40 \div 7$ • Will not divide evenly
$40 \div 8 = 5$ • Factors are repeating

1, 2, 4, 5, 8, 10, 20, and 40 are the factors of 40.

You Try It 2

$$\begin{array}{r|r} & 44 \\ \hline 2 & 22 \\ 2 & 11 \\ 11 & 1 \end{array}$$
• $44 \div 2 = 22$
• $22 \div 2 = 11$
• $11 \div 11 = 1$

$44 = 2 \cdot 2 \cdot 11$

You Try It 3

$$\begin{array}{r|r} & 177 \\ \hline 3 & 59 \\ 59 & 1 \end{array}$$
• Try only 2, 3, 4, 7, and 11, because $11^2 > 59$.

$177 = 3 \cdot 59$

Solutions to Chapter 2 "You Try It"

SECTION 2.1

You Try It 1

	2	3	5
$12 =$	$(2 \cdot 2)$	3	
$27 =$		$(3 \cdot 3 \cdot 3)$	
$50 =$	2		$(5 \cdot 5)$

The LCM $= 2 \cdot 2 \cdot 3 \cdot 3 \cdot 3 \cdot 5 \cdot 5 = 2700.$

You Try It 2

	2	3	5
$36 =$	$(2 \cdot 2)$	$3 \cdot 3$	
$60 =$	$2 \cdot 2$	(3)	5
$72 =$	$2 \cdot 2 \cdot 2$	$3 \cdot 3$	

The GCF $= 2 \cdot 2 \cdot 3 = 12.$

You Try It 3

	2	3	5	11
$11 =$				11
$24 =$	$2 \cdot 2 \cdot 2$	3		
$30 =$	2	3	5	

Because no numbers are circled, the GCF $= 1.$

SECTION 2.2

You Try It 1 $4\dfrac{1}{4}$

You Try It 2 $\dfrac{17}{4}$

You Try It 3

$$\begin{array}{r} 4 \\ 5\overline{)\,22} \\ -20 \\ \hline 2 \end{array}$$
   $\dfrac{22}{5} = 4\dfrac{2}{5}$

You Try It 4

$$\begin{array}{r} 4 \\ 7\overline{)\,28} \\ -28 \\ \hline 0 \end{array}$$
   $\dfrac{28}{7} = 4$

Try It 5 $14\frac{^{+7}5}{^{×}8} = \frac{112 + 5}{8} = \frac{117}{8}$

SECTION 2.3

Try It 1 $45 \div 5 = 9, \qquad \frac{3}{5} = \frac{3 \cdot 9}{5 \cdot 9} = \frac{27}{45}$

$\frac{27}{45}$ is equivalent to $\frac{3}{5}$.

Try It 2   Write 6 as $\frac{6}{1}$.

$18 \div 1 = 18, \qquad 6 = \frac{6 \cdot 18}{1 \cdot 18} = \frac{108}{18}$

$\frac{108}{18}$ is equivalent to 6.

Try It 3 $\frac{16}{24} = \frac{\overset{1}{2} \cdot \overset{1}{2} \cdot \overset{1}{2} \cdot 2}{\underset{1}{2} \cdot \underset{1}{2} \cdot \underset{1}{2} \cdot 3} = \frac{2}{3}$

Try It 4 $\frac{8}{56} = \frac{\overset{1}{2} \cdot \overset{1}{2} \cdot \overset{1}{2}}{\underset{1}{2} \cdot \underset{1}{2} \cdot \underset{1}{2} \cdot 7} = \frac{1}{7}$

Try It 5 $\frac{15}{32} = \frac{3 \cdot 5}{2 \cdot 2 \cdot 2 \cdot 2 \cdot 2} = \frac{15}{32}$

Try It 6 $\frac{48}{36} = \frac{\overset{1}{2} \cdot \overset{1}{2} \cdot 2 \cdot 2 \cdot \overset{1}{3}}{\underset{1}{2} \cdot \underset{1}{2} \cdot 3 \cdot 3} = \frac{4}{3} = 1\frac{1}{3}$

SECTION 2.4

Try It 1

$\begin{aligned} &\frac{3}{8} \\ +&\frac{7}{8} \\ \hline &\frac{10}{8} = \frac{5}{4} = 1\frac{1}{4} \end{aligned}$

• The denominators are the same. Add the numerators. Place the sum over the common denominator.

Try It 2

$\begin{aligned} &\frac{7}{9} = \frac{35}{45} \\ +&\frac{11}{15} = \frac{33}{45} \\ \hline &\frac{68}{45} = 1\frac{23}{45} \end{aligned}$

• The LCD is 45.

Try It 3

$\begin{aligned} &\frac{5}{12} = \frac{20}{48} \\ +&\frac{9}{16} = \frac{27}{48} \\ \hline &\frac{47}{48} \end{aligned}$

• The LCD is 48.

You Try It 4

$\begin{aligned} &\frac{3}{4} = \frac{30}{40} \\ &\frac{4}{5} = \frac{32}{40} \\ +&\frac{5}{8} = \frac{25}{40} \\ \hline &\frac{87}{40} = 2\frac{7}{40} \end{aligned}$

• The LCD is 40.

You Try It 5 $7 + \frac{6}{11} = 7\frac{6}{11}$

You Try It 6

$\begin{aligned} &29 \\ +&17\frac{5}{12} \\ \hline &46\frac{5}{12} \end{aligned}$

You Try It 7

$\begin{aligned} &7\frac{4}{5} = 7\frac{24}{30} \\ &6\frac{7}{10} = 6\frac{21}{30} \\ +&13\frac{11}{15} = 13\frac{22}{30} \\ \hline &26\frac{67}{30} = 28\frac{7}{30} \end{aligned}$

• The LCD is 30.

You Try It 8

Strategy   To find the total time spent on the activities, add the three times $\left(4\frac{1}{2}, 3\frac{3}{4}, \text{ and } 1\frac{1}{3}\right)$.

Solution

$\begin{aligned} &4\frac{1}{2} = 4\frac{6}{12} \\ &3\frac{3}{4} = 3\frac{9}{12} \\ +&1\frac{1}{3} = 1\frac{4}{12} \\ \hline &8\frac{19}{12} = 9\frac{7}{12} \end{aligned}$

The total time spent on the three activities was $9\frac{7}{12}$ hours.

You Try It 9

Strategy To find the overtime pay:
▶ Find the total number of overtime hours $\left(1\frac{2}{3} + 3\frac{1}{3} + 2\right)$.
▶ Multiply the total number of hours by the overtime hourly wage (36).

Solution

$$1\frac{2}{3}$$
$$3\frac{1}{3}$$
$$+ 2$$
$$\overline{6\frac{3}{3}} = 7 \text{ hours}$$

$$\begin{array}{r} 36 \\ \times\ 7 \\ \hline 252 \end{array}$$

Jeff earned \$252 in overtime pay.

SECTION 2.5

You Try It 1

$$\frac{16}{27}$$
$$-\frac{7}{27}$$
$$\overline{\frac{9}{27}} = \frac{1}{3}$$

• The denominators are the same. Subtract the numerators. Place the difference over the common denominator.

You Try It 2

$$\frac{13}{18} = \frac{52}{72}$$
$$-\frac{7}{24} = \frac{21}{72}$$
$$\overline{\frac{31}{72}}$$

• LCD = 72

You Try It 3

$$\frac{8}{9} = \frac{16}{18}$$
$$-\frac{5}{6} = \frac{15}{18}$$
$$\overline{\frac{1}{18}}$$

• LCD = 18

You Try It 4

$$21\frac{7}{9} = 21\frac{28}{36} = 20\frac{64}{36}$$
$$-\ 7\frac{11}{12} = 7\frac{33}{36} = 7\frac{33}{36}$$
$$\overline{\hspace{3cm} 13\frac{31}{36}}$$

• LCD = 36

You Try It 5

$$8 = 7\frac{13}{13}$$
$$-2\frac{4}{13} = 2\frac{4}{13}$$
$$\overline{5\frac{9}{13}}$$

• LCD = 13

You Try It 6

Strategy To find the time remaining before the pla lands, subtract the number of hours alread in the air $\left(2\frac{3}{4}\right)$ from the total time of the t $\left(5\frac{1}{2}\right)$.

Solution

$$5\frac{1}{2} = 5\frac{2}{4} = 4\frac{6}{4}$$
$$-2\frac{3}{4} = 2\frac{3}{4} = 2\frac{3}{4}$$
$$\overline{\hspace{2cm} 2\frac{3}{4} \text{ hours}}$$

The plane will land in $2\frac{3}{4}$ hours.

You Try It 7

Strategy To find the amount of weight to be lost du the third month:
▶ Find the total weight loss during the first two months $\left(7\frac{1}{2} + 5\frac{3}{4}\right)$.
▶ Subtract the total weight loss from the (24 pounds).

Solution

$$7\frac{1}{2} = 7\frac{2}{4}$$
$$+5\frac{3}{4} = 5\frac{3}{4}$$
$$\overline{12\frac{5}{4}} = 13\frac{1}{4} \text{ pounds lost}$$

$$24 = 23\frac{4}{4}$$
$$-13\frac{1}{4} = 13\frac{1}{4}$$
$$\overline{10\frac{3}{4} \text{ pounds}}$$

The patient must lose $10\frac{3}{4}$ pounds to achie the goal.

SECTION 2.6

You Try It 1

$$\frac{4}{21} \times \frac{7}{44} = \frac{4 \cdot 7}{21 \cdot 44}$$

$$= \frac{\overset{1}{2} \cdot \overset{1}{2} \cdot \overset{1}{7}}{3 \cdot \underset{1}{7} \cdot \underset{1}{2} \cdot \underset{1}{2} \cdot 11} = \frac{1}{33}$$

Try It 2

$$\frac{7}{12} \times \frac{5}{6} = \frac{7 \cdot 5}{12 \cdot 6}$$

$$= \frac{7 \cdot 5}{2 \cdot 2 \cdot 3 \cdot 2 \cdot 3} = \frac{35}{72}$$

Try It 3

$$\frac{5}{16} \times \frac{12}{25} = \frac{5 \cdot 12}{16 \cdot 25}$$

$$= \frac{\overset{1}{\cancel{5}} \cdot \overset{1}{\cancel{2}} \cdot \overset{1}{\cancel{2}} \cdot 3}{2 \cdot 2 \cdot 2 \cdot 2 \cdot \cancel{5} \cdot 5} = \frac{3}{20}$$

Try It 4

$$5\frac{2}{5} \times \frac{5}{9} = \frac{27}{5} \times \frac{5}{9} = \frac{27 \cdot 5}{5 \cdot 9}$$

$$= \frac{\overset{1}{\cancel{3}} \cdot \overset{1}{\cancel{3}} \cdot 3 \cdot \overset{1}{\cancel{5}}}{\cancel{5} \cdot \cancel{3} \cdot \cancel{3}} = \frac{3}{1} = 3$$

Try It 5

$$3\frac{2}{5} \times 6\frac{1}{4} = \frac{17}{5} \times \frac{25}{4} = \frac{17 \cdot 25}{5 \cdot 4}$$

$$= \frac{17 \cdot \overset{1}{\cancel{5}} \cdot 5}{\cancel{5} \cdot 2 \cdot 2} = \frac{85}{4} = 21\frac{1}{4}$$

Try It 6

Strategy

To find the value of the house today, multiply the old value of the house (170,000) by $2\frac{1}{2}$.

Solution

$$170{,}000 \times 2\frac{1}{2} = \frac{170{,}000}{1} \times \frac{5}{2}$$

$$= \frac{170{,}000 \cdot 5}{1 \cdot 2}$$

$$= 425{,}000$$

The value of the house today is $425,000.

Try It 7

Strategy

To find the cost of the air compressor:

► Multiply to find the value of the drying chamber $\left(\frac{4}{5} \times 160{,}000\right)$.

► Subtract the value of the drying chamber from the total value of the two items (160,000).

Solution

$$\frac{4}{5} \times \frac{160{,}000}{1} = \frac{640{,}000}{5}$$

$$= 128{,}000 \quad \text{• Value of the drying chamber}$$

$$160{,}000 - 128{,}000 = 32{,}000$$

The cost of the air compressor was $32,000.

SECTION 2.7

You Try It 1

$$\frac{3}{7} \div \frac{2}{3} = \frac{3}{7} \times \frac{3}{2} = \frac{3 \cdot 3}{7 \cdot 2} = \frac{9}{14}$$

You Try It 2

$$\frac{3}{4} \div \frac{9}{10} = \frac{3}{4} \times \frac{10}{9}$$

$$= \frac{3 \cdot 10}{4 \cdot 9} = \frac{\overset{1}{\cancel{3}} \cdot \overset{1}{\cancel{2}} \cdot 5}{2 \cdot 2 \cdot \cancel{3} \cdot 3} = \frac{5}{6}$$

You Try It 3

$$\frac{5}{7} \div 6 = \frac{5}{7} \div \frac{6}{1}$$

$$= \frac{5}{7} \times \frac{1}{6} = \frac{5 \cdot 1}{7 \cdot 6}$$

$$= \frac{5}{7 \cdot 2 \cdot 3} = \frac{5}{42}$$

You Try It 4

$$12\frac{3}{5} \div 7 = \frac{63}{5} \div \frac{7}{1} = \frac{63}{5} \times \frac{1}{7}$$

$$= \frac{63 \cdot 1}{5 \cdot 7} = \frac{3 \cdot 3 \cdot \overset{1}{\cancel{7}}}{5 \cdot \cancel{7}}$$

$$= \frac{9}{5} = 1\frac{4}{5}$$

You Try It 5

$$3\frac{2}{3} \div 2\frac{2}{5} = \frac{11}{3} \div \frac{12}{5}$$

$$= \frac{11}{3} \times \frac{5}{12} = \frac{11 \cdot 5}{3 \cdot 12}$$

$$= \frac{11 \cdot 5}{3 \cdot 2 \cdot 2 \cdot 3} = \frac{55}{36} = 1\frac{19}{36}$$

You Try it 6

$$2\frac{5}{6} \div 8\frac{1}{2} = \frac{17}{6} \div \frac{17}{2}$$

$$= \frac{17}{6} \times \frac{2}{17} = \frac{17 \cdot 2}{6 \cdot 17}$$

$$= \frac{\overset{1}{\cancel{17}} \cdot \overset{1}{\cancel{2}}}{2 \cdot 3 \cdot \cancel{17}} = \frac{1}{3}$$

You Try It 7

$$6\frac{2}{5} \div 4 = \frac{32}{5} \div \frac{4}{1}$$

$$= \frac{32}{5} \times \frac{1}{4} = \frac{32 \cdot 1}{5 \cdot 4}$$

$$= \frac{2 \cdot 2 \cdot 2 \cdot \overset{1}{\cancel{2}} \cdot \overset{1}{\cancel{2}}}{5 \cdot \cancel{2} \cdot \cancel{2}} = \frac{8}{5} = 1\frac{3}{5}$$

You Try It 8

Strategy   To find the number of products, divide the number of minutes in 1 hour (60) by the time to assemble one product $\left(7\frac{1}{2}\right)$.

Solution $60 \div 7\dfrac{1}{2} = \dfrac{60}{1} \div \dfrac{15}{2} = \dfrac{60}{1} \cdot \dfrac{2}{15}$

$$= \dfrac{60 \cdot 2}{1 \cdot 15} = 8$$

The factory worker can assemble 8 products in 1 hour.

You Try It 9

Strategy   To find the length of the remaining piece:

▶ Divide the total length of the board (16) by the length of each shelf $\left(3\frac{1}{3}\right)$. This will give you the number of shelves cut, with a certain fraction of a shelf left over.

▶ Multiply the fractional part of the result in step 1 by the length of one shelf to determine the length of the remaining piece.

Solution $16 \div 3\dfrac{1}{3} = \dfrac{16}{1} \div \dfrac{10}{3}$

$$= \dfrac{16}{1} \times \dfrac{3}{10} = \dfrac{16 \cdot 3}{1 \cdot 10}$$

$$= \dfrac{2 \cdot 2 \cdot 2 \cdot \overset{1}{\cancel{2}} \cdot 3}{\underset{1}{\cancel{2}} \cdot 5} = \dfrac{24}{5}$$

$$= 4\dfrac{4}{5}$$

There are 4 pieces that are each $3\frac{1}{3}$ feet long. There is 1 piece that is $\frac{4}{5}$ of $3\frac{1}{3}$ feet long.

$\dfrac{4}{5} \times 3\dfrac{1}{3} = \dfrac{4}{5} \times \dfrac{10}{3}$

$$= \dfrac{4 \cdot 10}{5 \cdot 3} = \dfrac{2 \cdot 2 \cdot 2 \cdot \overset{1}{\cancel{5}}}{\underset{1}{\cancel{5}} \cdot 3}$$

$$= \dfrac{8}{3} = 2\dfrac{2}{3}$$

The length of the piece remaining is $2\frac{2}{3}$ feet.

SECTION 2.8

You Try It 1 $\dfrac{9}{14} = \dfrac{27}{42}$ $\dfrac{13}{21} = \dfrac{26}{42}$ $\dfrac{9}{14} > \dfrac{13}{21}$

You Try It 2 $\left(\dfrac{1}{13}\right)^2 \cdot \left(\dfrac{1}{4} + \dfrac{1}{6}\right) \div \dfrac{5}{13}$

$$= \left(\dfrac{1}{13}\right)^2 \cdot \left(\dfrac{5}{12}\right) \div \dfrac{5}{13}$$

$$= \left(\dfrac{1}{169}\right) \cdot \left(\dfrac{5}{12}\right) \div \dfrac{5}{13}$$

$$= \left(\dfrac{1 \cdot 5}{13 \cdot 13 \cdot 12}\right) \div \dfrac{5}{13}$$

$$= \left(\dfrac{1 \cdot 5}{13 \cdot 13 \cdot 12}\right) \times \dfrac{13}{5}$$

$$= \dfrac{1 \cdot \overset{1}{\cancel{5}} \cdot \overset{1}{\cancel{13}}}{\underset{1}{\cancel{13}} \cdot 13 \cdot 12 \cdot \underset{1}{\cancel{5}}} = \dfrac{1}{156}$$

Solutions to Chapter 3 "You Try It"

SECTION 3.1

You Try It 1   The digit 4 is in the thousandths place.

You Try It 2   Fifty-five and six thousand eighty-three ten-thousandths

You Try It 3   806.00491   • 1 is in the hundred-thousandths place.

You Try It 4

   Given place value

3.675849

   4 < 5

3.675849 rounded to the nearest ten-thousandth is 3.6758.

You Try It 5

   Given place value

48.907

   0 < 5

48.907 rounded to the nearest tenth is 48.9.

You Try It 6

   Given place value

31.8652

   8 > 5

31.8652 rounded to the nearest whole number is 32.

You Try It 7   0.15   0.107

$\dfrac{15}{100}$ $\dfrac{107}{1000}$ • Write the numbers as fractions.

$\dfrac{150}{1000}$ $\dfrac{107}{1000}$ • Write the fractions with common denominator.

$\dfrac{150}{1000} > \dfrac{107}{1000}$ • Compare the fractions

0.15 > 0.107

SECTION 3.2

Try It 1

$$\begin{array}{r}
\overset{1\ 2}{4.62} \\
27.9 \\
+\ \ 0.62054 \\
\hline
33.14054
\end{array}$$

• Place the decimal points on a vertical line.

Try It 2

$$\begin{array}{r}
\overset{1}{6.05} \\
12. \\
+\ \ 0.374 \\
\hline
18.424
\end{array}$$

Try It 3

Strategy Find the number of minutes for Facebook (19.2) and for Hulu (215.5) in the table. Then add the numbers.

Solution $19.2 + 215.5 = 234.7$

The total number of minutes watched per viewer for Internet users on Facebook and Hulu was 234.7 minutes.

Try It 4

Strategy To find the total income, add the four commissions (985.80, 791.46, 829.75, and 635.42) to the salary (875).

Solution $875 + 985.80 + 791.46 + 829.75 + 635.42$
$= 4117.43$

Anita's total income was $4117.43.

SECTION 3.3

Try It 1

$$\begin{array}{r}
\overset{11\ \ 9}{\overset{6\ \not{1}\ 10\,13}{\not{7}\,\not{2}.\not{0}\,\not{3}\,9}} \\
-\ \ \ 8.4\,7 \\
\hline
6\,3.5\,6\,9
\end{array}$$
Check:
$$\begin{array}{r}
\overset{1\ 1\ 1}{8.47} \\
+\ 63.569 \\
\hline
72.039
\end{array}$$

Try It 2

$$\begin{array}{r}
\overset{14\ \ 9}{\overset{2\ \ 4\ 10\,10}{\not{3}\,\not{5}.\not{0}\,\not{0}}} \\
-\ \ \ 9.6\,7 \\
\hline
2\,5.3\,3
\end{array}$$
Check:
$$\begin{array}{r}
\overset{1\ 1\ 1}{9.67} \\
+\ 25.33 \\
\hline
35.00
\end{array}$$

Try It 3

$$\begin{array}{r}
\overset{16}{\overset{2\ 6\ 9\ 9\ 10}{\not{3}.\not{7}\,\not{0}\,\not{0}\,\not{0}}} \\
-\ 1.9\,7\,1\,5 \\
\hline
1.7\,2\,8\,5
\end{array}$$
Check:
$$\begin{array}{r}
\overset{1\ 1\ 1\ 1}{1.9715} \\
+\ 1.7285 \\
\hline
3.7000
\end{array}$$

Try It 4

Strategy To find the amount of change, subtract the cost of your breakfast (6.85) from 10.

Solution

$$\begin{array}{r}
10.00 \\
-\ 6.85 \\
\hline
3.15
\end{array}$$

Your change was $3.15.

You Try It 5

Strategy To find the new balance:

▶ Add to find the total of the three checks (1025.60 + 79.85 + 162.47).
▶ Subtract the total from the previous balance (2472.69).

Solution

$$\begin{array}{r}
1025.60 \\
79.85 \\
+\ 162.47 \\
\hline
1267.92
\end{array}
\qquad
\begin{array}{r}
2472.69 \\
-\ 1267.92 \\
\hline
1204.77
\end{array}$$

The new balance is $1204.77.

SECTION 3.4

You Try It 1

$$\begin{array}{r}
870 \\
\times\ \ \ 4.6 \\
\hline
522\ 0 \\
3480 \\
\hline
4002.0
\end{array}$$

• 1 decimal place

• 1 decimal place

You Try It 2

$$\begin{array}{r}
0.000086 \\
\times\ \ \ \ \ \ 0.057 \\
\hline
602 \\
430 \\
\hline
0.000004902
\end{array}$$

• 6 decimal places
• 3 decimal places

• 9 decimal places

You Try It 3

$$\begin{array}{r}
4.68 \\
\times\ 6.03 \\
\hline
1404 \\
28\ 080 \\
\hline
28.2204
\end{array}$$

• 2 decimal places
• 2 decimal places

• 4 decimal places

You Try It 4 $6.9 \times 1000 = 6900$

You Try It 5 $4.0273 \times 10^2 = 402.73$

You Try It 6

Strategy To find the total bill:

▶ Find the number of gallons of water used by multiplying the number of gallons used per day (5000) by the number of days (62).
▶ Find the cost of water by multiplying the cost per 1000 gallons (1.39) by the number of 1000-gallon units used.
▶ Add the cost of the water to the meter fee (133.70).

Solution Number of gallons = $5000(62) = 310{,}000$

$$\text{Cost of water} = \frac{310{,}000}{1000} \times 1.39 = 430.90$$

Total cost = $430.90 + 133.70 = 564.60$

The total bill is $564.60.

You Try It 7

Strategy To find the cost of running the freezer for 210 hours, multiply the hourly cost (0.035) by the number of hours the freezer has run (210).

Solution

$$
\begin{array}{r}
0.035 \\
\times\ \ \ 210 \\
\hline
350 \\
70\ \ \\
\hline
7.350
\end{array}
$$

The cost of running the freezer for 210 hours is $7.35.

You Try It 8

Strategy To find the total cost of the electronic drum kit:
- ▶ Multiply the monthly payment (37.18) by the number of months (18).
- ▶ Add that product to the down payment (175.00).

Solution

$$
\begin{array}{r}
37.18 \\
\times\ \ \ 18 \\
\hline
29744 \\
3718\ \ \\
\hline
669.24
\end{array}
\qquad
\begin{array}{r}
175.00 \\
+\ 669.24 \\
\hline
844.24
\end{array}
$$

The total cost of the electronic drum kit is $844.24.

SECTION 3.5

You Try It 1

$$
\begin{array}{r}
2.7 \\
0.052.\overline{)\ 0.140.4} \\
-\ 104\ \ \ \\
\hline
36\ 4 \\
-\ 36\ 4 \\
\hline
0
\end{array}
$$

• Move the decimal point 3 places to the right in the divisor and the dividend. Write the decimal point in the quotient directly above the decimal point in the dividend.

You Try It 2

$$
\begin{array}{r}
0.4873 \approx 0.487 \\
76\overline{)\ 37.0420} \\
-\ 30\ 4\ \ \ \ \ \\
\hline
6\ 64 \\
-\ 6\ 08 \\
\hline
562 \\
-\ 532 \\
\hline
300 \\
-\ 228 \\
\hline
\end{array}
$$

• Write the decimal point in the quotient directly above the decimal point in the dividend.

You Try It 3

$$
\begin{array}{r}
72.73 \approx 72.7 \\
5.09.\overline{)\ 370.20.00} \\
-\ 356\ 3\ \ \ \ \ \ \\
\hline
13\ 90 \\
-\ 10\ 18 \\
\hline
3\ 720 \\
-\ 3\ 563 \\
\hline
1570 \\
-\ 1527
\end{array}
$$

You Try It 4 $309.21 \div 10{,}000 = 0.030921$

You Try It 5 $42.93 \div 10^4 = 0.004293$

You Try It 6

Strategy To find how many times greater the average hourly earnings were, divide the 2010 average hourly earnings (19.07) by the 1980 average hourly earnings (6.85).

Solution $19.07 \div 6.85 \approx 2.8$

The average hourly earnings in 2010 were about 2.8 times greater than in 1980.

You Try It 7

Strategy To find the average number of people watching TV per day:
- ▶ Add the numbers of people watching each day of the week.
- ▶ Divide the total number of people watching by 7.

Solution $91.9 + 89.8 + 90.6 + 93.9 + 78.0 + 77.1 + 87.7 =$

$$\frac{609}{7} = 87$$

An average of 87 million people watch television per day.

SECTION 3.6

You Try It 1

$$
\begin{array}{r}
0.611 \\
18\overline{)\ 11.000} \\
-\ 10\ 8\ \ \ \\
\hline
20 \\
-\ 18 \\
\hline
20 \\
-\ 18 \\
\hline
2
\end{array}
$$

• Divide the numerator by the denominator. Continue to divide until the remainder is 0 or the remainder repeats.

$$\frac{11}{18} = 0.6\overline{1}$$

• Use a bar over the repeating digit.

Try It 2

$$
\begin{array}{r}
0.28 \\
25\overline{)7.00} \\
-5\ 0 \\
\hline
2\ 00 \\
-2\ 00 \\
\hline
0
\end{array}
$$
• The remainder is 0.

$$\frac{7}{25} = 0.28$$

Try It 3

$$
\begin{array}{r}
2.166 \\
6\overline{)13.000} \\
-12 \\
\hline
1\ 0 \\
-6 \\
\hline
40 \\
-36 \\
\hline
40 \\
-36 \\
\hline
4
\end{array}
$$
• The remainder repeats.

$$\frac{13}{6} = 2.1\overline{6}$$

Try It 4 $\quad 0.0005 = \dfrac{5}{10,000} = \dfrac{1}{2000}$

Try It 5

$$\frac{5}{6} \qquad 0.83$$

$$\frac{5}{6} \qquad \frac{83}{100}$$
• Write the decimal as a fraction.

$$\frac{250}{300} \qquad \frac{249}{300}$$
• Write the fractions with a common denominator.

$$\frac{250}{300} > \frac{249}{300}$$
• Compare the fractions.

$$\frac{5}{6} > 0.83$$

lutions to Chapter 4 "You Try It"

CTION 4.1

Try It 1 $\quad \dfrac{20 \text{ pounds}}{24 \text{ pounds}} = \dfrac{20}{24} = \dfrac{5}{6}$

20 pounds : 24 pounds = 20 : 24 = 5 : 6

20 pounds to 24 pounds = 20 to 24
$\qquad\qquad\qquad\qquad\qquad = 5$ to 6

Try It 2 $\quad \dfrac{64 \text{ miles}}{8 \text{ miles}} = \dfrac{64}{8} = \dfrac{8}{1}$

64 miles : 8 miles = 64 : 8 = 8 : 1

64 miles to 8 miles = 64 to 8 = 8 to 1

You Try It 3

Strategy To find the ratio, write the ratio of board feet of cedar (12,000) to board feet of ash (18,000) in simplest form.

Solution $\quad \dfrac{12,000}{18,000} = \dfrac{2}{3}$

The ratio is $\frac{2}{3}$.

You Try It 4

Strategy To find the ratio, write the ratio of the amount spent on radio advertising (450,000) to the amount spent on radio and television advertising (450,000 + 600,000) in simplest form.

Solution $\quad \dfrac{\$450,000}{\$450,000 + \$600,000} = \dfrac{450,000}{1,050,000} = \dfrac{3}{7}$

The ratio is $\frac{3}{7}$.

SECTION 4.2

You Try It 1 $\quad \dfrac{15 \text{ pounds}}{12 \text{ trees}} = \dfrac{5 \text{ pounds}}{4 \text{ trees}}$

You Try It 2 $\quad \dfrac{260 \text{ miles}}{8 \text{ hours}}$

$$
\begin{array}{r}
32.5 \\
8\overline{)260.0}
\end{array}
$$

32.5 miles/hour

You Try It 3

Strategy To find the per-foot cost of the pipe, divide the total cost ($22.40) by the number of feet purchased (40 feet).

Solution $\quad 22.40 \div 40 = 0.56$

The cost of the pipe is $.56/foot.

SECTION 4.3

You Try It 1

$6 \times 15 = 90$; $10 \times 9 = 90$

The cross products are equal.
The proportion is true.

You Try It 2

$6 \times 90 = 540$; $32 \times 8 = 256$

The cross products are not equal.
The proportion is not true.

You Try It 3

$$\frac{n}{14} = \frac{3}{7}$$
• Find the cross products. Then solve for n.

$n \times 7 = 14 \times 3$

$n \times 7 = 42$

$\qquad n = 42 \div 7$

$\qquad n = 6$

Check: $\dfrac{6}{14} \quad \dfrac{3}{7}$ $\quad 14 \times 3 = 42$; $6 \times 7 = 42$

You Try It 4

$$\frac{5}{7} = \frac{n}{20}$$
$$5 \times 20 = 7 \times n$$
$$100 = 7 \times n$$
$$100 \div 7 = n$$
$$14.3 \approx n$$

• Find the cross products. Then solve for n.

You Try It 5

$$\frac{15}{20} = \frac{12}{n}$$
$$15 \times n = 20 \times 12$$
$$15 \times n = 240$$
$$n = 240 \div 15$$
$$n = 16$$

• Find the cross products. Then solve for n.

Check: $\dfrac{15}{20} \times \dfrac{12}{16}$ $20 \times 12 = 240$ $15 \times 16 = 240$

You Try It 6

$$\frac{12}{n} = \frac{7}{4}$$
$$12 \times 4 = n \times 7$$
$$48 = n \times 7$$
$$48 \div 7 = n$$
$$6.86 \approx n$$

You Try It 7

$$\frac{n}{12} = \frac{4}{1}$$
$$n \times 1 = 12 \times 4$$
$$n \times 1 = 48$$
$$n = 48 \div 1$$
$$n = 48$$

Check: $\dfrac{48}{12} \times \dfrac{4}{1}$ $12 \times 4 = 48$ $48 \times 1 = 48$

You Try It 8

Strategy

To find the number of tablespoons of fertilizer needed, write and solve a proportion using n to represent the number of tablespoons of fertilizer.

Solution

$$\frac{3 \text{ tablespoons}}{4 \text{ gallons}} = \frac{n \text{ tablespoons}}{10 \text{ gallons}}$$
$$3 \times 10 = 4 \times n$$
$$30 = 4 \times n$$
$$30 \div 4 = n$$
$$7.5 = n$$

• The unit "tablespoons" is in the numerator. The unit "gallons" is in the denominator.

For 10 gallons of water, 7.5 tablespoons of fertilizer are required.

You Try It 9

Strategy

To find the number of jars that can be packed in 15 boxes, write and solve a proportion using n to represent the number of jars.

Solution

$$\frac{24 \text{ jars}}{6 \text{ boxes}} = \frac{n \text{ jars}}{15 \text{ boxes}}$$
$$24 \times 15 = 6 \times n$$
$$360 = 6 \times n$$
$$360 \div 6 = n$$
$$60 = n$$

60 jars can be packed in 15 boxes.

Solutions to Chapter 5 "You Try It"

SECTION 5.1

You Try It 1

a. $125\% = 125 \times 0.01 = 1.25$

$$125\% = 125 \times \frac{1}{100}$$
$$= \frac{125}{100} = \frac{5}{4} = 1\frac{1}{4}$$

b. $8.5\% = 8.5 \times 0.01 = 0.085$

$$8.5\% = 8.5 \times \frac{1}{100}$$
$$= 8\frac{1}{2} \times \frac{1}{100}$$ • $8.5 = 8\frac{5}{10} = 8\frac{1}{2}$
$$= \frac{17}{2} \times \frac{1}{100}$$
$$= \frac{17}{200}$$ • Multiply the fract

c. $0.25\% = 0.25 \times 0.01 = 0.0025$

$$0.25\% = 0.25 \times \frac{1}{100}$$
$$= \frac{1}{4} \times \frac{1}{100}$$ • $0.25 = \frac{25}{100} = \frac{1}{4}$
$$= \frac{1}{400}$$ • Multiply the fract

You Try It 2

$$33\frac{1}{3}\% = 33\frac{1}{3} \times \frac{1}{100}$$
$$= \frac{100}{3} \times \frac{1}{100}$$
$$= \frac{100}{300} = \frac{1}{3}$$

You Try It 3

$$0.048 = 0.048 \times 100\% = 4.8\%$$
$$3.6 = 3.6 \times 100\% = 360\%$$

You Try It 4

$$\frac{5}{16} \times \frac{100\%}{1}$$
$$= \frac{500\%}{16} = 31.25\%$$ • Write in decimal fo

You Try It 5

$$\frac{5}{6} = \frac{5}{6} \times \frac{100\%}{1} = \frac{500\%}{6} = 83\frac{1}{3}\%$$

SECTION 5.2

You Try It 1

Percent $\times$ base $=$ amount
$$0.063 \times 150 = n$$
$$9.45 = n$$

Try It 2

Percent × base = amount

$$\frac{1}{6} \times 66 = n \qquad \bullet \; 16\frac{2}{3}\% = \frac{1}{6}$$
$$11 = n$$

Try It 3

Strategy To determine the amount that came from corporations, write and solve the basic percent equation, using n to represent the amount. The percent is 5%. The base is $291 billion.

Solution Percent × base = amount
$$5\% \times 291 = n$$
$$0.05 \times 291 = n$$
$$14.55 = n$$

Corporations gave $14.55 billion to charities.

Try It 4

Strategy To find the new hourly wage:
- Find the amount of the raise. Write and solve the basic percent equation, using n to represent the amount of the raise (amount). The percent is 8%. The base is $33.50.
- Add the amount of the raise to the old wage (33.50).

Solution
$$8\% \times 33.50 = n \qquad\qquad 33.50$$
$$0.08 \times 33.50 = n \qquad\qquad +\;2.68$$
$$2.68 = n \qquad\qquad\quad 36.18$$

The new hourly wage is $36.18.

SECTION 5.3

Try It 1 Percent × base = amount
$$n \times 32 = 16$$
$$n = 16 \div 32$$
$$n = 0.50$$
$$n = 50\%$$

Try It 2 Percent × base = amount
$$n \times 15 = 48$$
$$n = 48 \div 15$$
$$n = 3.2$$
$$n = 320\%$$

Try It 3 Percent × base = amount
$$n \times 45 = 30$$
$$n = 30 \div 45$$
$$n = \frac{2}{3} = 66\frac{2}{3}\%$$

Try It 4

Strategy To find what percent of the income the income tax is, write and solve the basic percent equation, using n to represent the percent. The base is $33,500, and the amount is $5025.

Solution
$$n \times 33,500 = 5025$$
$$n = 5025 \div 33,500$$
$$n = 0.15 = 15\%$$

The income tax is 15% of the income.

You Try It 5

Strategy To find the percent of wireless subscribers not using a smartphone:
- Subtract to find the number of subscribers not using a smartphone (302.9 million − 112.1 million).
- Write and solve the basic percent equation, using n to represent the percent. The base is 302.9 million, and the amount is the number of wireless subscribers not using a smartphone.

Solution 302.9 million − 112.1 million = 190.8 million

There were 190.8 million wireless subscribers not using a smartphone.
$$n \times 302.9 = 190.8$$
$$n = 190.8 \div 302.9$$
$$n \approx 0.6299$$

Approximately 63.0% of the wireless subscribers were not using a smartphone.

SECTION 5.4

You Try It 1 Percent × base = amount
$$0.86 \times n = 215$$
$$n = 215 \div 0.86$$
$$n = 250$$

You Try It 2 Percent × base = amount
$$0.025 \times n = 15$$
$$n = 15 \div 0.025$$
$$n = 600$$

You Try It 3 Percent × base = amount
$$\frac{1}{6} \times n = 5 \qquad \bullet \; 16\frac{2}{3}\% = \frac{1}{6}$$
$$n = 5 \div \frac{1}{6}$$
$$n = 30$$

You Try It 4

Strategy To find the original value of the car, write and solve the basic percent equation, using n to represent the original value (base). The percent is 42%, and the amount is $10,458.

Solution
$$42\% \times n = 10,458$$
$$0.42 \times n = 10,458$$
$$n = 10,458 \div 0.42$$
$$n = 24,900$$

The original value of the car was $24,900.

You Try It 5

Strategy   To find the difference between the original price and the sale price:

▶ Find the original price. Write and solve the basic percent equation, using n to represent the original price (base). The percent is 80%, and the amount is $89.60.
▶ Subtract the sale price (89.60) from the original price.

Solution

$$80\% \times n = 89.60$$
$$0.80 \times n = 89.60$$
$$n = 89.60 \div 0.80$$
$$n = 112.00 \quad \text{(original price)}$$
$$112.00 - 89.60 = 22.40$$

The difference between the original price and the sale price is $22.40.

SECTION 5.5

You Try It 1

$$\frac{26}{100} = \frac{22}{n}$$
$$26 \times n = 100 \times 22$$
$$26 \times n = 2200$$
$$n = 2200 \div 26$$
$$n \approx 84.62$$

You Try It 2

$$\frac{16}{100} = \frac{n}{132}$$
$$16 \times 132 = 100 \times n$$
$$2112 = 100 \times n$$
$$2112 \div 100 = n$$
$$21.12 = n$$

You Try It 3

Strategy   To find the number of days it snowed, write and solve a proportion, using n to represent the number of days it snowed (amount). The percent is 64%, and the base is 150.

Solution

$$\frac{64}{100} = \frac{n}{150}$$
$$64 \times 150 = 100 \times n$$
$$9600 = 100 \times n$$
$$9600 \div 100 = n$$
$$96 = n$$

It snowed 96 days.

You Try It 4

Strategy   To find the percent of alarms that were not false alarms:

▶ Subtract to find the number of alarms that were not false alarms (200 − 24).

▶ Write and solve a proportion, using n represent the percent of alarms that we not false. The base is 200, and the amo is the number of alarms that were not alarms.

Solution

$$200 - 24 = 176$$
$$\frac{n}{100} = \frac{176}{200}$$
$$n \times 200 = 100 \times 176$$
$$n \times 200 = 17{,}600$$
$$n = 17{,}600 \div 200$$
$$n = 88$$

88% of the alarms were not false alarms.

Solutions to Chapter 6 "You Try It"

SECTION 6.1

You Try It 1

Strategy   To find the unit cost, divide the cost of th package by the number of units in the pac age.

Solution   a. Unit cost $= \frac{\text{cost of the package}}{\text{number of units in the package}}$

$$= \frac{\$14.99}{12 \text{ apples}} \approx \$1.208 \text{ per app}$$

b. Unit cost $= \frac{\text{cost of the package}}{\text{number of units in the package}}$

$$= \frac{\$10.00}{15 \text{ pounds}} \approx \$.667 \text{ per poun}$$

You Try It 2

Strategy   To find the more economical purchase, co pare the unit costs.

Solution

$$8.70 \div 6 = 1.45$$
$$6.96 \div 4 = 1.74$$
$$\$1.45 < \$1.74$$

The more economical purchase is 6 cans for $8.70.

You Try It 3

Strategy   To find the total cost, multiply the unit co (9.96) by the number of units (7).

Solution

Unit cost	×	number of units	=	total cost
9.96	×	7	=	69.72

The total cost is $69.72.

TION 6.2

Try It 1

tegy To find the percent increase:

  ▸ Find the amount of the increase.
  ▸ Solve the basic percent equation for *percent*.

tion

New value	−	original value	=	amount of increase

$$3.83 \quad - \quad 3.46 \quad = \quad 0.37$$

Percent × base = amount
$$n \quad \times 3.46 = \quad 0.37$$
$$n = 0.37 \div 3.46$$
$$n \approx 0.11 = 11\%$$

The percent increase was 11%.

Try It 2

tegy To find the new hourly wage:

  ▸ Solve the basic percent equation for *amount*.
  ▸ Add the amount of the increase to the original wage.

tion Percent × base = amount
$$0.14 \quad \times 12.50 = \quad n$$
$$1.75 = n$$
$$12.50 + 1.75 = 14.25$$

The new hourly wage is $14.25.

Try It 3

tegy To find the markup, solve the basic percent equation for *amount*.

tion Percent × base = amount

Markup rate	×	cost	=	markup

$$0.20 \quad \times \quad 32 \quad = \quad n$$
$$6.4 = n$$

The markup is $6.40.

Try It 4

tegy To find the selling price:

  ▸ Find the markup by solving the basic percent equation for *amount*.
  ▸ Add the markup to the cost.

tion Percent × base = amount

Markup rate	×	cost	=	markup

$$0.55 \quad \times \quad 72 \quad = \quad n$$
$$39.60 = n$$

Cost	+	markup	=	selling price

$$72 \quad + \quad 39.60 \quad = \quad 111.60$$

The selling price is $111.60.

You Try It 5

Strategy To find the percent decrease:

  ▸ Find the amount of the decrease.
  ▸ Solve the basic percent equation for *percent*.

Solution

Original value	−	new value	=	amount of decrease

$$88{,}000{,}000 - 84{,}227{,}000 = 3{,}773{,}000$$

Percent × base = amount
$$n \quad \times 88{,}000{,}000 = 3{,}773{,}000$$
$$n = 3{,}773{,}000 \div 88{,}000{,}000$$
$$n \approx 0.043$$

The percent decrease is 4.3%.

You Try It 6

Strategy To find the visibility in the fog:

  ▸ Find the amount of decrease by solving the basic percent equation for *amount*.
  ▸ Subtract the amount of decrease from the original visibility.

Solution Percent × base = amount
$$0.40 \quad \times \quad 5 \quad = \quad n$$
$$2 = n$$
$$5 - 2 = 3$$

The visibility in the fog was 3 miles.

You Try It 7

Strategy To find the discount rate:

  ▸ Find the discount.
  ▸ Solve the basic percent equation for *percent*.

Solution

Regular price	−	sale price	=	discount

$$12.50 \quad - \quad 10.99 \quad = \quad 1.51$$

Percent × base = amount

Discount rate	×	regular price	=	discount

$$n \quad \times \quad 12.50 \quad = \quad 1.51$$
$$n = 1.51 \div 12.50$$
$$n = 0.1208$$

The discount rate is 12.1%.

You Try It 8

Strategy To find the sale price:

  ▸ Find the discount by solving the basic percent equation for *amount*.
  ▸ Subtract to find the sale price.

Solution

Percent × base = amount

| Discount rate | × | regular price | = | discount |

0.15 × 225 = n

33.75 = n

| Regular price | − | discount | = | sale price |

225 − 33.75 = 191.25

The sale price is $191.25.

SECTION 6.3

You Try It 1

Strategy

To find the simple interest due, multiply the principal (15,000) times the annual interest rate (8% = 0.08) times the time in years (18 months = $\frac{18}{12}$ years = 1.5 years).

Solution

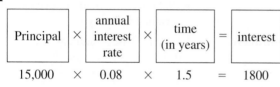

| Principal | × | annual interest rate | × | time (in years) | = | interest |

15,000 × 0.08 × 1.5 = 1800

The interest due is $1800.

You Try It 2

Strategy

To find the maturity value:
- ▶ Use the simple interest formula to find the simple interest due.
- ▶ Find the maturity value by adding the principal and the interest.

Solution

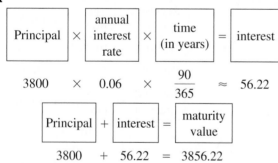

| Principal | × | annual interest rate | × | time (in years) | = | interest |

3800 × 0.06 × $\frac{90}{365}$ ≈ 56.22

| Principal | + | interest | = | maturity value |

3800 + 56.22 = 3856.22

The maturity value is $3856.22.

You Try It 3

Strategy

To find the monthly payment:
- ▶ Find the maturity value by adding the principal and the interest.
- ▶ Divide the maturity value by the length of the loan in months (12).

Solution

Principal + interest = maturity value

1900 + 152 = 2052

Maturity value ÷ length of the loan = payment

2052 ÷ 12 = 171

The monthly payment is $171.

You Try It 4

Strategy

To find the finance charge, multiply the principal, or unpaid balance (1250), times monthly interest rate (1.6%) times the number of months (1).

Solution

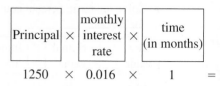

| Principal | × | monthly interest rate | × | time (in months) |

1250 × 0.016 × 1 = 20

The finance charge is $20.

You Try It 5

Strategy

To find the interest earned:
- ▶ Find the new principal by multiplying the original principal (1000) by the factor found in the Compound Interest Table (3.29066).
- ▶ Subtract the original principal from the new principal.

Solution

1000 × 3.29066 = 3290.66

The new principal is $3290.66.

3290.66 − 1000 = 2290.66

The interest earned is $2290.66.

SECTION 6.4

You Try It 1

Strategy

To find the mortgage:
- ▶ Find the down payment by solving the basic percent equation for *amount*.
- ▶ Subtract the down payment from the purchase price.

Solution

Percent × base = amount

| Percent | × | purchase price | = | down payment |

0.25 × 1,500,000 = n

375,000 = n

| Purchase price | − | down payment | = | mortgage |

1,500,000 − 375,000 = 1,125,000

The mortgage is $1,125,000.

You Try It 2

Strategy

To find the loan origination fee, solve the basic percent equation for *amount*.

Solution

Percent × base = amount

| Points | × | mortgage | = | fee |

0.045 × 180,000 = n

8100 = n

The loan origination fee was $8100.

Try It 3

Strategy   To find the mortgage payment:

▶ Find the down payment.
▶ Subtract the down payment from the purchase price to find the mortgage.
▶ Multiply the mortgage by the factor in the Monthly Payment Table for a 20-year loan at 6%.

Solution   Percent × purchase price = down payment

$$0.30 \times 185{,}000 = 55{,}000$$

The down payment is $55,500.

$$
\boxed{\begin{array}{c}\text{Purchase}\\\text{price}\end{array}} - \boxed{\begin{array}{c}\text{down}\\\text{payment}\end{array}} = \boxed{\text{mortgage}}
$$

$$185{,}000 - 55{,}500 = 129{,}500$$

The mortgage is $129,500.

The factor from the Monthly Payment Table is 0.0071643.

$$129{,}500 \times 0.0071643 \approx 927.78$$

The monthly mortgage payment is $927.78.

Try It 4

Strategy   To find the amount of the first month's payment that is interest and the amount that is principal:

▶ Find the monthly simple interest rate.
▶ Use the basic percent equation to find the interest owed for the first month.
▶ Subtract the interest owed for the first month from the monthly payment to find the amount of the payment that is principal.

Solution   Monthly simple interest rate

$$= \frac{\text{annual interest rate}}{12}$$

$$= \frac{0.045}{12} = 0.00375$$

Percent × base = amount

$$0.00375 \times 296{,}000 = 1110$$

The interest owed for the first month is $1110.

$$
\boxed{\begin{array}{c}\text{Monthly}\\\text{payment}\end{array}} - \boxed{\begin{array}{c}\text{amount}\\\text{to}\\\text{interest}\end{array}} = \boxed{\begin{array}{c}\text{amount}\\\text{to}\\\text{principal}\end{array}}
$$

$$1413.15 - 1110.00 = 303.15$$

The amount of the payment that goes to the principal is $303.15.

SECTION 6.5

Try It 1

Strategy   To find the amount financed:

▶ Find the down payment by solving the basic percent equation for *amount*.
▶ Subtract the down payment from the purchase price.

Solution   Percent × base = amount

$$
\boxed{\text{Percent}} \times \boxed{\begin{array}{c}\text{purchase}\\\text{price}\end{array}} = \boxed{\begin{array}{c}\text{down}\\\text{payment}\end{array}}
$$

$$0.20 \times 19{,}200 = n$$
$$3840 = n$$

The down payment is $3840.

$$19{,}200 - 3840 = 15{,}360$$

The amount financed is $15,360.

You Try It 2

Strategy   To find the license fee, solve the basic percent equation for *amount*.

Solution   Percent × base = amount

$$
\boxed{\text{Percent}} \times \boxed{\begin{array}{c}\text{purchase}\\\text{price}\end{array}} = \boxed{\begin{array}{c}\text{license}\\\text{fee}\end{array}}
$$

$$0.015 \times 27{,}350 = n$$
$$410.25 = n$$

The license fee is $410.25.

You Try It 3

Strategy   To find the cost, multiply the cost per mile (0.41) by the number of miles driven (23,000).

Solution $$23{,}000 \times 0.41 = 9430$$

The cost is $9430.

You Try It 4

Strategy   To find the cost per mile for car insurance, divide the cost for insurance (360) by the number of miles driven (15,000).

Solution $$360 \div 15{,}000 = 0.024$$

The cost per mile for insurance is $.024.

You Try It 5

Strategy   To find the monthly payment:

▶ Subtract the down payment from the purchase price to find the amount financed.
▶ Multiply the amount financed by the factor found in the Monthly Payment Table.

Solution $$25{,}900 - 6475 = 19{,}425$$

$$19{,}425 \times 0.0244129 \approx 474.22$$

The monthly payment is $474.22.

SECTION 6.6

You Try It 1

Strategy   To find the worker's earnings:

▶ Find the worker's overtime wage by multiplying the hourly wage by 2.
▶ Multiply the number of overtime hours worked by the overtime wage.

Solution $28.50 \times 2 = 57$

The hourly wage for overtime is $57.

$57 \times 8 = 456$

The construction worker earns $456.

You Try It 2

Strategy   To find the monthly salary, divide the annual salary by the number of months in a year (12).

Solution $70,980 \div 12 = 5915$

The contractor's monthly salary is $5915.

You Try It 3

Strategy   To find the total earnings:

▸ Find the sales over $50,000.
▸ Multiply the commission rate by sales over $50,000.
▸ Add the commission to the annual salary.

Solution $175,000 - 50,000 = 125,000$

Sales over $50,000 totaled $125,000.

$125,000 \times 0.095 = 11,875$

Earnings from commissions totaled $11,875.

$37,000 + 11,875 = 48,875$

The insurance agent earned $48,875.

SECTION 6.7

You Try It 1

Strategy   To find the current balance:

▸ Subtract the amount of the check from old balance.
▸ Add the amount of each deposit.

Solution

$$
\begin{array}{rl}
302.46 & \\
-\ \ 20.59 & \text{check} \\
\hline
281.87 & \\
176.86 & \text{first deposit} \\
+\ \ 94.73 & \text{second deposit} \\
\hline
553.46 &
\end{array}
$$

The current checking account balance is $553.46.

You Try It 2

$$
\begin{array}{lr}
\text{Current checkbook} & \\
\text{balance:} & 623.41 \\
\text{Check: 237} & +\ \ 78.73 \\
\hline
 & 702.14 \\
\text{Interest:} & +\ \ \ \ 2.11 \\
\hline
 & 704.25 \\
\text{Deposit:} & -523.84 \\
\hline
 & 180.41
\end{array}
$$

Closing bank balance from bank statement $180.41

Checkbook balance: $180.41

The bank statement and the checkbook bal

nswers to Chapter 1 Selected Exercises

REP TEST

8   **2.** 1 2 3 4 5 6 7 8 9 10   **3.** a and D; b and E; c and A; d and B; e and F; f and C

CTION 1.1

. False   **b.** True   **c.** True   **d.** True   **3.** 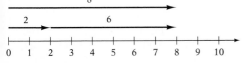   **5.**

number line: 0 1 2 3 4 5 6 7 8 9 10 11 12   number line: 0 1 2 3 4 5 6 7 8 9 10 11 12

37 < 49   **9.** 101 > 87   **11.** 2701 > 2071   **13.** 107 > 0   **15.** Yes   **17.** Three thousand seven hundred ninety
Fifty-eight thousand four hundred seventy-three   **21.** Four hundred ninety-eight thousand five hundred twelve
Six million eight hundred forty-two thousand seven hundred fifteen   **25.** 357   **27.** 63,780   **29.** 7,024,709   **31.** 5000 + 200 + 80 + 7
50,000 + 8000 + 900 + 40 + 3   **35.** 200,000 + 500 + 80 + 3   **37.** 400,000 + 3000 + 700 + 5   **39.** No   **41.** 850
4000   **45.** 53,000   **47.** 630,000   **49.** 250,000   **51.** 72,000,000   **53.** No. Round 3846 to the nearest hundred.

CTION 1.2

Addition Property of Zero   **3.** Associative Property of Addition   **5.** Commutative Property of Addition   **7.** 28   **9.** 125   **11.** 102
154   **15.** 1489   **17.** 828   **19.** 1584   **21.** 102,317   **23.** 79,326   **25.** 1804   **27.** 1579   **29.** 19,740   **31.** 7420
120,570   **35.** 207,453   **37.** 24,218   **39.** 11,974   **41.** 9323   **43.** 77,139   **45.** 14,383   **47.** 9473   **49.** 33,247   **51.** 5058
1992   **55.** 68,263   **57.** Cal.: 17,754   **59.** Cal.: 2872   **61.** Cal.: 101,712   **63.** Cal.: 158,763   **65.** Cal.: 261,595
　　　　　　　　　　　　Est.: 17,700   　　　　Est.: 2900   　　　　Est.: 101,000   　　　　Est.: 158,000   　　　　Est.: 260,000
Cal.: 946,718   **69.** Commutative Property of Addition   **71.** There were 144,928 multiple births during the year.
Est.: 940,000
The total gross income from the eight *Harry Potter* movies was $2,390,100,000.   **75.** The total gross income from the two highest-grossing
ry Potter movies was $698,600,000.   **77. a.** During the three days, 1285 miles will be driven.   **b.** At the end of the trip, the odometer will
69,977 miles.   **79.** 14,636,300 barrels of crude oil are produced and imported per day.   **81.** No. For example, 0 + 2 = 2

8
2   6
number line: 0 1 2 3 4 5 6 7 8 9 10

CTION 1.3

4; 5 + 4 = 9   **3.** 11; 0 + 11 = 11   **5.** 4   **7.** 9   **9.** 22   **11.** 60   **13.** 66   **15.** 31   **17.** 901   **19.** 791   **21.** 1125   **23.** 3131
47   **27.** 925   **29.** 4561   **31.** 3205   **33.** 1222   **35.** 5 and 3   **37.** 53   **39.** 29   **41.** 8   **43.** 37   **45.** 58   **47.** 574
337   **51.** 1423   **53.** 754   **55.** 2179   **57.** 6489   **59.** 889   **61.** 71,129   **63.** 698   **65.** 29,405   **67.** 49,624   **69.** 628
6532   **73.** 4286   **75.** 4042   **77.** 5209   **79.** 10,378   **81.** ii and iii   **83.** 11,239   **85.** 8482   **87.** 625   **89.** 76,725
23   **93.** 4648   **95.** Cal.: 29,837   **97.** Cal.: 36,668   **99.** Cal.: 101,998
　　　　　　　　　　Est.: 30,000   　　Est.: 40,000   　　Est.: 100,000
. **a.** The honey bee has 91 more smell genes than the mosquito.   **b.** The mosquito has eight more taste genes than the fruit fly.
The honey bee has the best sense of smell.   **d.** The honey bee has the worst sense of taste.   **103.** The difference between the maximum
ption heights is 15 feet.   **105.** 202,345 more women than men earned a bachelor's degree.   **107. a.** The smallest expected increase occurs
n 2010 to 2012.   **b.** The greatest expected increase occurs from 2018 to 2020.   **109.** Your new credit card balance is $360.

CHECK YOUR PROGRESS: CHAPTER 1*

1. [1.1A]   **2.** 107 > 97   [1.1A]   **3.** Eighty-two thousand seven hundred forty-three   [1.1B]   **4.** Two million five hundred thirty thousand twenty-one   [1.1B]   **5.** 23,401   [1.1B]   **6.** 903,003   [1.1B]
7. 60,000 + 3000 + 200 + 90 + 1   [1.1C]   **8.** 592,000   [1.1D]   **9.** 46,000   [1.1D]   **10.** 843,995   [1.2A]   **11.** 14,632   [1.2A]
12. 197,523   [1.2A]   **13.** 7058   [1.3B]   **14.** 8538   [1.3B]   **15.** The national debt is about $14,800,000,000,000.   [1.1D]
16. Colonial Falls is 160 feet higher than Yosemite Falls.   [1.3C]   **17.** Janice contributed a total of $130.   [1.2B]   **18.** Boys grow 60 centimeters from birth to age 5.   [1.3C]   **19.** Girls grow the most between birth and age 1.   [1.3C]   **20.** The golfer's total score was 275.   [1.2B]

SECTION 1.4

1. 6 × 2 or 6 · 2   **3.** 4 × 7 or 4 · 7   **5.** Multiplication Property of One   **7.** Commutative Property of Multiplication   **9.** 12   **11.** 35
13. 25   **15.** 0   **17.** 72   **19.** 198   **21.** 335   **23.** 2492   **25.** 5463   **27.** 4200   **29.** 6327   **31.** 1896   **33.** 5056   **35.** 16
37. 46,963   **39.** 59,976   **41.** 19,120   **43.** 19,790   **45.** 140   **47.** 22,456   **49.** 18,630   **51.** 336   **53.** 910   **55.** 63,063
57. 33,520   **59.** 380,834   **61.** 541,164   **63.** 400,995   **65.** 105,315   **67.** 428,770   **69.** 260,000   **71.** 344,463   **73.** 41,808
75. 189,500   **77.** 401,880   **79.** 1,052,763   **81.** 4,198,388   **83.** Answers will vary. For example, 5 and 20   **85.** 198,423
87. 18,834   **89.** 260,178   **91.** Cal.: 440,076   **93.** Cal.: 6,491,166   **95.** Cal.: 18,728,744   **97.** Cal.: 57,691,192
　　　　　　　　　　　　　　　Est.: 450,000　　　　　Est.: 6,300,000　　　　　Est.: 18,000,000　　　　　Est.: 54,000,000
99. The area is 2808 square feet.   **101.** The car could travel 516 miles on 12 gallons of gas.   **103. a.** eHarmony can take credit for 3794 marriages a week.   **b.** eHarmony can take credit for 197,830 marriages a year.   **105.** The estimated cost of the electricians' labor is $5100.   **107.** The total cost is $2138.   **109.** There are 12 accidental deaths each hour, 288 deaths each day, and 105,120 deaths each year.   **111.** 21,978 × 4 = 87,912

SECTION 1.5

1. 2; 2 × 4 = 8   **3.** 6; 6 × 5 = 30   **5.** 6   **7.** 12   **9.** 7   **11.** 16   **13.** 210   **15.** 44   **17.** 703   **19.** 910
21. 5006   **23.** 6050   **25.** 1075   **27.** 1   **29.** 3 r1   **31.** 9 r7   **33.** 16 r1   **35.** 10 r4   **37.** 90 r3   **39.** 120 r5
41. 309 r3   **43.** 1160 r4   **45.** 708 r2   **47.** 3825 r1   **49.** 5710 r3   **51.** 11,430   **53.** 510   **55.** False
57. 1 r38   **59.** 1 r26   **61.** 21 r21   **63.** 30 r22   **65.** 5 r40   **67.** 9 r17   **69.** 200 r21   **71.** 303 r1   **73.** 67 r13
75. 708 r49   **77.** 1086 r7   **79.** 5007 r55   **81.** 12 r456   **83.** 4 r160   **85.** 160 r27   **87.** 1669 r14   **89.** 7950
91. Cal.: 5129   **93.** Cal.: 21,968   **95.** Cal.: 24,596   **97.** Cal.: 2836   **99.** Cal.: 3024   **101.** Cal.: 32,036
　　Est.: 5000　　　　　Est.: 20,000　　　　　Est.: 22,500　　　　　Est.: 3000　　　　　Est.: 3000　　　　　Est.: 30,000
103. Melissa's monthly salary is $5754.   **105.** The cost of the gold alloy in each necklace is $750.   **107.** The nursing student's average exam score was 88.   **109.** The monthly payment is $130.   **111.** The average monthly claim for theft was $25,000.   **113.** The average number of hours worked by employees in the United Kingdom is 33 hours.   **115.** Employees in the country with the most number of hours worked per year (Greece) work an average of 15 hours more per week than do employees in the country with the least number of hours worked per year (Germany).
117. On average, the U.S. Postal Service processed 390 million pieces of mail per day.   **119.** The total of the deductions is $350.
121. 49,500,000 more cases of eggs were sold by retail stores.   **123.** The average monthly expense for housing is $976.
125. The total amount paid is $11,860.   **127.** Subtraction   **129.** Division

SECTION 1.6

1. Five   **3.** i and iii   **5.** 2^3 **7.** $6^3 \cdot 7^4$ **9.** $2^3 \cdot 3^3$ **11.** $5 \cdot 7^5$ **13.** $3^3 \cdot 6^4$ **15.** $3^3 \cdot 5 \cdot 9^3$ **17.** 8   **19.** 400   **21.** 900
23. 972   **25.** 120   **27.** 360   **29.** 0   **31.** 90,000   **33.** 540   **35.** 4050   **37.** 11,025   **39.** 25,920   **41.** 4,320,000   **43.** 5
45. 23   **47.** 6   **49.** 5   **51.** 18   **53.** 10   **55.** 7   **57.** 8   **59.** 6   **61.** 52   **63.** 26   **65.** 52   **67.** 42   **69.** 16   **71.** 6
73. 8   **75.** 3   **77.** 4   **79.** 13   **81.** 0   **83.** $(2 \cdot 3 + 8) \cdot 4 - 2$ **85.** $2 \cdot (3 + 8 \cdot 4 - 2)$ **87.** No   **89.** No   **91. a.** 6561
b. 43,046,721   **c.** 43,046,721

SECTION 1.7

1. ii, iii, v, vi   **3.** 1, 2, 4   **5.** 1, 2, 5, 10   **7.** 1, 7   **9.** 1, 3, 9   **11.** 1, 13   **13.** 1, 2, 3, 6, 9, 18   **15.** 1, 2, 4, 7, 8, 14, 28, 56
17. 1, 3, 5, 9, 15, 45   **19.** 1, 29   **21.** 1, 2, 11, 22   **23.** 1, 2, 4, 13, 26, 52   **25.** 1, 2, 41, 82   **27.** 1, 3, 19, 57
29. 1, 2, 3, 4, 6, 8, 12, 16, 24, 48   **31.** 1, 5, 19, 95   **33.** 1, 2, 3, 6, 9, 18, 27, 54   **35.** 1, 2, 3, 6, 11, 22, 33, 66
37. 1, 2, 4, 5, 8, 10, 16, 20, 40, 80   **39.** 1, 2, 3, 4, 6, 8, 12, 16, 24, 32, 48, 96   **41.** 1, 2, 3, 5, 6, 9, 10, 15, 18, 30, 45, 90
43. True   **45.** 2 · 3   **47.** Prime   **49.** 2 · 2 · 2 · 3   **51.** 3 · 3 · 3   **53.** 2 · 2 · 3 · 3   **55.** Prime   **57.** 2 · 3 · 3 · 5
59. 5 · 23   **61.** 2 · 3 · 3   **63.** 2 · 2 · 7   **65.** Prime   **67.** 2 · 31   **69.** 2 · 11   **71.** Prime   **73.** 2 · 3 · 11
75. 2 · 37   **77.** Prime   **79.** 5 · 11   **81.** 2 · 2 · 2 · 3 · 5   **83.** 2 · 2 · 2 · 2 · 2 · 5   **85.** 2 · 2 · 2 · 3 · 3 · 3
87. 5 · 5 · 5 · 5   **89.** False   **91.** Answers will vary. For example, 21, 33, 27, and 39

---

*Note: The numbers in brackets following the answers to the Check Your Progress exercises are a reference to the objective that corresponds to the problem. For example, the reference [1.2A] stands for Section 1.2, Objective A. This notation will be used for all Prep Tests, Check Your Progress exercises, Chapter Reviews, Chapter Tests, and Cumulative Reviews throughout the text.

HAPTER 1 REVIEW EXERCISES

00   [1.6A]   **2.** 10,000 + 300 + 20 + 7   [1.1C]   **3.** 1, 2, 3, 6, 9, 18   [1.7A]   **4.** 12,493   [1.2A]   **5.** 1749   [1.3B]
135   [1.5A]   **7.** 101 > 87   [1.1A]   **8.** $5^2 \cdot 7^5$ [1.6A]   **9.** 619,833   [1.4B]   **10.** 5409   [1.3B]   **11.** 1081   [1.2A]
2   [1.6B]   **13.** 45,700   [1.1D]   **14.** Two hundred seventy-six thousand fifty-seven   [1.1B]   **15.** 1306 r59   [1.5C]
2,011,044   [1.1B]   **17.** 488 r2   [1.5B]   **18.** 17   [1.6B]   **19.** 32   [1.6B]   **20.** $2 \cdot 2 \cdot 2 \cdot 3 \cdot 3$ [1.7B]
2133   [1.3A]   **22.** 22,761   [1.4B]   **23.** The total pay for last week's work is $768.   [1.4C]   **24.** He drove 27 miles
gallon of gasoline.   [1.5D]   **25.** Each monthly car payment is $560.   [1.5D]   **26.** The total income from commissions
2567.   [1.2B]   **27.** The total amount deposited is $301. The new checking account balance is $817.   [1.2B]   **28.** The total
he car payments is $2952.   [1.4C]   **29.** More males were enrolled in U.S. colleges in 2009 than in 2005.   [1.1A]
The difference between the numbers of males and females enrolled in U.S. colleges in 2005 is 2,575,625.   [1.3C]   **31.** The number of
es enrolled in U.S. colleges increased by 1,313,579 students from 2005 to 2009.   [1.3C]   **32.** 2,940,236 more students were enrolled
.S. colleges in 2009 than in 2005.   [1.3C]

HAPTER 1 TEST

432   [1.6A; Example 3]   **2.** Two hundred seven thousand sixty-eight   [1.1B; Example 3]   **3.** 15,069   [1.3B; Example 3]
1, 2, 4, 5, 10, 20   [1.7A; Example 1]   **5.** 6,854,144   [1.4B; HOW TO 3]   **6.** 9   [1.6B; Example 4]
900,000 + 6000 + 300 + 70 + 8   [1.1C; Example 6]   **8.** 75,000   [1.1D; Example 8]   **9.** 1121 r27   [1.5C; Example 8]
$3^3 \cdot 7^2$ [1.6A; Example 1]   **11.** 54,915   [1.2A; Example 1]   **12.** $2 \cdot 2 \cdot 3 \cdot 7$ [1.7B; Example 2]   **13.** 4
B; Example 4]   **14.** 726,104   [1.4A; Example 1]   **15.** 1,204,006   [1.1B; Example 4]   **16.** 8710 r2   [1.5B; Example 5]
21 > 19   [1.1A; Example 2]   **18.** 703   [1.5A; Example 3]   **19.** 96,798   [1.2A; Example 3]   **20.** 19,922
B; Example 4]   **21.** The difference between projected total enrollment in 2016 and 2013 is 1,908,000 students.   [1.3C; Example 6]
The projected enrollment in pre-kindergarten through grade 12 in 2016 is 59,781,000 students.   [1.2B; HOW TO 4]
3000 boxes were needed to pack the lemons.   [1.5D; Example 10]   **24.** A hummingbird will beat its wings 46,800 times in 900 seconds.
C; You Try It 3]   **25.** The average speed was 66 miles per hour.   [1.5D; HOW TO 3]

nswers to Chapter 2 Selected Exercises

REP TEST

20   [1.4A]   **2.** 120   [1.4A]   **3.** 9   [1.4A]   **4.** 10   [1.2A]   **5.** 7   [1.3A]   **6.** 2 r3   [1.5C]   **7.** 1, 2, 3, 4, 6, 12   [1.7A]
59   [1.6B]   **9.** 7   [1.3A]   **10.** 44 < 48   [1.1A]

ECTION 2.1

5, 10, 15, 20   **3.** 10, 20, 30, 40   **5.** Multiples of 6: 6, 12, 18, 24, 30, 36, 42, 48, 54, 60; multiples of 8: 8, 16, 24, 32, 40, 48, 56, 64, 72, 80;
mmon multiples: 24, 48; least common multiple: 24   **7.** 1, 2, 4, 5, 10, 20   **9.** 1, 2, 4, 7, 14, 28   **11.** 40   **13.** 24   **15.** 12
24   **19.** 60   **21.** 56   **23.** 32   **25.** 36   **27.** 660   **29.** 9384   **31.** 24   **33.** 30   **35.** 24   **37.** 576   **39.** 420
True   **43.** 1   **45.** 3   **47.** 5   **49.** 25   **51.** 1   **53.** 4   **55.** 4   **57.** 4   **59.** 1   **61.** 7   **63.** 5   **65.** 8
1   **69.** 25   **71.** 8   **73.** True   **75.** They will have another day off together in 12 days.   **79. a.** No   **b.** Yes   **c.** Yes   **d.** Yes

ECTION 2.2

Improper fraction; greater than 1   **3.** Proper fraction; less than 1   **5.** $\frac{3}{4}$ **7.** $\frac{7}{8}$ **9.** $1\frac{1}{2}$ **11.** $2\frac{5}{8}$ **13.** $3\frac{3}{5}$ **15.** $\frac{5}{4}$
$\frac{8}{3}$ **19.** $\frac{27}{8}$ **21.**   **23.**   **25.** False   **27.** $5\frac{1}{3}$ **29.** 2   **31.** $3\frac{1}{4}$ **33.** $14\frac{1}{2}$ **35.** 17
$1\frac{7}{9}$ **39.** $1\frac{4}{5}$ **41.** 23   **43.** $1\frac{15}{16}$ **45.** $6\frac{1}{3}$ **47.** 5   **49.** 1   **51.** $\frac{14}{3}$ **53.** $\frac{26}{3}$ **55.** $\frac{59}{8}$ **57.** $\frac{25}{4}$ **59.** $\frac{121}{8}$
$\frac{41}{12}$ **63.** $\frac{34}{9}$ **65.** $\frac{38}{3}$ **67.** $\frac{38}{7}$ **69.** $\frac{63}{5}$ **71.** $\frac{41}{9}$ **73.** $\frac{117}{14}$ **77.** Answers will vary. For example, $\frac{17}{8}$

CTION 2.3

No. 5 does not divide evenly into 7.   **3.** $\frac{5}{10}$ **5.** $\frac{9}{48}$ **7.** $\frac{12}{32}$ **9.** $\frac{9}{51}$ **11.** $\frac{12}{16}$ **13.** $\frac{27}{9}$ **15.** $\frac{20}{60}$ **17.** $\frac{44}{60}$
$\frac{12}{18}$ **21.** $\frac{35}{49}$ **23.** $\frac{10}{18}$ **25.** $\frac{21}{3}$ **27.** $\frac{35}{45}$ **29.** $\frac{60}{64}$ **31.** $\frac{21}{98}$ **33.** $\frac{30}{48}$ **35.** $\frac{15}{42}$ **37.** $\frac{102}{144}$ **39.** $\frac{1}{3}$
$\frac{1}{2}$ **43.** $\frac{1}{6}$ **45.** $1\frac{1}{9}$ **47.** 0   **49.** $\frac{9}{22}$ **51.** 3   **53.** $\frac{4}{21}$ **55.** $\frac{12}{35}$ **57.** $\frac{7}{11}$ **59.** $1\frac{1}{3}$ **61.** $\frac{3}{5}$ **63.** $\frac{1}{11}$
4   **67.** $\frac{1}{3}$ **69.** $\frac{3}{5}$ **71.** $2\frac{1}{4}$ **73.** $\frac{1}{5}$ **75.** Answers will vary. For example, $\frac{4}{6}, \frac{6}{9}, \frac{8}{12}, \frac{10}{15}, \frac{12}{8}$.   **77. a.** $\frac{4}{25}$ **b.** $\frac{4}{25}$

SECTION 2.4

1. 2, 5, 7 **3.** 8 **5.** 18 **7.** $\dfrac{3}{7}$ **9.** $\dfrac{2}{3}$ **11.** $\dfrac{4}{7}$ **13.** 1 **15.** $1\dfrac{4}{11}$ **17.** $3\dfrac{2}{5}$ **19.** $1\dfrac{3}{8}$ **21.** $1\dfrac{7}{15}$ **23.** $1\dfrac{5}{12}$

25. A whole number other than 1 **27.** The number 1 **29.** $1\dfrac{1}{6}$ **31.** $\dfrac{13}{14}$ **33.** $\dfrac{53}{60}$ **35.** $1\dfrac{1}{56}$ **37.** $\dfrac{23}{60}$ **39.** $1\dfrac{17}{18}$

41. $1\dfrac{11}{48}$ **43.** $1\dfrac{9}{20}$ **45.** $2\dfrac{17}{120}$ **47.** $2\dfrac{5}{72}$ **49.** $\dfrac{39}{40}$ **51.** $1\dfrac{19}{24}$ **53.** ii **55.** $10\dfrac{1}{12}$ **57.** $9\dfrac{2}{7}$ **59.** $9\dfrac{47}{48}$ **61.** $8\dfrac{3}{13}$

63. $16\dfrac{29}{120}$ **65.** $24\dfrac{29}{40}$ **67.** $33\dfrac{7}{24}$ **69.** $10\dfrac{5}{36}$ **71.** $10\dfrac{5}{12}$ **73.** $14\dfrac{73}{90}$ **75.** $10\dfrac{13}{48}$ **77.** The length of the pole is $9\dfrac{7}{8}$ feet.

79. $9\dfrac{5}{24}$ **81.** $14\dfrac{1}{18}$ **83.** $11\dfrac{11}{12}$ **85.** No **87.** The length of the shaft is $8\dfrac{9}{16}$ inches. **89.** The sum represents the height of the tab

91. The total length of the course is $10\dfrac{1}{2}$ miles. **93.** The wall is $6\dfrac{5}{8}$ inches thick.

95. The minimum length of the bolt needed is $1\dfrac{3}{8}$ inches. **97.** $\dfrac{1}{2}, \dfrac{1}{3}, \dfrac{1}{4}$ **99.** $\dfrac{1}{3} + \dfrac{1}{4}$ **101.** $\dfrac{1}{4} + \dfrac{1}{6}$

SECTION 2.5

1. 5, 3, 2 **3.** $\dfrac{11}{18}$ **5.** $\dfrac{2}{17}$ **7.** $\dfrac{1}{3}$ **9.** $\dfrac{1}{10}$ **11.** $\dfrac{5}{13}$ **13.** $\dfrac{1}{3}$ **15.** $\dfrac{4}{7}$ **17.** $\dfrac{1}{4}$ **19.** Yes **21.** $\dfrac{1}{2}$ **23.** $\dfrac{19}{56}$

25. $\dfrac{1}{2}$ **27.** $\dfrac{11}{60}$ **29.** $\dfrac{1}{32}$ **31.** $\dfrac{19}{60}$ **33.** $\dfrac{5}{72}$ **35.** $\dfrac{11}{60}$ **37.** $\dfrac{29}{60}$ **39.** i **41.** $5\dfrac{1}{5}$ **43.** $4\dfrac{7}{8}$ **45.** $\dfrac{16}{21}$ **47.** $5\dfrac{1}{2}$

49. $7\dfrac{5}{24}$ **51.** $1\dfrac{2}{5}$ **53.** $15\dfrac{11}{18}$ **55.** The distance is $21\dfrac{3}{4}$ inches. **57.** $15\dfrac{11}{20}$ **59.** $4\dfrac{37}{45}$ **61.** No **63.** The missing dimension

is $9\dfrac{1}{2}$ inches. **65.** The desk is $\dfrac{3}{4}$ inch shorter than a standard size desk. **67. a.** The hikers plan to travel $17\dfrac{17}{24}$ miles the first two days.

b. There will be $9\dfrac{19}{24}$ miles left to travel on the third day. **69.** The difference represents how much farther the hikers plan to travel on the

second day than on the first day. **71. a.** Yes **b.** The wrestler needs to lose $3\dfrac{1}{4}$ pounds to reach the desired weight.

73. $\dfrac{11}{15}$ of the electrician's income is not spent on housing. **75.** $6\dfrac{1}{8}$

CHECK YOUR PROGRESS: CHAPTER 2

1. 36 [2.1A] **2.** 18 [2.1A] **3.** 70 [2.1A] **4.** 252 [2.1A] **5.** 6 [2.1B] **6.** 27 [2.1B] **7.** 1 [2.1B] **8.** 5 [2.1

9. $\dfrac{4}{5}$ [2.3B] **10.** $\dfrac{1}{3}$ [2.3B] **11.** Simplest form [2.3B] **12.** 9 [2.3B] **13.** $\dfrac{2}{3}$ [2.4A] **14.** $\dfrac{1}{2}$ [2.5A] **15.** $\dfrac{7}{18}$ [2.5B

16. $\dfrac{3}{5}$ [2.4B] **17.** $1\dfrac{25}{48}$ [2.4B] **18.** $\dfrac{21}{52}$ [2.5B] **19.** $\dfrac{23}{48}$ [2.5B] **20.** $\dfrac{17}{20}$ [2.4B] **21.** $9\dfrac{1}{6}$ [2.4C] **22.** $18\dfrac{11}{18}$ [2.4C]

23. $6\dfrac{5}{14}$ [2.5C] **24.** $2\dfrac{19}{56}$ [2.5C] **25.** $13\dfrac{13}{18}$ [2.4C] **26.** $17\dfrac{1}{20}$ [2.4C] **27.** $3\dfrac{1}{4}$ [2.5C] **28.** $2\dfrac{5}{12}$ [2.5C]

SECTION 2.6

1. 2, 9, $\dfrac{10}{27}$ **3.** Yes **5.** $\dfrac{7}{12}$ **7.** $\dfrac{7}{48}$ **9.** $\dfrac{1}{48}$ **11.** $\dfrac{11}{14}$ **13.** 6 **15.** $\dfrac{5}{12}$ **17.** 6 **19.** $\dfrac{2}{3}$ **21.** $\dfrac{3}{16}$ **23.** $\dfrac{21}{80}$

25. 10 **27.** $\dfrac{1}{15}$ **29.** $\dfrac{2}{3}$ **31.** $\dfrac{7}{26}$ **33.** 4 **35.** $\dfrac{4}{9}$ **37.** Answers will vary. For example, $\dfrac{3}{4}$ and $\dfrac{4}{3}$. **39.** $1\dfrac{1}{3}$ **41.** $2\dfrac{1}{2}$

43. $\dfrac{9}{34}$ **45.** 10 **47.** $16\dfrac{2}{3}$ **49.** 1 **51.** $\dfrac{1}{2}$ **53.** 30 **55.** 42 **57.** $12\dfrac{2}{3}$ **59.** $1\dfrac{4}{5}$ **61.** $1\dfrac{2}{3}$ **63.** $1\dfrac{2}{3}$ **65.** 0

67. $27\dfrac{2}{3}$ **69.** $8\dfrac{1}{16}$ **71.** 8 **73.** The distance is 54 feet. **75.** 9 **77.** $\dfrac{5}{8}$ **79.** $3\dfrac{1}{40}$ **81.** Less than **83.** The cost is $11.

85. The length is $3\dfrac{1}{12}$ feet. **87.** The area is $27\dfrac{9}{16}$ square feet. **89.** Each year, about 36 million acres of corn are turned into ethanol.

91. The weight is $54\dfrac{19}{36}$ pounds. **93.** The total cost of the material is $363. **95.** $\dfrac{1}{2}$ **97.** A

CTION 2.7

3. $\dfrac{5}{4}$ **5.** 9, 4, $\dfrac{27}{32}$ **7.** $\dfrac{5}{6}$ **9.** 1   **11.** 0   **13.** $\dfrac{1}{2}$ **15.** $\dfrac{1}{6}$ **17.** $\dfrac{7}{10}$ **19.** 2   **21.** 2   **23.** $\dfrac{1}{6}$ **25.** 6

$\dfrac{1}{15}$ **29.** 2   **31.** $2\dfrac{1}{2}$ **33.** 3   **35.** $1\dfrac{1}{6}$ **37.** $3\dfrac{1}{3}$ **39.** True   **41.** 6   **43.** $\dfrac{1}{2}$ **45.** $\dfrac{1}{30}$ **47.** $1\dfrac{4}{5}$ **49.** 13   **51.** 3

$\dfrac{1}{5}$ **55.** $\dfrac{11}{28}$ **57.** 120   **59.** $\dfrac{11}{40}$ **61.** $\dfrac{33}{40}$ **63.** $4\dfrac{4}{9}$ **65.** $\dfrac{13}{32}$ **67.** $10\dfrac{2}{3}$ **69.** $\dfrac{12}{53}$ **71.** $4\dfrac{62}{191}$ **73.** 68   **75.** $8\dfrac{2}{7}$

$3\dfrac{13}{49}$ **79.** 4   **81.** $1\dfrac{3}{5}$ **83.** $\dfrac{9}{34}$ **85.** False   **87.** Less than   **89.** There are 12 servings in 16 ounces of cereal.

Each acre costs $24,000.   **93.** The nut will make 12 turns in moving $1\dfrac{7}{8}$ inches.   **95. a.** The total weight of the fat and bone is

pounds.   **b.** The chef can cut 28 servings from the roast.   **97.** The distance between each pair of posts is $2\dfrac{3}{4}$ inches.   **99.** $\dfrac{1}{2}$

$\dfrac{1}{2}$ **103.** $\dfrac{2}{3}$ **105.** $\dfrac{2}{3}$ **107.** The recommended maximum monthly payment is $1500.

The board measures 14 inches by 7 inches by $1\dfrac{3}{4}$ inches when closed.   **111.** Each column is $2\dfrac{1}{4}$ inches wide.

Three times more people use Safari.   **115.** The unnamed browsers represent $\dfrac{1}{10}$ of the world browser market.

CTION 2.8

Equal to   **3.** Less than   **5.** $\dfrac{11}{40} < \dfrac{19}{40}$ **7.** $\dfrac{2}{3} < \dfrac{5}{7}$ **9.** $\dfrac{5}{8} > \dfrac{7}{12}$ **11.** $\dfrac{7}{9} < \dfrac{11}{12}$ **13.** $\dfrac{13}{14} > \dfrac{19}{21}$ **15.** $\dfrac{7}{24} < \dfrac{11}{30}$ **17.** $\dfrac{4}{5}$

$\dfrac{25}{144}$ **21.** $\dfrac{2}{9}$ **23.** $\dfrac{3}{125}$ **25.** $\dfrac{4}{45}$ **27.** $\dfrac{1}{30}$ **29.** $1\dfrac{1}{5}$ **31.** $\dfrac{17}{24}$ **33.** $\dfrac{7}{8}$ **35.** $1\dfrac{3}{8}$ **37.** $\dfrac{7}{8}$ **39.** $\dfrac{12}{125}$ **41.** $\dfrac{11}{32}$

$\dfrac{17}{24}$ **45.** $\dfrac{14}{15}$ **47.** $2\dfrac{7}{10}$ **49.** $\dfrac{21}{44}$ **51.** $\dfrac{25}{39}$ **53.** $1\dfrac{1}{9}$ **55.** $\dfrac{43}{48}$ **57. a.** More people choose a fast-food restaurant on the

is of its location.   **b.** Location was the criterion cited by the most people.   **59.** $\left(\dfrac{7}{8} + \dfrac{2}{3}\right) \cdot \dfrac{1}{2} + \dfrac{5}{6}$

IAPTER 2 REVIEW EXERCISES

$\dfrac{2}{3}$ [2.3B]   **2.** $\dfrac{3}{16}$ [2.8B]   **3.** $\dfrac{13}{4}$ [2.2A]   **4.** $\dfrac{32}{44}$ [2.3A]   **5.** $\dfrac{11}{18} < \dfrac{17}{24}$ [2.8A]   **6.** $14\dfrac{19}{42}$ [2.5C]   **7.** $\dfrac{5}{36}$ [2.8B]

$9\dfrac{1}{24}$ [2.6B]   **9.** 2 [2.7B]   **10.** $\dfrac{25}{48}$ [2.5B]   **11.** $3\dfrac{1}{3}$ [2.7B]   **12.** 4 [2.1B]   **13.** $\dfrac{24}{36}$ [2.3A]   **14.** $\dfrac{3}{4}$ [2.7A]

$1\dfrac{13}{18}$ [2.4B]   **16.** $16\dfrac{1}{2}$ [2.6B]   **17.** 36 [2.1A]   **18.** $\dfrac{4}{11}$ [2.3B]   **19.** $1\dfrac{1}{8}$ [2.4A]   **20.** $\dfrac{1}{8}$ [2.6A]   **21.** $18\dfrac{13}{54}$ [2.4C]

5 [2.1B]   **23.** $3\dfrac{2}{5}$ [2.2B]   **24.** $\dfrac{1}{15}$ [2.8B]   **25.** $5\dfrac{7}{8}$ [2.4C]   **26.** 54 [2.1A]   **27.** $\dfrac{1}{3}$ [2.5A]   **28.** $\dfrac{19}{7}$ [2.2B]

2 [2.7A]   **30.** $\dfrac{1}{15}$ [2.6A]   **31.** $10\dfrac{1}{8}$ [2.5C]   **32.** $1\dfrac{7}{8}$ [2.2A]   **33.** The total rainfall for the 3 months was $21\dfrac{7}{24}$ inches.

D]   **34.** The cost per acre was $36,000. [2.7C]   **35.** The second checkpoint is $4\dfrac{3}{4}$ miles from the finish line. [2.5D]

The car can travel 243 miles. [2.6C]

IAPTER 2 TEST

$\dfrac{4}{9}$ [2.6A; Example 1]   **2.** 8 [2.1B; Example 2]   **3.** $1\dfrac{3}{7}$ [2.7A; Example 2]   **4.** $\dfrac{7}{24}$ [2.8B; You Try It 2]

$\dfrac{49}{5}$ [2.2B; Example 5]   **6.** 8 [2.6B; Example 5]   **7.** $\dfrac{5}{8}$ [2.3B; Example 3]   **8.** $\dfrac{3}{8} < \dfrac{5}{12}$ [2.8A; Example 1]

$\dfrac{5}{6}$ [2.8B; Example 2]   **10.** 120 [2.1A; Example 1]   **11.** $\dfrac{1}{4}$ [2.5A; Example 1]   **12.** $3\dfrac{3}{5}$ [2.2B; Example 3]

$2\dfrac{2}{19}$ [2.7B; Example 4]   **14.** $\dfrac{45}{72}$ [2.3A; Example 1]   **15.** $1\dfrac{61}{90}$ [2.4B; Example 4]   **16.** $13\dfrac{81}{88}$ [2.5C; Example 4]

$\dfrac{7}{48}$ [2.5B; Example 2]   **18.** $\dfrac{19}{96}$ [2.8B; You Try It 2]   **19.** $1\dfrac{11}{12}$ [2.4A; Example 1]   **20.** $22\dfrac{4}{15}$ [2.4C; Example 7]

$\dfrac{11}{4}$ [2.2A; Example 2]   **22.** The electrician earns $840. [2.6C; Example 6]   **23.** 11 lots were available for sale. [2.7C; Example 8]

24. The actual length of wall A is $12\frac{1}{2}$ feet. The actual length of wall B is 18 feet. The actual length of wall C is $15\frac{3}{4}$ feet. [2.7C, Example 8]

25. The total rainfall for the 3-month period was $21\frac{11}{24}$ inches. [2.4D, Example 8]

CUMULATIVE REVIEW EXERCISES

1. 290,000 [1.1D] **2.** 291,278 [1.3B] **3.** 73,154 [1.4B] **4.** 540 r12 [1.5C] **5.** 1 [1.6B] **6.** $2 \cdot 2 \cdot 11$ [1.7B]

7. 210 [2.1A] **8.** 20 [2.1B] **9.** $\frac{23}{3}$ [2.2B] **10.** $6\frac{1}{4}$ [2.2B] **11.** $\frac{15}{48}$ [2.3A] **12.** $\frac{2}{5}$ [2.3B] **13.** $1\frac{7}{48}$ [2.4B]

14. $14\frac{11}{48}$ [2.4C] **15.** $\frac{13}{24}$ [2.5B] **16.** $1\frac{7}{9}$ [2.5C] **17.** $\frac{7}{20}$ [2.6A] **18.** $7\frac{1}{2}$ [2.6B] **19.** $1\frac{1}{20}$ [2.7A] **20.** $2\frac{5}{8}$ [2.7

21. $\frac{1}{9}$ [2.8B] **22.** $5\frac{5}{24}$ [2.8B] **23.** The amount in the checking account at the end of the week was $862. [1.3C] **24.** The total income from the tickets was $1410. [1.4C] **25.** The total weight is $12\frac{1}{24}$ pounds. [2.4D] **26.** The length of the remaining piece is $4\frac{17}{24}$ feet. [2.5D] **27.** The car travels 225 miles on $8\frac{1}{3}$ gallons of gas. [2.6C] **28.** 25 parcels can be sold from the remaining land. [2.7C]

Answers to Chapter 3 Selected Exercises

PREP TEST

1. $\frac{3}{10}$ [2.2A] **2.** 36,900 [1.1D] **3.** Four thousand seven hundred ninety-one [1.1B] **4.** 6842 [1.1B] **5.** 9394 [1.2A] **6.** 1638 [1.3B] **7.** 76,804 [1.4B] **8.** 278 r18 [1.5C]

SECTION 3.1

1. Thousandths **3.** Ten-thousandths **5.** 0.3 **7.** 0.853 **9.** $\frac{59}{100}$ **11.** Thirty-seven hundredths **13.** Nine and four tenths **15.** Fifty-three ten-thousandths **17.** Forty-five thousandths **19.** Twenty-six and four hundredths **21.** 3.0806 **23.** 407.03 **25.** 246.024 **27.** 73.02684 **29.** 6.2 **31.** 21.0 **33.** 18.41 **35.** 72.50 **37.** 936.291 **39.** 47 **41.** 7015 **43.** 2.97527 **45.** 700 **47.** 0.18 ounce **49.** 26.2 miles **51.** Answers will vary. For example, 0.572 **53.** $0.278 > 0.203$ **55.** $0.045 > 0.038$ **57.** $0.037 < 0.13$ **59.** $0.031 > 0.00987$ **61.** $0.02883 < 0.0305$ **63.** $0.0072 > 0.0008294$ **65.** Answers will vary. For example, **a.** 0.15 **b.** 1.05 **c.** 0.001

SECTION 3.2

3. 150.1065 **5.** 95.8446 **7.** 69.644 **9.** 92.883 **11.** 113.205 **13.** 110.7666 **15.** 1.6466 **17.** 107.642 **19.** Cal.: 234.192 Est.: 234 **21.** Cal.: 781.943 Est.: 782 **23.** Yes **25.** The length of the shaft is 4.35 feet. **27.** The perimeter is 3.53 meters. **29.** The total average number of viewers per day for the three news programs was 21.1 million. **31.** No, a 4-foot rope cannot be wrapped around the box. **33.** Three possible answers are bread, butter, and mayonnaise; raisin bran, butter, and bread; and lunch meat, milk, and popcorn. **35.** $\frac{79}{1000} + \frac{13}{100}; \frac{209}{1000}$ **37.** $\frac{53}{1000} + \frac{9}{100} + \frac{1077}{10,000}; \frac{2507}{10,000}$

SECTION 3.3

1. 6.19 **3.** 0.0095 **5.** 5.627 **7.** 113.6427 **9.** 6.7098 **11.** 215.697 **13.** 53.8776 **15.** 72.7091 **17.** 0.3142 **19.** 1.023 **21.** 261.166 **23.** 655.32 **25.** 342.9268 **27.** 8.628 **29.** 184.728 **31.** 0.27598 **33.** $7.01 - 2.325$ **35.** $19.35 - 8.967$ **37.** Cal.: 2.74506 Est.: 3 **39.** Cal.: 7.14925 Est.: 7 **41.** The missing dimension is 2.59 feet. **43.** The average price of a ticket increased by $.62. **45.** 33.5 million more people watched Super Bowl XLII than watched the Super Bowl post-game show. **47. a.** 0.1 **b.** 0.01 **c.** 0.001 **49.** $\frac{87}{100} - \frac{531}{1000}; \frac{339}{1000}$ **51.** $\frac{97}{1000} - \frac{69,531}{1,000,000}; \frac{27,469}{1,000,000}$

ECK YOUR PROGRESS: CHAPTER 3

$\frac{7}{10}$ [3.1C]   **2.** $\frac{17}{1000}$ [3.1C]   **3.** $\frac{93}{100}$ [3.1C]   **4.** $\frac{87}{100,000}$ [3.1C]   **5.** Twenty-three and forty-five thousandths [3.1A]

305.0057 [3.1A]   **7.** 357.80 [3.1B]   **8.** 0.357 < 0.4 [3.1C]   **9.** 0.056 > 0.0107 [3.1C]   **10.** 0.00319 < 0.005 [3.1C]

16.18 [3.2A]   **12.** 17.97 [3.3A]   **13.** 116.217 [3.3A]   **14.** 90.3972 [3.2A]   **15.** 1000 [3.2A]   **16.** 18.1508 [3.3A]

ECTION 3.4

10^2 **3.** 10^6 **5.** 10,000,000   **7.** 3   **9.** 5   **11.** 0.36   **13.** 0.25   **15.** 6.93   **17.** 1.84   **19.** 0.74   **21.** 39.5
2.72   **25.** 0.603   **27.** 13.50   **29.** 4.316   **31.** 0.1323   **33.** 0.03568   **35.** 0.0784   **37.** 0.076   **39.** 34.48
580.5   **43.** 20.148   **45.** 0.04255   **47.** 0.17686   **49.** 0.19803   **51.** 0.429   **53.** 2.116   **55.** 0.476   **57.** 1.022
2.318   **61.** The height of the diving board is 9.8424 feet.   **63.** 3.2   **65.** 6.5   **67.** 6285.6   **69.** 35,700   **71.** 6.3
3.9   **75.** 49,000   **77.** 6.7   **79.** 0.012075   **81.** 0.0117796   **83.** 0.31004   **85.** 0.082845   **87.** 5.175
Cal.: 91.2   **91.** Cal.: 1.0472   **93.** Cal.: 3.897   **95.** Cal.: 11.2406   **97.** Cal.: 0.371096   **99.** Cal.: 31.8528
Est.: 90   Est.: 0.8   Est.: 4.5   Est.: 12   Est.: 0.32   Est.: 30
. The amount received is $14.06.   **103.** A U.S. homeowner's average annual cost of electricity is $1244.04.   **105.** The accountant's
eage deduction is $258.02.   **107.** The deduction for driving a car 2374 miles for business   **109.** You will pay $5.96 in taxes.
. The area is 23.625 square feet.   **113. a.** The CRNA's overtime pay is $2240.25.   **b.** The CRNA's total income is $5680.25.
. The federal government would have saved $125,120,000.   **117. a.** The total cost for grade 1 is $56.32.   **b.** The total cost
grade 2 is $74.04.   **c.** The total cost for grade 3 is $409.56.   **d.** The total cost is $539.92.

. $1\frac{3}{10} \times 2\frac{31}{100} = \frac{13}{10} \times \frac{231}{100} = \frac{3003}{1000} = 3\frac{3}{1000} = 3.003$

ECTION 3.5

right; whole; right; divided   **3.** 0.82   **5.** 4.8   **7.** 89   **9.** 60   **11.** 84.3   **13.** 32.3   **15.** 5.06   **17.** 1.3   **19.** 0.11   **21.** 3.8
. 6.3   **25.** 0.6   **27.** 2.5   **29.** 1.1   **31.** 0.81   **33.** 0.09   **35.** 40.70   **37.** 0.46   **39.** 0.019   **41.** 0.360   **43.** 0.103
. 0.009   **47.** 1   **49.** 3   **51.** 1   **53.** 57   **55.** The length is 1.0375 meters.   **57.** 0.407   **59.** 4.267   **61.** 0.01037
. 0.008295   **65.** 0.032   **67.** 0.23627   **69.** 0.000053   **71.** 0.0018932   **73.** 18.42   **75.** 16.07   **77.** 0.0135
. 0.023678   **81.** 0.112   **83.** Cal.: 11.1632   **85.** Cal.: 884.0909   **87.** Cal.: 1.8269   **89.** Cal.: 58.8095   **91.** Cal.: 72.3053
Est.: 10   Est.: 1000   Est.: 1.5   Est.: 50   Est.: 100
. **a.** Use division to find the cost.   **b.** Use multiplication to find the cost.   **95.** The trucker must drive 35 miles.   **97.** 6.23 yards are gained
. carry.   **99.** Three complete shelves can be cut from a 12-foot board.   **101.** The monthly payment was $213.46.   **103.** The car travels
.5 miles on 1 gallon of gasoline.   **105.** You will use 0.405 barrel of oil.   **107.** 2.57 million more women than men were attending institutions
. higher learning.   **109.** The Army's advertising budget was 4.2 times greater than the Navy's advertising budget.   **111.** The population of
.s segment is expected to be 2.1 times greater in 2030 than in 2000.   **115.** ×   **117.** ×   **119.** ÷   **121.** 2.53   **123.** 0.27

ECTION 3.6

Thousandths   **3.** Tenths   **5.** Hundredths   **7.** Greater than 1   **9.** Less than 1   **11.** $0.\overline{6}$ **13.** 0.875   **15.** $0.7\overline{2}$ **17.** $0.\overline{60}$
. $0.47\overline{2}$ **21.** $0.\overline{729}$ **23.** $0.9\overline{25}$ **25.** $0.4\overline{729}$ **27.** 0.85   **29.** $0.\overline{857142}$ **31.** 0.34375   **33.** 3.85   **35.** $4.2\overline{36}$ **37.** $\frac{2}{5}$

. $\frac{12}{25}$ **41.** $\frac{97}{200}$ **43.** $3\frac{3}{4}$ **45.** $3\frac{7}{40}$ **47.** $11\frac{1}{250}$ **49.** $9\frac{279}{1000}$ **51.** $\frac{28}{125}$ **53.** $\frac{13}{250}$ **55.** $\frac{3}{20,000}$ **57.** 0.31   **59.** 0.163

. 0.089   **63.** 0.7059   **65.** $\frac{7}{8} < 0.9$ **67.** $0.13 > \frac{5}{40}$ **69.** $\frac{12}{55} < 0.22$ **71.** $0.55 < \frac{5}{9}$ **73.** $\frac{17}{18} > 0.94$ **75.** $\frac{22}{7} > 3.14$

. 0.5, 0.75, 0.625, 0.5625, 0.3, 0.35, 0.59375, 0.575, 0.28, 0.38   **79.** 2 and 5   **81.** Answers will vary. For example, $\frac{5}{6} = 0.8\overline{3}$, $\frac{4}{11} = 0.\overline{36}$,

. $= 0.\overline{692307}$. No.

HAPTER 3 REVIEW EXERCISES

54.5 [3.5A]   **2.** 833.958 [3.2A]   **3.** 0.055 < 0.1 [3.1C]   **4.** Twenty-two and ninety-two ten-thousandths [3.1A]

0.05678 [3.1B]   **6.** 0.2125 [3.6A]   **7.** $\frac{3}{8}$ [3.6B]   **8.** 36.714 [3.2A]   **9.** 34.025 [3.1A]   **10.** $\frac{5}{8} > 0.62$ [3.6C]

. $0.3\overline{18}$ [3.6A]   **12.** $\frac{33}{50}$ [3.6B]   **13.** 22.8635 [3.3A]   **14.** 7.94 [3.1B]   **15.** 8.932 [3.4A]   **16.** Three hundred forty-two
d thirty-seven hundredths [3.1A]   **17.** 3.06753 [3.1A]   **18.** 25.7446 [3.4A]   **19.** 6.594 [3.5A]   **20.** 4.8785 [3.3A]
. The airline saved 49.1 million gallons of fuel. The average cost per gallon of fuel is $2.67. [3.2B; 3.5B]   **22.** The new balance in your
count is $661.51. [3.3B]   **23.** The number who drove is 6.4 times greater than the number who flew. [3.5B]   **24.** During a 5-day school
eek, 9.5 million gallons of milk are served. [3.4B]

CHAPTER 3 TEST

1. $0.0068 > 0.000963$ [3.1C; Example 7]   **2.** 4.087 [3.3A; Example 1]   **3.** Forty-five and three hundred two ten-thousandths [3.1A; Example 2]   **4.** 209.07086 [3.1A; Example 3]   **5.** $\frac{33}{40}$ [3.6B; HOW TO 3]   **6.** $\frac{13}{8} > 0.72$ [3.6C; You Try It 5]   **7.** 1.538 [3.5A; Example 3]   **8.** 27.76626 [3.3A; Example 2]   **9.** 25.8808 [3.3A; Example 3]   **10.** 0.325 [3.6A; HOW TO 1]   **11.** 7.095 [3.1B; Example 4]   **12.** 23.2 [3.5A; Example 1]   **13.** 458.581 [3.2A; Example 2]   **14.** $0.68\overline{1}$ [3.6A; Example 1]   **15.** 0.00548 [3.4A; You Try It 3]   **16.** 255.957 [3.2A; You Try It 1]   **17.** 17,149.6 [3.4A; You Try It 5]   **18.** 0.0015923 [3.5A; Example 5]   **19.** The cost is $21.60. [3.4B; Example 7]   **20.** The monthly payment is $395.40. [3.5B; Example 7]   **21.** Your total income is $3087.14. [3.2B; You Try It 4]   **22.** The cost of the call is $4.63. [3.4B; Example 8]

CUMULATIVE REVIEW EXERCISES

1. 235 r17 [1.5C]   **2.** 128 [1.6A]   **3.** 3 [1.6B]   **4.** 72 [2.1A]   **5.** $4\frac{2}{5}$ [2.2B]   **6.** $\frac{37}{8}$ [2.2B]   **7.** $\frac{25}{60}$ [2.3A]   **8.** $1\frac{17}{48}$ [2.4B]   **9.** $8\frac{35}{36}$ [2.4C]   **10.** $5\frac{23}{36}$ [2.5C]   **11.** $\frac{1}{12}$ [2.6A]   **12.** $9\frac{1}{8}$ [2.6B]   **13.** $1\frac{2}{9}$ [2.7A]   **14.** $\frac{19}{20}$ [2.7B]   **15.** $\frac{3}{16}$ [2.8B]   **16.** $2\frac{5}{18}$ [2.8B]   **17.** Sixty-five and three hundred nine ten-thousandths [3.1A]   **18.** 504.6991 [3.2A]   **19.** 21.0764 [3.3A]   **20.** 55.26066 [3.4A]   **21.** 2.154 [3.5A]   **22.** $0.7\overline{3}$ [3.6A]   **23.** $\frac{17}{40}$ [3.6B]   **24.** $\frac{8}{9} < 0.98$ [3.6C]   **25.** Sweden mandates 14 more vacation days than Germany. [1.3C]   **26.** The patient must lose $7\frac{3}{4}$ pounds during the third month to achieve the goal. [2.5D]   **27.** Your checking account balance is $617.38. [3.3B]   **28.** The resulting thickness is 1.395 inches. [3.3B]   **29.** You paid $6008.80 in income tax last year. [3.4B]   **30.** The amount of each payment is $46.37. [3.5B]

Answers to Chapter 4 Selected Exercises

PREP TEST

1. $\frac{4}{5}$ [2.3B]   **2.** $\frac{1}{2}$ [2.3B]   **3.** 24.8 [3.6A]   **4.** 4×33 [1.4A]   **5.** 4 [1.5A]

SECTION 4.1

1. 3 to 8   **3.** $\frac{1}{5}$ 1:5 1 to 5   **5.** $\frac{2}{1}$ 2:1 2 to 1   **7.** $\frac{3}{8}$ 3:8 3 to 8   **9.** $\frac{1}{1}$ 1:1 1 to 1   **11.** $\frac{7}{10}$ 7:10 7 to 10   **13.** $\frac{1}{2}$ 1:2 1 to 2   **15.** $\frac{2}{1}$ 2:1 2 to 1   **17.** $\frac{5}{2}$ 5:2 5 to 2   **19.** $\frac{5}{7}$ 5:7 5 to 7   **21.** days   **23.** The ratio is $\frac{3}{8}$.   **25.** The ratio is $\frac{1}{3}$.   **27.** The ratio is $\frac{13}{22,000}$.   **29.** The ratio is $\frac{1}{5}$.   **31.** The ratio is $\frac{3}{250}$.   **35.** Answers will vary.

SECTION 4.2

3. $\frac{3 \text{ pounds}}{4 \text{ people}}$ **5.** $\frac{\$20}{3 \text{ boards}}$ **7.** $\frac{20 \text{ miles}}{1 \text{ gallon}}$ **9.** $\frac{8 \text{ gallons}}{1 \text{ hour}}$ **11.** Divide the number of gallons per minute by 60.   **13.** 1   **15.** 2.5 feet/second   **17.** $975/week   **19.** 110 trees/acre   **21.** $18.84/hour   **23.** 35.6 miles/gallon   **25.** The car got 42.6 miles/gallon.   **27.** The rate is 7.4 miles per dollar.   **29.** The average number of rides per day was 1220.   **31.** The cost per viewer is $.03.   **33.** The rate is 12 gallons/minute.   **35.** The cost is 2,715,580 yen.   **37. a.** Australia has the least population density.   **b.** There are 851 more people per square mile in India than in the United States.   **41.** The car gets about 3.6 gallons per 100 miles.   **43.** 0.004 ppm

CHECK YOUR PROGRESS: CHAPTER 4

1. $\frac{1}{4}$, 1:4 [4.1A]   **2.** $\frac{2}{3}$, 2:3 [4.1A]   **3.** $\frac{5}{12}$, 5:12 [4.1A]   **4.** $24/hour [4.2B]   **5.** 10.4 yards/second [4.2B]   **6.** 29.2 miles/gallon [4.2B]   **7.** The recommended amount of fertilizer is 0.025 gallon/square foot. [4.2C]   **8.** Whole milk has 18.75 calories/ounce. [4.2C]   **9.** The cost per rose is $4.25. [4.2C]   **10.** The cost per page is $.0425. [4.2C]

SECTION 4.3

1. $n = 45 \div 15$ **3.** $72 \div 9 = n$ **5.** True   **7.** Not true   **9.** Not true   **11.** True   **13.** True   **15.** True   **17.** True   **19.** Not true   **21.** True   **23.** Yes   **25.** Yes   **27.** 3   **29.** 105   **31.** 2   **33.** 60   **35.** 2.22   **37.** 6.67   **39.** 21.33   **41.** 16.25   **43.** 2.44   **45.** 47.89   **47.** A 0.5-ounce serving contains 50 calories.   **49.** The car can travel 329 miles.   **51.** 12.5 gallons of water are required.   **53.** The distance is 16 miles.   **55.** 1.25 ounces are required.   **57.** 160,000 people would vote.   **59.** The monthly payment is $176.75.   **61.** 750 defective circuit boards are expected in a run of 25,000.   **63.** A bowling ball would weigh about 2.67 pounds on the moon.   **65.** The dividend would be $1071.

CHAPTER 4 REVIEW EXERCISES

1. True [4.3A]   **2.** $\frac{2}{5}$ 2:5 2 to 5 [4.1A]   **3.** 62.5 miles/hour [4.2B]   **4.** True [4.3A]   **5.** 68 [4.3B]
6. $12.50/hour [4.2B]   **7.** $1.75/pound [4.2B]   **8.** $\frac{2}{7}$ 2:7 2 to 7 [4.1A]   **9.** 36 [4.3B]   **10.** 19.44 [4.3B]
11. $\frac{2}{5}$ 2:5 2 to 5 [4.1A]   **12.** Not true [4.3A]   **13.** $\frac{\$35}{4\,hours}$ [4.2A]   **14.** 27.2 miles/gallon [4.2B]
15. $\frac{1}{1}$ 1:1 1 to 1 [4.1A]   **16.** True [4.3A]   **17.** 65.45 [4.3B]   **18.** $\frac{100\,miles}{3\,hours}$ [4.2A]   **19.** The ratio is $\frac{2}{5}$. [4.1B]
20. The property tax is $6400. [4.3C]   **21.** The ratio is $\frac{3}{8}$. [4.1B]   **22.** The cost per phone is $37.50. [4.2C]
23. 1344 blocks would be needed. [4.3C]   **24.** The ratio is $\frac{5}{2}$. [4.1B]   **25.** The turkey costs $.93/pound. [4.2C]
26. The average was 56.8 miles/hour. [4.2C]   **27.** The cost is $493.50. [4.3C]   **28.** The cost is $44.75/share. [4.2C]
29. 22.5 pounds of fertilizer will be used. [4.3C]   **30.** The ratio is $\frac{1}{2}$. [4.1B]

CHAPTER 4 TEST

1. $3836.40/month [4.2B; Example 2]   **2.** $\frac{1}{6}$ 1:6 1 to 6 [4.1A; You Try It 1]   **3.** $\frac{9\,supports}{4\,feet}$ [4.2A; Example 1]
4. Not true [4.3A; Example 2]   **5.** $\frac{3}{1}$ 3:1 3 to 1 [4.1A; Example 2]   **6.** 144 [4.3B; HOW TO 3]
7. 30.5 miles/gallon [4.2B; Apply the Concept]   **8.** $\frac{1}{3}$ 1:3 1 to 3 [4.1A; You Try It 1]   **9.** True [4.3A; Example 1]
10. 40.5 [4.3B; Example 3]   **11.** $\frac{3\,feet}{2\,boards}$ [4.2A; Example 1]   **12.** $\frac{3}{5}$ 3:5 3 to 5 [4.1A; You Try It 1]
13. The dividend is $625. [4.3C; Example 9]   **14.** The ratio is $\frac{1}{12}$. [4.1B; Example 3]   **15.** The plane's speed is
275 miles/hour. [4.2C; Example 3]   **16.** The college student's body contains 132 pounds of water. [4.3C; Example 8]
17. The cost of the lumber is $1.73/foot. [4.2C; You Try It 3]   **18.** The amount of medication required is 0.875 ounce.
[4.3C; Example 8]   **19.** The ratio is $\frac{4}{5}$. [4.1B; Example 4]   **20.** 36 defective hard drives are expected to be found in the
production of 1200 hard drives. [4.3C; You Try It 9]

CUMULATIVE REVIEW EXERCISES

1. 9158 [1.3B]   **2.** $2^4 \cdot 3^3$ [1.6A]   **3.** 3 [1.6B]   **4.** $2 \cdot 2 \cdot 2 \cdot 2 \cdot 2 \cdot 5$ [1.7B]   **5.** 36 [2.1A]   **6.** 14 [2.1B]
7. $\frac{5}{8}$ [2.3B]   **8.** $8\frac{3}{10}$ [2.4C]   **9.** $5\frac{11}{18}$ [2.5C]   **10.** $2\frac{5}{6}$ [2.6B]   **11.** $4\frac{2}{3}$ [2.7B]   **12.** $\frac{23}{30}$ [2.8B]
13. Four and seven hundred nine ten-thousandths [3.1A]   **14.** 2.10 [3.1B]   **15.** 1.990 [3.5A]   **16.** $\frac{3}{50}$ [3.6B]
17. $\frac{1}{8}$ [4.1A]   **18.** $\frac{29¢}{2\,pencils}$ [4.2A]   **19.** 33.4 miles/gallon [4.2B]   **20.** 4.25 [4.3B]   **21.** The car's speed is
52 miles/hour. [4.2C]   **22.** 36 [4.3B]   **23.** Your new balance is $744. [1.3C]   **24.** The monthly payment is $570. [1.5D]
25. 105 pages remain to be read. [2.6C]   **26.** The cost per acre was $36,000. [2.7C]   **27.** The change was $35.24. [3.3B]
28. Your monthly salary is $3468.25. [3.5B]   **29.** 25 inches will erode in 50 months. [4.3C]   **30.** 1.6 ounces are required. [4.3C]

Answers to Chapter 5 Selected Exercises

PREP TEST

1. $\frac{19}{100}$ [2.6B]   **2.** 0.23 [3.4A]   **3.** 47 [3.4A]   **4.** 2850 [3.4A]   **5.** 4000 [3.5A]   **6.** 32 [2.7B]   **7.** 62.5 [3.6A]
8. $66\frac{2}{3}$ [2.2B]   **9.** 1.75 [3.5A]

SECTION 5.1

1. 100   **3.** left   **5.** 0.72, $\frac{18}{25}$ **7.** 0.23, $\frac{23}{100}$ **9.** 0.36, $\frac{9}{25}$ **11.** 0.59, $\frac{59}{100}$ **13.** 0.41, $\frac{41}{100}$ **15.** 0.254, $\frac{127}{500}$ **17.** 0.579, $\frac{579}{1000}$
19. 0.062, $\frac{31}{500}$ **21.** 0.064, $\frac{8}{125}$ **23.** 0.0025, $\frac{1}{400}$ **25.** 0.0055, $\frac{11}{2000}$ **27.** $\frac{2}{3}$ **29.** $\frac{5}{6}$ **31.** $\frac{1}{9}$ **33.** $\frac{5}{11}$ **35.** $\frac{3}{70}$ **37.** $\frac{1}{15}$
39. Greater than   **41.** 73%   **43.** 1%   **45.** 294%   **47.** 0.6%   **49.** 310.6%   **51.** 70%   **53.** 85%   **55.** 40%   **57.** 12.5%
59. 150%   **61.** 225%   **63.** 87.5%   **65.** 48%   **67.** $44\frac{4}{9}$%   **69.** $166\frac{2}{3}$%   **71.** $38\frac{8}{9}$%   **73.** Less than   **75.** 6% of those surveyed named
something other than corn on the cob, cole slaw, corn bread, or fries.   **77.** $\frac{53}{1000}$, 0.053   **79.** $\frac{3}{20}$, 0.15   **81.** 0.5%   **83.** 62.5%

SECTION 5.2

1. Percent × base = amount   **3.** Greater than   **5.** 8   **7.** 10.8   **9.** 0.075   **11.** 80   **13.** 51.895   **15.** 7.5   **17.** 13   **19.** 3.75
21. 20   **23.** 5% of 95   **25.** 79% of 16   **27.** Less than   **29.** The number of people in the United States aged 18 to 24 without life insurance is
less than 50 million.   **31.** There will be 138.49 million more passengers.   **33.** The piece contains 29.25 grams of gold, 8.75 grams of silver, and
7 grams of copper.   **35.** 99 million returns were filed electronically.   **37.** The total cost is $30,952.16. The monthly payment is $644.84.
39. The withholding tax is $0.   **41.** The withholding tax is $577.72.   **43.** No

CHECK YOUR PROGRESS: CHAPTER 5

1. $0.85, \frac{17}{20}$ [5.1A] **2.** $0.04, \frac{1}{25}$ [5.1A] **3.** $0.0025, \frac{1}{400}$ [5.1A] **4.** $1.80, 1\frac{4}{5}$ [5.1A] **5.** 15% [5.1B] **6.** 2.7% [5.1B]
7. 145% [5.1B] **8.** 0.125% [5.1B] **9.** 60% [5.1B] **10.** 42.5% [5.1B] **11.** $41\frac{2}{3}\%$ [5.1B] **12.** 170% [5.1B]
13. 29.4 [5.2A] **14.** 13.75 [5.2A] **15.** 39.6 [5.2A] **16.** 0.156 [5.2A] **17.** The weekly pay increase was $72.25. [5.2B]

SECTION 5.3

1. Greater than **3.** Greater than **5.** 32% **7.** $16\frac{2}{3}\%$ **9.** 200% **11.** 37.5% **13.** 18% **15.** 0.25% **17.** 20% **19.** 400%
21. 2.5% **23.** 37.5% **25.** 0.25% **27.** 70% of couples disagree about financial matters. **29.** Approximately 25.4% of the vegetables
were wasted. **31.** 27.1% of Americans with diabetes have not been diagnosed. **33.** 98.5% of the slabs did meet safety requirements.
35. 26.7% of the total is spent on veterinary care. **39. a.** $5 per share **b.** 20% **c.** 25% **d.** No

SECTION 5.4

1. Greater than **3.** Less than **5.** 75 **7.** 50 **9.** 100 **11.** 85 **13.** 1200 **15.** 19.2 **17.** 7.5 **19.** 32 **21.** 200 **23.** 9
25. 504 **27.** 15.8 million travelers allowed their children to miss school to go on a trip. **29.** 24,350 runners started the Boston Marathon in
2011. **31.** A large cargo ship uses 300 tons of fuel per day. **33. a.** 3000 boards were tested. **b.** 2976 of the boards tested were not defecti▪
35. a. 80% **b.** 70% **c.** 75% **d.** 74%; no **e.** When both tests have the same number of points

SECTION 5.5

1. $\frac{\text{percent}}{100} = \frac{\text{amount}}{\text{base}}$ **3.** percent **5.** 65 **7.** 25% **9.** 75 **11.** 12.5% **13.** 400 **15.** 19.5 **17.** 14.8% **19.** 62.62 **21.** 15
23. a. ii and iii **b.** i and iv **25.** The drug will be effective for 4.8 hours. **27. a.** $175 million is generated annually from sales of Thin Mir
b. $63 million is generated annually from sales of Trefoil shortbread cookies. **29.** 57.7% of baby boomers have attended college.
31. The U.S. total turkey production was 7 billion pounds. **33.** The 110th Senate had the larger percentage of Republicans. **35.** The rose-go
ring contains 4.5 grams of gold, 1.2 grams of copper, and 0.3 gram of silver.

CHAPTER 5 REVIEW EXERCISES

1. 60 [5.2A] **2.** 20% [5.3A] **3.** 175% [5.1B] **4.** 75 [5.4A] **5.** $\frac{3}{25}$ [5.1A] **6.** 19.36 [5.2A] **7.** 150% [5.3A]
8. 504 [5.4A] **9.** 0.42 [5.1A] **10.** 5.4 [5.2A] **11.** 157.5 [5.4A] **12.** 0.076 [5.1A] **13.** 77.5 [5.2A] **14.** $\frac{1}{6}$ [5.1A]
15. 160% [5.5A] **16.** 75 [5.5A] **17.** 38% [5.1B] **18.** 10.9 [5.4A] **19.** 7.3% [5.3A] **20.** 613.3% [5.3A]
21. The student answered 85% of the questions correctly. [5.5B] **22.** The company spent $4500 on newspaper advertising. [5.2B]
23. 34.3% of energy costs is spent on electricity. [5.3B] **24.** The total cost of the camcorder was $1041.25. [5.2B]
25. Approximately 78.6% of the women wore sunscreen often. [5.3B] **26.** The world's population in 2000 was approximately 6,100,000,000
people. [5.4B] **27.** The cost of the computer system 4 years ago was $3000. [5.5B] **28.** The total cranberry crop that year was 572 millio
pounds. [5.3B/5.5B]

CHAPTER 5 TEST

1. 0.973 [5.1A; Example 1] **2.** $\frac{5}{6}$ [5.1A; Example 2] **3.** 30% [5.1B; Example 3] **4.** 163% [5.1B; Example 3]
5. 150% [5.1B; HOW TO 2] **6.** 92.5% [5.1B; Example 4] **7.** 50.05 [5.2A; Example 1] **8.** 61.36 [5.2A; Example 1]
9. $61\frac{1}{9}\%$ [5.1B; HOW TO 3] **10.** $\frac{3}{400}$ [5.1A; Example 1C] **11.** 80 [5.4A; Example 2] **12.** 28.3 [5.4A; Example 2]
13. 143.0 [5.5A; Example 1] **14.** 1000% [5.5A; Example 1] **15.** The amount spent for advertising is $45,000. [5.2B; Example 3]
16. 1170 pounds of vegetables were not spoiled. [5.2B; Example 4] **17.** 14.7% of the daily recommended amount of potassium is
provided. [5.3B; Example 4] **18.** 9.1% of the daily recommended number of calories is provided. [5.3B; Example 4] **19.** The number o▪
temporary employees is 16% of the number of permanent employees. [5.3B; Example 4] **20.** The student answered approximately 91.3% of
the questions correctly. [5.3B; Example 5] **21.** 32,000 digital cameras were tested. [5.4B; Example 4] **22.** The increase was 60% of the
original price. [5.3B; Example 5] **23.** The dollar increase in the hourly wage is $1.74. [5.5B; Example 3] **24.** The population now is 220
of the population 10 years ago. [5.3B; Example 5/5.5B; Example 4] **25.** The value of the car is $25,000. [5.5B; Example 3]

CUMULATIVE REVIEW EXERCISES

1. 4 [1.6B] **2.** 240 [2.1A] **3.** $10\frac{11}{24}$ [2.4C] **4.** $12\frac{41}{48}$ [2.5C] **5.** $12\frac{4}{7}$ [2.6B] **6.** $\frac{7}{24}$ [2.7B] **7.** $\frac{4}{9}$ [2.8B] **8.** $\frac{13}{36}$ [2.8B
9. 3.08 [3.1B] **10.** 1.1196 [3.3A] **11.** 34.2813 [3.5A] **12.** 3.625 [3.6A] **13.** $1\frac{3}{4}$ [3.6B] **14.** $\frac{3}{8} < 0.87$ [3.6C]
15. 53.3 [4.3B] **16.** $19.20/hour [4.2B] **17.** $\frac{11}{60}$ [5.1A] **18.** $72\frac{2}{9}\%$ [5.1B] **19.** 19.56 [5.2A/5.5A] **20.** $133\frac{1}{3}\%$ [5.3A/5.5A
21. 9.92 [5.4A/5.5A] **22.** 342.9% [5.3A/5.5A] **23.** Sergio's take-home pay is $592. [2.6C] **24.** The monthly payment is
$292.50. [3.5B] **25.** 420 gallons were used during the month. [3.5B] **26.** The real estate tax is $10,000. [4.3C] **27.** 7346 hotels are
located along interstate highways. [5.2B/5.5B] **28.** 45% of the people did not favor the candidate. [5.3B/5.5B] **29.** The approximate
average number of hours spent watching TV in a week is 61.3 hours. [5.2B/5.5B] **30.** 18% of the children tested had levels of lead that
exceeded federal standards. [5.3B/5.5B]

Glossary

lend In addition, one of the numbers added. [1.2]

lition The process of finding the total of two numbers. [1.2]

dition Property of Zero Zero added to a number does not change the number. [1.2]

proximation An estimated value obtained by rounding an exact value. 1.1]

sociative Property of Addition Numbers to be added can be grouped with parentheses, for example) in any order; the sum will be the same. 1.2]

sociative Property of Multiplication Numbers to be multiplied can be grouped (with parentheses, for example) in any order; the product will be the same. [1.4]

erage The sum of all the numbers divided by the number of those numbers. [1.5]

lancing a checkbook Determining whether the checking account balance is accurate. [6.7]

nk statement A document showing all the transactions in a bank account during the month. [6.7]

sic percent equation Percent times base equals amount. [5.2]

rrowing In subtraction, taking a unit from the next larger place value in the minuend and adding it to the number in the given place value in order to make that number larger than the number to be subtracted from it. [1.3]

rrying In addition, transferring a number to another column. [1.2]

eck A printed form that, when filled out and signed, instructs a bank to pay a specified sum of money to the person named on it. [6.7]

ecking account A bank account that enables you to withdraw money or make payments to other people, using checks. [6.7]

mmission That part of the pay earned by a salesperson that is calculated as a percent of the salesperson's sales. [6.6]

mmon factor A number that is a factor of two or more numbers is a common factor of those numbers. [2.1]

mmon multiple A number that is a multiple of two or more numbers is a common multiple of those numbers. [2.1]

ommutative Property of Addition Two numbers can be added in either order; the sum will be the same. [1.2]

ommutative Property of Multiplication Two numbers can be multiplied in either order; the product will be the same. [1.4]

mposite number A number that has whole-number factors besides 1 and itself. For instance, 18 is a composite number. [1.7]

mpound interest Interest computed not only on the original principal but also on interest already earned. [6.3]

ost The price that a business pays for a product. [6.2]

ross product In a proportion, the product of the numerator on the left side of the proportion times the denominator on the right, and the product of the denominator on the left side of the proportion times the numerator on the right. [4.3]

ecimal A number written in decimal notation. [3.1]

ecimal notation Notation in which a number consists of a whole-number part, a decimal point, and a decimal part. [3.1]

decimal part In decimal notation, that part of the number that appears to the right of the decimal point. [3.1]

decimal point In decimal notation, the point that separates the whole-number part from the decimal part. [3.1]

denominator The part of a fraction that appears below the fraction bar. [2.2]

deposit slip A form for depositing money in a checking account. [6.7]

difference In subtraction, the result of subtracting two numbers. [1.3]

discount The difference between the regular price and the sale price. [6.2]

discount rate The percent of a product's regular price that is represented by the discount. [6.2]

dividend In division, the number into which the divisor is divided to yield the quotient. [1.5]

division The process of finding the quotient of two numbers. [1.5]

divisor In division, the number that is divided into the dividend to yield the quotient. [1.5]

down payment The percent of a home's purchase price that the bank, when issuing a mortgage, requires the borrower to provide. [6.4]

equivalent fractions Equal fractions with different denominators. [2.3]

expanded form The number 46,208 can be written in expanded form as $40,000 + 6000 + 200 + 0 + 8$. [1.1]

exponent In exponential notation, the raised number that indicates how many times the number to which it is attached is taken as a factor. [1.6]

exponential notation The expression of a number to some power, indicated by an exponent. [1.6]

factor In multiplication, one of the numbers in a product. [1.4]

factors of a number The whole-number factors of a number divide that number evenly. [1.7]

finance charges Interest charges on purchases made with a credit card. [6.3]

fixed-rate mortgage A mortgage in which the monthly payment remains the same for the life of the loan. [6.4]

fraction The notation used to represent the number of equal parts of a whole. [2.2]

fraction bar The bar that separates the numerator of a fraction from the denominator. [2.2]

graph of a whole number A heavy dot placed directly above that number on the number line. [1.1]

greater than A number that appears to the right of a given number on the number line is greater than the given number. [1.1]

greatest common factor (GCF) The largest common factor of two or more numbers. [2.1]

hourly wage Pay calculated on the basis of a certain amount for each hour worked. [6.6]

improper fraction A fraction greater than or equal to 1. [2.2]

interest Money paid for the privilege of using someone else's money. [6.3]

interest rate The percent used to determine the amount of interest. [6.3]

inverting a fraction Interchanging the numerator and denominator. [2.7]

least common denominator (LCD) The least common multiple of denominators. [2.4]

least common multiple (LCM) The smallest common multiple of two or more numbers. [2.1]

less than A number that appears to the left of a given number on the number line is less than the given number. [1.1]

license fees Fees charged for authorization to operate a vehicle. [6.5]

loan origination fee The fee a bank charges for processing mortgage papers. [6.4]

markup The difference between selling price and cost. [6.2]

markup rate The percent of a product's cost that is represented by the markup. [6.2]

maturity value of a loan The principal of a loan plus the interest owed on it. [6.3]

minuend In subtraction, the number from which another number (the subtrahend) is subtracted. [1.3]

mixed number A number greater than 1 that has a whole-number part and a fractional part. [2.2]

monthly mortgage payment One of 12 payments due each year to the lender of money to buy real estate. [6.4]

mortgage The amount borrowed to buy real estate. [6.4]

multiples of a number The products of that number and the numbers 1, 2, 3, ... [2.1]

multiplication The process of finding the product of two numbers. [1.4]

Multiplication Property of One The product of a number and 1 is the number. [1.4]

Multiplication Property of Zero The product of a number and zero is zero. [1.4]

number line A line on which a number can be graphed. [1.1]

numerator The part of a fraction that appears above the fraction bar. [2.2]

Order of Operations Agreement A set of rules that tells us in what order to perform the operations that occur in a numerical expression. [1.6]

percent Parts per hundred. [5.1]

percent decrease A decrease of a quantity, expressed as a percent of its original value. [6.2]

percent increase An increase of a quantity, expressed as a percent of its original value. [6.2]

period In a number written in standard form, each group of digits separated from other digits by a comma or commas. [1.1]

place value The position of each digit in a number written in standard form determines that digit's place value. [1.1]

place-value chart A chart that indicates the place value of every digit in a number. [1.1]

points A term banks use to mean percent of a mortgage; used to express the loan origination fee. [6.4]

prime factorization The expression of a number as the product of its prime factors. [1.7]

prime number A number whose only whole-number factors are 1 and itself. For instance, 13 is a prime number. [1.7]

principal The amount of money originally deposited or borrowed. [6.

product In multiplication, the result of multiplying two numbers. [1.4

proper fraction A fraction less than 1. [2.2]

property tax A tax based on the value of real estate. [6.4]

proportion An expression of the equality of two ratios or rates. [4.3]

quotient In division, the result of dividing the divisor into the dividen [1.5]

rate A comparison of two quantities that have different units. [4.2]

ratio A comparison of two quantities that have the same units. [4.1]

reciprocal of a fraction The fraction with the numerator and denomir interchanged. [2.7]

remainder In division, the quantity left over when it is not possible to separate objects or numbers into a whole number of equal groups. [1

repeating decimal A decimal in which a block of one or more digits repeats forever. [3.6]

rounding Giving an approximate value of an exact number. [1.1]

salary Pay based on a weekly, biweekly, monthly, or annual time sche ule. [6.6]

sale price The reduced price. [6.2]

sales tax A tax levied by a state or municipality on purchases. [6.5]

selling price The price for which a business sells a product to a custon [6.2]

service charge An amount of money charged by a bank for handling a transaction. [6.7]

simple interest Interest computed on the original principal. [6.3]

simplest form of a fraction A fraction is in simplest form when there no common factors in the numerator and denominator. [2.3]

simplest form of a rate A rate is in simplest form when the numbers t make up the rate have no common factor. [4.2]

simplest form of a ratio A ratio is in simplest form when the two num bers do not have a common factor. [4.1]

solve a proportion Find a solution of a proportion. [4.3]

standard form A whole number is in standard form when it is written using the digits 0, 1, 2, . . . , 9. An example is 46,208. [1.1]

subtraction The process of finding the difference between two number [1.3]

subtrahend In subtraction, the number that is subtracted from another number (the minuend). [1.3]

sum In addition, the total of the numbers added. [1.2]

terminating decimal A decimal that has a finite number of digits after decimal point, which means that it comes to an end and does not go c forever. [3.6]

total cost The unit cost multiplied by the number of units purchased. [6

true proportion A proportion in which the fractions are equal. [4.3]

unit cost The cost of one item. [6.1]

unit rate A rate in which the number in the denominator is 1. [4.2]

whole numbers The whole numbers are 0, 1, 2, 3, ... [1.1]

whole-number part In decimal notation, that part of the number that appears to the left of the decimal point. [3.1]

Index

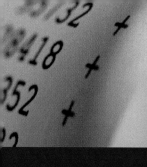

For your lifelong learning solutions, visit **custom.cengage.com**

Visit our corporate website at **cengage.com**

ISBN-13: 978-1-285-88401-1
ISBN-10: 1-285-88401-9

90000

EAN

9 781285 884011